Pain Sensations and Reactions

Pain Sensations and Reactions

Pain Sensations and Reactions

JAMES D. HARDY, Ph.D.,

Associate Professor of Physiology, Cornell University Medical College

HAROLD G. WOLFF, M.D.,

Professor of Medicine (Neurology), Cornell University Medical College

HELEN GOODELL, B.S.,

Research Fellow in Medicine, Cornell University Medical College

WITH A FOREWORD BY

EDWIN G. BORING. Ph.D.,

Professor of Psychology, Harvard University

THE WILLIAMS & WILKINS COMPANY

BALTIMORE • 1952

Printed for
The Williams & Wilkins Company
by the
Waverly Press, Inc.
Baltimore 2, Md., U. S. A.

FOREWORD

The steady onward flow of science is resolvable into the sum of many little spurts. These spurts appear as discoveries, if you take the larger analytical view, or as crucial personal insights, if you take the finer view. You cannot analyze the course of science much more minutely than to get down to the individual insight—the sudden perception of a novel relationship between old items— which comes as an inspiration to a scientist at some particular time and moment. Newton had such insight soon after he went to the Stourbridge Fair in 1666 and bought himself a prism. Long before that everyone knew that sunlight through a prism is broken up into spectral colors, but it was Newton's inspiration to see that this fact means that white, seemingly so simple, is actually a mixture of colors. Out of this newly perceived relationship came the laws of color mixture and the beginnings of psychophysical optics. Fechner, lying in bed on Tuesday morning, 22 October 1850, had the insight that Weber's experiments on sensory intensities provide a way for writing the quantitative relations between mind and body, or, more particularly, between sensation and its stimulus. Out of this inspiration grew the whole of psychophysical research and, thus, in a way, of the new experimental psychology. Let us, therefore, take a look at the scientific history of pain and at some of the crucial insights that contributed to it, in order to see how the understanding of the nature of pain has advanced by both spurts and slow hard work up to the level at which Dr. Hardy, Dr. Wolff and Miss Goodell describe it in this volume.

Originally—from the eighteenth century on back—pain was regarded as an unpleasant quality in the sense of touch, which was Aristotle's fifth sense. As sensation, pain was a quality of experience, like redness, bitterness, or warmth. As unpleasant, it was a sign of something to be avoided, rejected, escaped from, or terminated. Thus, pain came mostly to be thought of as a warning or a signal of harm. Because the two so often went together, common sense confused pain, a quality, with unpleasantness, the

v

awareness of harm. Language also failed to discriminate between these two meanings. Pain, in the dictionary, is still suffering, the opposite of pleasure, and the sign of difficulty, effort and unpleasantness ("he was at pains to . . .," "a painful memory," "painful meeting"). Yet by no means is everything that is unpleasant, that is, disliked or rejected, accompanied by the sensation of pain. Most unpleasantness is not in fact painful in this strict sense of the word, and some sensory pains are actually pleasant and seem desirable (like the aches of stretching, the prick-pains that act as counterirritants to itching, and the pains that are welcome in masochistic ecstasy). Although this confusion still exists in language and in common sense, Dr. Hardy and his associates are perfectly clear. When they say *pain*, they mean the sensory quality and imply nothing about pleasantness or unpleasantness. When they consider the escape or rejection concomitants of sensory pain, they rightly talk of *reactions* to pain or to noxious stimulation. Unpleasantness is reaction and not a conscious quality.

The first thing that happened scientifically to pain was, in a sense, negative. In 1846 Ernst Heinrich Weber ruled pain out of the sense of touch in his famous handbook chapter on the sense of touch (*Tastsinn*) and common sensibility or feeling (*Gemeingefühl*). Touch he divided into the pressure sense, the temperature sense (warmth and cold), and the sense of locality; whereas pain he placed with common sensibility, a catch-all category for those many vague organic perceptions that are known mostly by their biological functions—hunger, thirst, dizziness, nausea, and their like. Weber was a physiologist of great influence, for he had formulated what came later to be called Weber's Law of sensory intensities, and he was the first to experiment on touch, and he did all the pioneer experiments on the tactual error of localization and on the tactual discrimination of two points by the compass test. It was plain to him that pressure, warmth, and cold are true sensations because they have their proper stimuli—physical pressure for the pressure sense, excess or deficiency of physical heat for the temperature sense. Pain, on the other hand, seemed to him to have no proper stimulus but to represent a bodily need, like hunger or nausea. In recognizing this difference, Weber rendered science a service, but his contribution was negative, for the positive account of pain waited to come later.

After Weber there was no important change in the status of pain until the last two decades of the century. At that time the theory of specific nerve energies, supported by two great scientists, Johannes Müller and Helmholtz, was attracting attention. This theory affirms that there is a separate set of nerve fibers for every sensory quality, and it implies that these fibers have their separate endings at the sense-organ as well as at the brain. In the early 1880's Blix and Goldscheider independently undertook to explore the skin with very small stimuli, hoping thus to find different end-organs in it and so to determine the number of its specific qualities ("energies"). They both found tiny spots that are sensitive only to pressure, warmth, or cold, respectively, but they remained in some doubt about pain, although it is easily shown that a needle, applied with a constant moderate force, sometimes elicits the pricking quality from the skin and sometimes not. These "pain spots" lie very close together and you can always get pain from the skin if you push the needle far enough. Goldscheider, therefore, went over to the current theory that pain, a form of common sensibility, comes from the very intense excitation of any sense.

It was Max von Frey who scotched that view and in 1894 rescued pain from common sensibility. von Frey mapped separately pressure, warmth, cold, and pain spots. He worked out separate simple laws of stimulation for pressure and pain, laws which showed how the two senses differ. He made the argument that was accepted for many years as to the nature of the four kinds of neural receptor organs in the skin. In doing all this he established pain as a special sense, defined by its special quality, and set it up definitely as something different from unpleasantness and the reactions that usually, but not always, accompany pain.

One can lay it down as a premise that a successful scientific attack on the problems of sensation is bound to be psychophysical. Certainly the first thing to do for a sense is to show how sensation depends upon stimulation. The stimulus needs to be known, and understanding does not get far until the stimulus can be measured. When you can measure the stimulus, you can determine thresholds of sensation—the absolute threshold at which a difference between sensations becomes just noticeable. With control of the stimulus you can also determine equivalent sensations—the green that is just as bright as a standard yellow, and presently the pricking pain that is just as intense as a radiant-heat pain. Research on vision advanced rapidly as soon as the stimulus could be controlled, when the wave-length and energy of light could be measured and the accompanying visual sensation specified. Psychophysics advanced the knowledge of hearing in the same way. Nowadays we can set up true sensory scales of color, brightness, tonal pitch, and loudness, and relate these sensory scales to the corresponding values of the physical scales of the stimuli. That is psychophysics at work.

von Frey's work was psychophysical but it was only preliminary. The next outstanding contribution to the psychophysics of pain is the present one by Dr. Hardy and his associates. They have made, it seems to me, two notable contributions and are perhaps on their way to making a third.

The first important insight that they had was to see how to provide a measurable stimulus for pain. Weber had found no proper stimulus. von Frey used either heavy forces applied to small surfaces, or needles, but it is plain that distributed force is not a natural stimulus to pain and that a needle acts by destruction of tissue and does not have its effectiveness properly measured by the force applied to it. Dr. Hardy and his colleagues used radiant heat. They were not the first to elicit pain in this fashion, but they were the first to use this stimulus systematically to determine thresholds and equivalent sensations by means of it. They have developed a quantitative technique that is standardized and that yields more reliable results than can be obtained from other available methods. Thus, they have established an important advance in the psychophysics of pain.

The next major contribution of these investigators was to measure the intensity of pain itself—not the magnitude of the pain stimulus but the intensity of the sensory quality. That is their scale of dols. You can now plot sensation against **stimulus** by plotting dols against mc./sec./cm². This is, for pain, Fechner's fundamental problem for psychophysics as he thought it out in bed in 1850. You can relate one pain stimulus to another by determining what value of each is required to give a certain number of dols. You can aid the clinician by showing him how great is the pain under different disease conditions. That was the second phase of the current advance and it had to be second. To develop the dol scale required the availability of a well-controlled, reliably variable stimulus, like radiant heat. The dol scale is a scale of equal intervals of felt pain, and it must have a zero-point somewhere near 0 dols. New research will doubtless correct this scale and locate its zero more exactly; yet the fact remains that this is the first successful quantification of the pain sensation that we have ever had, and as such it is a crucial achievement.

Radiant heat is a much better stimulus for pain than is a needle, yet you still cannot say that radiant heat is the "true" stimulus to pain with the meaning that you have when you say that wavelength is the true stimulus to hue. You can find a threshold for pain in mc./sec./cm². without believing that heat is the normal and proper stimulus to pain. What is needed to answer this question about the "proper" or "true" stimulus is a statement of invariance. You need to be able to say that the pain sensation remains invariant as long as some measured property of the stimulus remains invariant, invariant under all the possible transformations of the stimulus—mechanical, thermal, electrical, chemical, in whatever form they are found to be adequate. You need to be able to say what for a given pain is the same, whether that pain comes from a needle-thrust, from radiant heat, from cold, from pressure, from acid, or from electrical stimulation.

Dr. Hardy and his associates think they have the answer to this question. They think that pain is aroused by noxious stimulation, by the destruction of tissue. They know that radiant heat is not the "true" stimulus, because heat is not invariant for a constant intensity of pain: a little heat for a long time is as effective as more heat for less time. They have evidence that temperature may, in this situation, be invariant, and they wonder whether

this fact does not indicate that destruction of tissue is the true
stimulus. How to translate thermal effect into mechanical, electrical, or chemical they do not yet know, nor what "cold" is as
effective as what "heat", but they are, I am certain, on the right
track. The publication of this handbook will stimulate research
on pain and the authors will be joined by other investigators.

Meanwhile we can congratulate Dr. Hardy, Dr. Wolff, and Miss
Goodell and ourselves that they have brought the psychophysics
of pain so far along that von Frey's techniques of the 1890's
now seem primitive. von Frey, himself a physiologist, competent
in physics and always concerned with technique, a pioneer now
twenty years dead, would have been the first to congratulate them
in this year, the hundredth anniversary of his birth.

                                          EDWIN G. BORING

Harvard University

PREFACE

As originally conceived, this monograph was intended to present in one volume the experimental results of our collaborative researches on pain, obtained (with war interruption) during the past thirteen years. However, the scope of the book has been broadened to present a more rounded view of the subject of pain sensation and reactions. The material presented is largely the work of the authors, and bearing, as it does, this imprint, crosses the lines of various scientific disciplines from physics through psychology and physiology to medicine, neurology and psychiatry. Thus, in Chapter III, on methods, Chapter IV, on pain thresholds, and Chapter X, on reactions to noxious stimulation, the concepts and methods bespeak the orientation of the physicist and physiologist. On the other hand, the last chapters of the book contain much that is derived from data about behavior and feelings and, since pain sensation is a psychological phenomenon, the methods of the psychologist have been employed throughout.

It is the aim of this essay to discuss the traditional concepts of pain, the newer data respecting the phenomenology of pain, and to outline a comprehensive theory of the pain experience compatible with available information. Although not attempting a complete review of the literature on pain, reference to the large body of recent data has been made where it has been pertinent to the discussion.

So many gaps still exist in our knowledge of pain that the present volume must be considered in the light of a report of progress and a statement of tentative theoretical formulations. It is hoped that it may serve as a starting point for future explorations into the many features of the universally interesting subject of pain.

The authors are indebted to the Directors of the Russell Sage Institute of Pathology for generosity in providing editorial assistance. The experimental work contained in this volume was supported by the Russell Sage Institute of Pathology, the New York Hospital, the Departments of Physiology, Medicine, Neurology, Surgery, Obstetrics and Gynecology, and Psychiatry of Cornell University Medical College, the Office of Naval Research,

and the United States Public Health Service. To Professor Edwin
G. Boring of Harvard University, and to Dr. Ward Edwards of
Johns Hopkins University, the authors are especially grateful for
having read the manuscript critically and corrected many of its
faults. Finally, the authors wish to thank Dr. Frederick Guder-
natsch for his painstaking review and correction of the manuscript, and Miss Margaret D. Meixner for her help and encouragement and her tireless editorial assistance during the preparation
of all the material.

For permission to use illustrations, data, and comment, the
authors wish to express their thanks to the publishers and editors
of the Journal of Clinical Investigation, the American Journal
of Physiology, Physiological Reviews, Journal of Neurophysiology, Proceedings of the Association for Research in Nervous and
Mental Disease, Journal of Pharmacology and Experimental Ther-
apeutics, Science, Anesthesiology, American Journal of Obstetrics
and Gynecology, and the Journal of Investigative Dermatology.
We also wish to express our appreciation to C C Thomas & Co.,
publishers of "Pain" by H. G. Wolff and S. Wolf, for permission
to use much of the subject matter included in Chapter II. Finally, our thanks are due the authors of monographs and those
represented in these journals, who generously allowed us to re-
print illustrations.

JAMES D. HARDY
HAROLD G. WOLFF
HELEN GOODELL

CONTENTS

Chapter I

DEVELOPMENT OF THE VARIOUS CONCEPTS CONCERNING PAIN

Pain is one of the most common experiences of man and the explanation of its nature probably one of his oldest preoccupations. During the time of Aristotle and for centuries after, the sensation of pain was considered the manifestation of an emotion, a "quale", i.e., a quality of the soul, and the epitome of unpleasantness (11, 477, 357). Pain, therefore, was not grouped with the traditional "five senses". Its position in the fields of psychology and physiology remained an uncertain one. This fact is prominent in discussions of the history of pain concepts (92) and of sensation in general (51) which deal with the various hypotheses that have been advanced to elucidate the pain experience. A brief review of these developments would seem desirable as a background against which more recent work can be properly evaluated. It is the purpose of the first chapter of this discussion to bring the earlier concepts of pain together in a modern statement of the nature of pain. These concepts can now be reviewed from the vantage point of several thousand years of contemplation and speculation, of a hundred years of experimentation by psychologists, physiologists and physicians, and of about 70 years of continued application of the quantitative methods of psychophysical study. This will enable us to appraise more clearly the advantages as well as the weaknesses of the methods upon which the experimental data and conclusions given in the following chapters are based.

The earliest ideas regarding the nature of pain stemmed from the realization that pain comes from many sources, some in the outside world, some within the body, and in the soul when one is miserable (12). Thus, pain was considered not a "quality" of external objects such as are color, form, hardness or coldness, but it was appraised as being a state of a general feeling of "unpleasantness". Opposed to "unpleasantness" was "pleasantness" and during his life the individual was thought to be continually passing

through various phases of "pleasure" and "pain" (12). "Pleasure"
and "pain" could not exist at one and the same time in an individual since the presence of one precluded the presence of its
opposite. Aristotle identified the perception of pain with the feelings it commonly evokes and used the word "pain" as the equivalent of "unpleasantness". The "five senses" concept—sight,
hearing, smell, taste and touch—excluded pain as a sensation since
the latter is not referrable to any quality of external objects. This
distinction survived for twenty centuries. As recently as 1939 Dallenbach wrote (92): "The doctrine of the five senses, which is
common sense today, is ascribed to Aristotle . . . ", indicating
thereby the great and enduring usefulness of Aristotle's formulation.

At the end of the eighteenth century Erasmus Darwin (96) was
among the first to begin an analysis of "unpleasantness". He,
indeed, regarded pain as a phase of unpleasantness and said, "Pain
results whenever the sensorial motions are stronger than usual."
In this he anticipated the "intensive" theory of pain: viz., that
pain results from too strong stimulation of any one of the five
senses. Here, now, was an opportunity for the application of
experimental methods; for, in this statement lies the implication
that if pain could be elicited without overstimulation of any of
the five "sensorial motions", or if even the strongest possible
stimulation of such did not arouse pain, there would be grave
doubt as to the complete identification of all pain sensation with
"unpleasantness". Darwin expanded the old concept to the extent of adding seven additional senses to the original five of
ancient classification. In reporting the following observation he
showed the way for a fruitful type of experimentation. He cites
on page 86 of his "Zoonomia" this observation on a patient with
violent cramps in the legs: "Though pricked with a pin in five or
six places, the patient declared he did not feel it in the least, nor
was he sensible of a very smart pinch. I then held a red hot poker
at some distance, and brought it gradually nearer till it came
within three inches, when he asserted that he felt it [heat] quite
distinctly. I suppose some violent irritation of the nerves of touch
had caused the cramps, and had left them paralytic; while the

nerves of heat having suffered no increase of stimulus, retained their irritability".

THE IMPACT OF NINETEENTH CENTURY NEUROPHYSIOLOGY

Over the years the concept of sensation had slowly been undergoing a fundamental change. To the question *"What do I feel?"* was added the question, "How do I feel it?" The answers to both questions are still subjects of investigation. The important discoveries of Charles Bell (26) regarding the functions of the dorsal roots of the spinal nerves as distinct from those of the ventral roots initiated a period of a century and a half of diligent search for the understanding of sensory phenomena. Bell pointed out the relationship, now known as the Bell-Magendie Law, viz., that the function of the dorsal roots is sensory and that of the ventral roots is motor. The recognition of this fundamental division of the nervous system established for sensation an anatomic basis as real as that of motor function. Bell's discovery justified the hope that some day sensory phenomena would lend themselves to a systematic analysis similar to that used for motor phenomena.

In 1834 Weber published his fundamental paper "De Tactu" (458), followed in 1846 by "Der Tastsinn und das Gemeingefühl" (459). In contrast to the older concepts he distinguished between touch and pain by classing touch as a sense of the skin and pain as belonging to the "Gemeingefühl". The latter expression means the common sensibility possessed by the skin as well as the internal organs. The "Tastsinn" or sense of touch included the pressure and the temperature senses. Weber's most pertinent remarks concerned the smallest difference between two weights that can still be perceived. This "just noticeable difference" (or "jnd"), he pointed out, depends on the magnitudes of the weights and is proportional to them. He extended his observations to visual and auditory discriminations. Although Weber himself formulated from his studies no general concept we shall here put down his statement as "Weber's Law", so termed by Fechner (120).

$$\frac{\Delta I}{I} = \text{constant}$$

in which I = intensity of stimulus,

ΔI = just noticeable difference in intensity between two stimuli.

As will be seen, the importance of this relationship lies in its providing the investigator with a tool for the study of sensation above the threshold.

At about that time, 1840, Johannes Müller (320) presented his theory of "specific nerve energies". He proposed five kinds of sensory nerves corresponding to the five traditional senses. The several types of nerves were thought each to carry a particular form of "energy" to the brain. The nature of the "energy" depended upon the special peripheral ending stimulated, together with the type of excitement carried by the particular nerve. Müller stated, "Sensation consists in the sensorium receiving through the medium of its nerves, as the result of the action of an external cause, a knowledge of certain qualities or conditions not of external bodies but of the nerves of sense themselves. . . . The immediate objects of our senses are merely particular states induced in the nerves, and felt as sensations either by the nerves themselves or by the sensorium." In other words, Müller attributed a higher degree of specificity to peripheral nerves than would be acceptable to a present-day physiologist. Müller's ten laws of specific nerve energies dispelled the idea that sensory nerves conduct to the brain non-corporeal copies of the objects perceived. The nerve pathways were considered to stand between the seat of consciousness and the external world. In this, Müller identified the sensation with a specific neural apparatus. This concept comes down to us unchanged so that today a sensation to be classed as such must be shown to have a functionally distinct set of afferent pathways and its specific integrative equipment. Thus, although it is now held that nerves do not carry "specific" energies but simply impulses, Müller's work forms the basis for a profitable classification of sensations. In addition, his theory furnished, during the latter part of the nineteenth century, the background and inspiration for much important research, as is attested by the flood of investigations which grew out of it.

About ten years after the publication of Müller's exhaustive

"Handbuch der Physiologie des Menschen", there came a most important discovery. In 1851, von Helmholtz (207, 208) first succeeded in measuring the velocity with which the nerve impulse travels, following the lead of DuBois-Reymond (102a), and opened the way for the development of modern electrophysiology. Here, the nature of nerve function itself came under the scrutiny of the experimentalist. Although no positive identification of this function with sensation can as yet be made, the information gained from studies of nerve action potentials forms part of the basis for our present day concepts of the nature of sensation and the relation of the latter to the peripheral sensory endings. This discovery effectively put an end to one of the aspects of Müller's idea of "specific nerve energies" as it became apparent that all nerve fibers carry electrical impulses which differ only in magnitude, frequency, and velocity. The three variables alone could not possibly account for both the number of sensory qualities and the variations of intensity in each. Yet, the other implications of Müller's doctrine still serve as the basis of sense classification. These include the specificity of the sensory endings, and afferent pathways, as well as a localized cerebral representation.

A step in placing pain in a sensory category of its own was made in 1858 when Schiff (384) reported his experiments on cord sections in dogs. He noted that by various partial incisions of the cord, pain apparently could be eliminated whereas touch remained. These crude experiments were open to such obvious objections that had it not been for the support lent to them from clinical observations of tabes dorsalis they would not be worth mentioning. However, the step was an experimental one based upon Müller's doctrine of specific nerve energies, and foreshadowed the modern surgical procedures for the relief of pain, such as rhizotomy and chordotomy.

Before tracing the history of investigations on pain through the last two decades of the nineteenth century it is important to consider the contribution of Fechner (120) who introduced in his "Elemente der Psychophysik", published in 1860, methods for measuring the intensity of sensation. While Fechner was not concerned primarily with any theories concerning the nature of pain, he started a movement for the application of quantitative methods in the study of sensation in general. It is these same methods that are being applied almost a hundred years later in the present study of pain. From a consideration of the form of Weber's Law, $\Delta I/I$ = constant, Fechner had concluded that the constant in this equation could be nothing other than the just noticeable difference in sensation, or ΔS. He then substituted this in Weber's Law to make

$$\frac{\Delta I}{I} \sim \Delta S$$

After making the assumption that sensation was measurable he integrated this equation and arrived at:

$$S = K \log I + C$$

where K and C are constants. Here one has the long sought relationship between the intensity of the stimulus and the intensity of the sensation which it evokes. This matter will be considered more fully in a later chapter, when the measurement of pain sensation is discussed. Fechner, the founder of psychophysics, is introduced here because, as the first to apply quantitative concepts to sensation, he was making strong headway against the then prevalent feeling that consciousness and sensation are beyond the realm of proper application of experimentation.

Stimulated by Müller's theory, Blix (44), in 1884, discovered the sensitive points in the skin. His observations were confirmed almost immediately and independently by Goldscheider (157), and Donaldson (101). Thus, opinion began to shift to the belief that stimulation of the skin can evoke one or more of four sensations: pressure, pain, heat, and cold. Blix showed that the skin is not uniformly sensitive throughout. With small heated or cooled metal rods he could arouse heat sensation from some spots and cold from others. Separate pain and pressure "spots" were also identified. His experiments gave results which fitted in so well with Müller's doctrine of "specific nerve energies" that they were immediately accepted. Herzen (214) had also come forward with observations on producing nerve block by means of pressure. He noted that when the blood is shut off from the arm by a tourniquet for several minutes, sensation in the occluded part became gradually altered. Sensations of cold and touch were lost first, then heat and superficial pain, and lastly deep pain. When the tourniquet was released, the return of sensations was in the reverse order. This phenomenon seemed to argue strongly in favor of the separateness, as sensations, of pain, touch, heat, and cold. von Frey (447) had gone a step further in his observations. Not only did he make more careful studies of particular sensitive points but he also excised the skin beneath such points and by histological examination identified the specific end organ type responsible for each sensation. Pain was conceived as being mediated by nerve fibers terminating in fine fibrils; cold by special large bulbous endings first described by Krause; warmth by the tightly coiled endings identified by Ruffini; and tactile sensation by networks of fibrillae contiguous with the hair follicles.

This formulation remains in many contemporary textbooks. However, other investigators were able to confirm the above observations only in the skin of the nipple and of the prepuce (22), but not in the skin over the forearm or other areas (499). The discrediting of the concept of end organ specificity re-opened the question of whether or not pain sensation has its special neural equipment and, indeed, if pain, according to Müller's doctrine, could at all be considered a sensation. So much for the experimental work of this period.

While such investigations were being carried out, three concepts of the nature of pain stood in mutual opposition. The first one was the so-called *intensive theory* which was based upon the concept that pain is the result of intense stimulation of any sensory equipment. This theory had such supporters as Külpe (246), and Wundt (501). To support his ideas, Wundt went even so far as to postulate the existence of a most ingenious neural mechanism. He assumed that the peripheral nerves of touch, heat, and cold were the only afferent pathways from the skin, as he saw no reason for assuming a special set of pathways for pain, or for considering pain a cutaneous sense. In his opinion the impulses from tactile or thermal stimulation, when reaching the cord, found two paths open: a primary low resistance pathway, "probably leading through the white matter", and a secondary high resistance pathway, "leading through the grey matter". "Impulses of moderate intensity" would take the primary pathway. When "excessive impulses" came they overflowed into the secondary paths and passed upward to give rise to pain. Such a concept admitted the separate nature of pain sensation, but moved the true pain fiber endings from the skin into the spinal cord.

Secondly, there was the older *emotion* theory which supposed pain to be a phase of unpleasantness, an emotional state initiated by some sensation. According to Marshall (306) ". . . pleasures and pains can in no proper sense be classed with sensation . . . , it appears to me neurologists are wasting valuable labor in the search for 'pain paths' and for 'pain localization' in the cortex of the brain, the paths in the spinal cord and the supposed nerve terminals which have attracted the attention of investigators, mediating some form of sensibility which under the conditions of the examination are always painful." Marshall voiced the prevalent opinion of the time by saying, ". . . pleasure and pain are two states which are too disparate to be commonly known by any one word, but so inseparably connected that they must be mentioned in one breath."

Thirdly, there was the group which supported the concept that pain is a *sensation* with its own distinct central and peripheral sensory mechanisms. von Frey, who conceived that each type of peripheral end organ mediated a specific sensory quality, may be considered the leader of this group whose views were adhered to generally by physiologists and physicians. Many psychologists also held these views and struggled bitterly in opposing the proponents of both the "intensive" and the "emotion" theories.

Strong (426) in 1895 called attention to the possibility that pain experience may include: ". . . 1) the feeling we have when the skin is cut or burnt, what the Germans call 'Schmerz', but also 2) the feeling of displeasure excited in us by this and other experiences, that which the Germans call 'Unlust'. . . . I hold that physical pain is not a compound of an indifferent sensation with a feeling of displeasure, but itself a sensation which calls forth displeasure."

As can be seen, each one of these three theories is the result of the particular types of investigation employed. The controversies arising from the differences in method have not yet ended. The final solution of the problem must be based on the combined evidence obtained by all the critical inquiries into the nature of pain; for only in this way will the entire complex designated by the term "pain experience" be adequately explained.

In considering the important contributions to the knowledge of pain made during the last decade of the nineteenth century, there must be mentioned the names of MacKenzie (303) and Head (202). MacKenzie was impressed with the fact that stimulation of a deep-lying structure, such as the pericardium or the dome of the diaphragm, gave rise to pain and tenderness in the skin of the pericardial and shoulder regions. This observation induced him to propose the idea of a "hyper-irritable focus" in spinal neurons, which could account for the superficial hyperalgesia associated with noxious stimulation of deeper structures. His studies of herpes zoster led to the discovery of the segmental distribution in the skin of sensory fibers in the superficial dermatomes.

MacKenzie's work prompted Head to propose an entirely new system for the classification of somesthetic sensations. He observed both on himself and on patients that following the transection of a cutaneous nerve the stimulation of skin areas within the distribution of the injured nerve revealed a zone of complete anesthesia surrounded by a band in which sensibility to light touch was lost, localization disturbed, but sensitivity to pain increased. The sensibility in this band Head called "protopathic" sensibility and the fine discriminative sense which was lost in the border between the anesthetic and normal skin he termed "epicritic sensibility". Normal cutaneous sensibility he thus postulated to be the sum of "epicritic" and "protopathic" sensibilities. "Deep" sensibility, his third category, he conceived as arising in subcutaneous structures. Boring (48) and Lanier (262) repeated Head's experiments, in general confirming the latter's observations but interpreting the results differently. These authors concluded that there exist four sensory modalities in the skin, i.e., touch, pain, warmth, and cold. The aberrations noted on the border of the anesthetic area were due to combination of skin senses differing from those felt in the normal skin with its overlapping sensory innervation. However, it seems useful to consider Head's observations as pointing to the width of the quality spectra of somesthetic sensation, notably as regards pain.

During the first quarter of the twentieth century the concepts supported by Goldscheider's experiments were re-explored. Goldscheider (155, 156) had demonstrated in 1894 that very rapid vibration of a fine hair against the skin (at a frequency of ca. 600 per second) gave rise to pain. From this observation he concluded that cutaneous pain was elicited by the intensive stimulation of touch receptors, and from these alone. This was contrary to the earlier reports of von Frey (447, 448, 449). Challenged by Goldscheider's claims he reported in 1922 (445) that pain could also be stimulated without mechanical contact by means of thermal radiation. He concluded from this that pain was not necessarily the result of just an intense touch sensation as claimed by Goldscheider. Later, Dallenbach (65, 425) and his students showed that when pain is induced by thermal radiation and the stimulus is kept constant at a level just above the pain threshold, the sensation fades from pain into warmth or coolness without inducing any touch sensation. They also concluded, as von Frey had done before, that pain does not result solely from an intense stimulation of touch (113).

More recently, (416) support of the intensive theory was offered especially by Nafe (326) who, in 1934, called attention to a possible relationship between the state of contraction of smooth muscle induced at various levels of temperature and the sensations which von Frey had shown were experienced at these temperatures. Nafe implied that the sensation which is evoked is dependent upon the degree of contraction of the smooth muscle which leads to a stimulation of the adjacent nerve endings—the more vigorous the contraction, the more intense the stimulation—the result being an alteration of the quality of the sensation from warmth, to heat, to pain, all being mediated by one and the same peripheral neural equipment. Pain, Nafe inferred, was associated with the most intense stimulation. This relationship is shown in table 1. In support of his position Nafe pointed out the difficulty encountered when attempting to identify the specific end organs claimed by von Frey, of heat, cold, pressure, and pain. Nafe also considered the sensibility of deep pain, cold, warmth, and pressure, pointing out that the presence of such senses in the viscera cannot be understood from a functional point of view. Also, he concluded that, if one assumes a special neural apparatus subserving pain in the viscera one would have to postulate for it some function of more importance to the body economy than the simple mediation of pain. Such a function would be the mediation of "non-painful" pain, and this he concluded could be the pressure sense. In this

TABLE 1

Nafe's parallelism between sensation, smooth muscle contraction, and temperature

EXPERIENCE	STIMULUS	MUSCLE ACTION
Pain	52°C.	Spastic contraction
Heat	45°C.	Constricting elements in dilating muscle
Warmth		Relaxation
"Zero"	33°C.	Physiological zero
Cold		Contraction
Cold heat	12°C.	Severe constriction
Pain	3°C.	Spastic contraction

connection he called attention to the experiments of Goldscheider and, later, of Heinbecker, Bishop and O'Leary (206) who found that a series of non-painful pricks or electrical sparks applied to the skin gave rise to a spectrum of sensation ranging from light touch, i.e., "non-painful pain", to actual pain as the frequency of stimulation was increased.

From all this Nafe concludes that pain is the result of a summation of effects originating in intense smooth muscle contractions integrated at the thalamocortical level. He implied that pain was akin to emotion and not a sensation, in this way combining the "intensive" with the "emotion" theory. The difficulty in accepting these views is that since Nafe originally stated his thesis many additional experimental data have been assembled which cannot be understood in terms of his concept.

The Contemporary Arguments for Considering Pain a Sensation

Inferences from Neuroanatomy and Neurophysiology

Although sensation itself cannot be studied by the methods of recording action potentials and of tracing neural pathways, current understanding of the mechanisms responsible for sensation is based on this very type of investigation. Adrian (1) has shown that nerve conduction consists of bursts of electrical alterations in the fibers. These nerve impulses which can be recorded by the oscillograph are alike except as regards their frequency and velocity. Adrian and Zotterman (4) also demonstrated that, when the skin of an animal is stimulated, increasing or decreasing the intensity of the stimulus does not change the size of the nerve impulses but only their number. This is an example of the "all-or-none" law which applies alike to a single nerve or muscle fiber. However, it is not to be inferred that the sensation obeys the all-or-none principle since graded intensities of sensation are the rule, as are also graded muscular responses. The two authors also showed that for tactile impulses

$$\text{Frequency} = \text{K log stimulus intensity.}$$

More recently, Hartline (198) demonstrated, by electrical recordings on the optic nerve of the Limulus eye, a similar relationship between frequency of nerve impulses and intensity of illumination. Two adjacent receptors may summate their responses so that impulse frequency depends not only upon stimulus intensity but also upon the number of receptors stimulated. This can be represented diagrammatically (see fig. 1).

If the electrodes are placed on the nerve before it reaches the synapse (see fig. 1, no. 1) the usual relationship is observed:

$$\text{Frequency} = \text{K log I.}$$

A recording taken at position 2, proximal to the synapse, gives the relationship for two or more receptors after they have converged into a common pathway. The relationship here is:

$$\text{Frequency} = \text{K log I} + \text{K}' \text{log A}$$

where A is the area of the retina (number of receptors) stimulated. This type of summative action known as "spatial summation" is to be distinguished from temporal summation. The latter means the evoking of a response by subliminal stimuli when these are presented sufficiently rapidly.

The precise data on the intimate relationship between the intensity of stimulation and the frequency of afferent nerve impulses have a direct bearing on our concept of sensation. Though there does not exist a one-to-one correspondence between the phenomena observed in the nerve and the qualities and intensities of

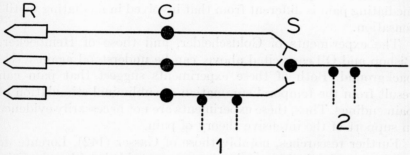

Fig. 1. Diagrammatic Representation of Electrical Recording of Action Potentials from Optic Nerve of Limulus Before (1), and After (2) Synapse

R, photoreceptor; G, ganglion cell; S. synapse

a sensory experience, nevertheless the intensity of sensation and the frequency of impulses in the nerve are both similarly dependent upon intensity of stimulation. For example, the critical fusion frequency for vision, which has been assumed to be an indication of the intensity of visual sensation, has been shown by Granit and Harper (169), by Ferry (123) and by Porter (344) to have the following dependence on the intensity of illumination and area of retina stimulated:

$$\text{Fusion frequency} = K \log I + K' \log A$$

where I and A have the same meanings as above. Furthermore, it has been shown that the thresholds for the temperature sensation depend on intensity of stimulus and on area stimulated in exactly this manner. From this it is reasonable to infer a causal relationship between frequency of nerve impulse and intensity of sensation.

Adrian, Cattell and Hoagland (3) recorded action potentials from afferent nerve fibers from the skin of a frog which they stimulated with puffs of air. They showed that intense stimulation of the skin evoked in the nerve a frequency of impulses which was as high as the total capacity of the nerve to conduct. Yet under these conditions the frog gave no pain response. However, the frog had sensitivity to pain and jumped vigorously when the skin was pricked with a pin. This is evidence that the neural equipment mediating pain is different from that involved in mediating tactile sensation.

The experiments of Goldscheider, and those of Heinbecker, Bishop and O'Leary cited above, can be understood against this background. Both of these experiments suggest that pain can result from the temporal summation of subliminal stimulation of pain endings. Thus, these experiments are not necessarily evidence in support of the intensive theory of pain.

Further researches, notably those of Gasser (142), Lorente de Nó (290), Lloyd (288) and others, have added evidence of the anatomical basis for sensation. The older experiments on blocking of nerve pathways by means of pressure, procaine, or cold, assumed new significance when the effects of these procedures and agents were analyzed in terms of nerve fiber diameter and function. For example, the double pain response which is observed when the skin at a distal portion of an extremity is noxiously stimulated can be explained in relation to the nerve fiber diameter. While fibers of widely varying diameters are involved, the fast component of the response is conducted mainly by the fibers of larger diameters, whereas the slower component is mediated for the most part by fibers of the smallest diameters. The concept of a central excitatory state, variously referred to by Sherrington (400) and MacKenzie (302) was elucidated by the anatomic and physiologic investigations of Gasser, of Lorente de Nò and of Lloyd who resorted to the use of the oscillograph. These observations became pertinent to the interpretation not only of motor phenomena, but of sensation as well. As will be shown in a subsequent chapter, the understanding of the production and maintenance of certain types of hyperalgesia and of itch sensation depends upon the concept of the central excitatory state, similar to that postulated by Sherrington. The latter was able to demonstrate that the activity of internuncial neurones exerted a controlling influence upon the level of excitability of motor neurones. Gasser showed that the reduction in the motor discharge over a ventral root could be accounted for by the excitation of the internuncial neurone pool when such excitation had been previously induced by shock to the dorsal root of the same segment. Such alteration in the central excitatory state results in some sort of inhibition. Lloyd confirmed these observations and noted further that inhibition occurs in monosynaptic reflexes as well as in those mediated through an internuncial neuron pool.

The relevance of Gasser's observations to pain may possibly be exemplified in recent observations of Kunkle et al (251). These authors observed that immersion of the middle finger into ice water caused pain which spread into the neighboring fingers. However, painful stimulation by an intense galvanic current applied to the digital nerve of the index finger just before immersion, blocked spread into this finger temporarily, while spread into the other fingers occurred as usual.

Lorente de Nò (291) inferred that all interneuronal connections fall into two categories (see diagrammatic sketch no. 1 in fig. 2). The first pathway is the type found commonly in sympathetic ganglia as well as in the neuraxis. It forms the basis for explaining the phenomena of mass discharge as well as for spatial summation. The second type of pathway (sketch no. 2, fig. 2) is found only in the spinal cord and brain and constitutes the basic anatomic arrangement for the maintenance of the central excitatory state.

The importance in perception of pain of the central excitatory state at the cord level has been mentioned above but the implications of the "feed-back system" of neuronal connections in the reticular substance of the brain may include also those supporting the excitatory events which determine consciousness. Defined from this point of view a sensory experience is the result of a particular pattern of excitatory states which is related to the afferent volleys of impulses induced by stimulating a specific peripheral apparatus. This concept is useful not only because it provides a reasonable way of looking at the relationship between consciousness and neural equipment, but also because it provides a basis for further investigation. These advantages have been evident in the investigations of Brodmann (59), of Cushing (91), and more recently of Foerster (128), Penfield (337), and others who resorted to direct stimulation of the cortex in order to localize the cortical responses to peripheral stimulation. The tracing of pathways and the success in locating specific sites of nuclear and cortical activity by the

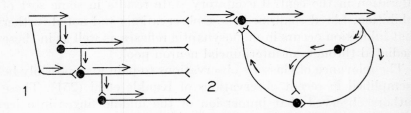

FIG. 2. DIAGRAM OF INTERNEURONAL CONNECTIONS ACCORDING TO LORENTE DE NÒ (291) (SLIGHTLY MODIFIED)

recording of action potentials associated with specific peripheral stimulation, have also helped in clarifying our understanding of the function of various parts of the brain and central nervous system.

As the anatomical methods of investigation were combined with those of physiology, the confusion concerning the sensory end organs in the skin as first assumed by von Frey has gradually become resolved. Structures which give rise to pain sensation have been definitely identified in the skin. Weddell, Sinclair and Feindel (462) demonstrated that cutaneous pain is subserved by the finer medullated and non-medullated nerve fibers bearing free endings which are arranged in the superficial layers of the epidermis in a plexiform interlocking manner. Weddell (461) in order to determine the neurohistology of a skin area from which pain alone could be evoked, outlined the pattern of sensory loss in a patient with a sciatic nerve lesion. The area from which pain could not be aroused was smaller than that from which touch could not be aroused, and this in turn was smaller than the area over which temperature sensibility has been lost. A piece of skin 2 by 3 cm. was removed from a zone in part of which pain only could be aroused and another where pain and touch could be evoked. In the portion from which pain alone could be elicited, fine nerve fibers were seen giving rise to superficial nerve nets; no thickened nerve fibers or specialized endings were seen. On the other hand, in the area in which both pain and touch could be evoked, a cutaneous nerve plexus was found, together with thickened nerve fibers ending around hair follicles and thinner ones giving rise to superficial fiber networks.

Finally, there is evidence that certain structures are equipped for and give rise to the pain sensation only. The tooth pulp (152), the structures of the sternal cavity (107), the middle meningeal artery (82), the arteries at the base of the brain and some of the scalp arteries (353), such as the temporal artery, seem to be equipped with afferent fibers which conduct impulses resulting in pain only. On the other hand, there are certain areas in the body from which pain cannot be elicited locally, as for example, the parenchyma of the brain. A similar area is found in most persons on the inside of the cheek opposite the second lower molar (Kiesow's area) (240).

Tower (438) introduced the useful concept of "sensory unit" in contrast to single afferent nerve endings. She made it seem likely that a "sensory unit" consists of many nerve endings, all being branches of one single fiber, and all connected with one neuron in the dorsal root ganglion. Such a single unit may arborize into an area of skin or cornea of about one centimeter in diameter. It is conceivable that larger units exist, as suggested by Weddell. Many pain fibers supply overlapping "sensory units" in a given area, although there is, of course, no continuity between the endings of different units. It would, thus, seem likely that the "painful spot" experienced as such when an area of normal skin is exposed to noxious stimulation exists only as a centrally integrated experience projected onto the periphery where it evidences itself in the form of localization. The "skin spot" is, so to speak, a "mind spot".

Such central representation areas have been established for vision in the occipital cortex, and for hearing in the temporal lobe. For touch, central areas for the various body regions have also been identified in the contralateral post-Rolandic region of the cortex. So far no separate areas for warmth, cold, and pain have been recognized. Electrical stimulation of the sensory cortex gives rise to an ill-defined sensation referred to some particular part of the body. It was also found that some individuals with tumors involving the cortex experience sustained or episodic pain referred to various areas on the opposite side of the body (311). In most instances the lesions involved the parietal or postparietal areas of the cortex.

Inferences from Physiology

A useful method of study productive of important results has been that based on quantitative techniques for measuring pain thresholds. Analgesics, such as codeine and morphine, have been shown to raise the pain threshold from thirty-five to eighty per cent above the control level while they had only a negligible effect on the thresholds for touch, hearing, smell, two-point discrimination, and vibration (470). It has also been observed that acetylsalicylic acid actually lowers the threshold for warmth while slightly raising the threshold for pain from radiant heat (185).

The earliest mention of the view that there are two types of cutaneous pain, viz., burning and pricking, was made by Gad and Goldscheider in 1892 (139). Since then, the two-fold nature of cutaneous pain has been explored extensively. Although investigators differ as to whether or not there are two qualities of cutaneous pain or merely two variations, all are agreed about the difference in speed of perception. Woollard, Weddell and Harpman (499), Boring (48), and more recently Bigelow, Harrison, Goodell and Wolff (32) are of the opinion that two qualities of pain do exist. Lewis (274) and Gasser (143) are less certain of any differences in sensation quality but find the difference in the speed of perception of special interest. According to Bigelow, Harrison, Goodell and Wolff, one type of pain is abrupt in onset and has a pricking quality which quickly terminates; the other type is slow in onset, never reaches an abrupt or pricking climax, and recedes more slowly. The latter pain has a burning quality whether initiated by a pin point or by heat.

Bishop (35, 34) suggested that "itch, non-painful prick, and pain, elicited by appropriate patterns of stimulation from the same point differ in quality as well as quantitatively." This shift in quality when there is a change in frequency of stimulation indicates, according to Bishop, "a central qualitative interpretation of sensory impulses depending on quantitative factors involving identical peripheral mechanisms within the single modality of pricking pain". It must be pointed out, however, that "stimulation from the same point" is not equivalent to stimulating the same single nerve ending, and, therefore, need not necessarily imply the existence of "identical peripheral mechanism" for touch as well as for itch, prick, and pain.

Gasser's experiments indicate that the pain first to be perceived when a pin is pressed into the skin or when a finger touches a very hot electric bulb (the so-called "first pain"), is carried mainly by the larger medullated fibers conducting at rates lying between 10 and 90 meters per second, whereas the slow pain (so-called "second pain") or that to come on after the above pricking pain has been experienced, is carried mainly by fine fibers at rates between 0.6 and 2 meters per second.

Bigelow, Harrison, Goodell and Wolff, using the radiation technique, studied these two types of pain. They measured the threshold of "pricking" pain and also the threshold of "burning" pain which was observed to be below the threshold for pricking pain. Burning pain was easily recognized as being distinct from pricking pain although it had certain properties in common with the latter. In both the threshold was raised after administering alcohol or morphine, and no spatial summation occurred as larger and larger areas were stimulated.

From observations of these two types of pain it became possible to understand certain pathological states. It appeared from studies of pricking pain threshold that there was no lowering of the pain threshold in patients with cutaneous hyperalgesia (179) or with some types of peripheral neuritis. Indeed, in most instances the pricking pain threshold was elevated. Yet experience forces the recognition of a lowered pain threshold for some types of pain. When a patient with nerve injury due to a tumor pressing upon the cervical roots was carefully studied it was demonstrated that the threshold of burning pain was actually lower than normal, whereas that of pricking pain, as previously observed, was considerably higher (482).

In summary, then, it may be inferred that the skin is endowed with at least two types of apparatus for perceiving noxious stimuli, one giving rise to pain of a burning quality and the other to pricking pain.

Inferences from Psychology

Boring (49) in his "Physical Dimensions of Consciousness" epitomizes the contemporary viewpoint regarding sensation. The modern concept has departed from the Descartes dualism of mind and physical world, and also from the position of those who would deny that conscious phenomena can be studied. Boring states frankly that sensations must be considered in the same light as physical phenomena with measurable dimensions. Even though the psychological dimensions are not completely independent of each other, they are, as Boring points out, not different in this respect from the physical dimensions of time, space, and mass which are also interrelated. At least four dimensions of sensation are required, according to this author. They have measurable aspects and thus are different from the former "attributes" of sensation which were descriptive only. These dimensions are quality, intensity, extension and duration.

The fruitfulness of this concept which has gradually been developed during the past one hundred years is seen in the rapidity with which one sensation after another has been subjected to analysis. For example, the dimension of intensity has been measured for both vision and hearing, in terms of "brils" for vision, and of "sones" for hearing (421). Similar measurements have been made for taste and smell (24). As regards pain, there appear to be at least three distinct quality categories, i.e., pricking, burning, and aching. However, there is at present no physical aspect known of the stimuli evoking pain to which quality may be quantitatively related. Therefore, it has not been possible either to obtain a measure of the quality of pain or to describe quantitatively a painful experience in terms of the sum of contributions from the various qualities of pain. Were this possible one could analyze the quality of the pain experience in terms of the fundamental qualities of which it is composed, i.e.,

$$P = xa + yp + zb$$

in which P refers to the quality of the painful experience composed of x amount of aching pain, y amount of pricking pain and z amount of burning pain.

Since this monograph is largely concerned with the dimensions of pain further elaboration at this point is unnecessary. Suffice it to say that until recently it had been doubted that the intensity dimension of pain could be measured although rough estimates of "more" or "less" were generally recognized as being useful. Extension and duration are important items in the study of pain and their recognition has led to distinctions between the effects of pain of short duration and of longer lasting pain, the latter having been designated "pathologic" pain (358, 236). As will be discussed in a later chapter it has been shown that the spreading of a noxious stimulus over a larger area does not increase the intensity of the resulting pain. However, the dimension "extension" as well as that of "duration" are of great significance when the overall reaction of the individual to pain is taken into account. On the whole, these dimensions of pain have received less attention than those of the other senses, but with the recognition of pain as a sensation a wider application of such experimental techniques has begun in this field (114).

Resulting from the difference in criteria which have been applied by different investigators for distinguishing one sensation from another, there has arisen a confusion as to the number and kind of sensations. Boring, in his analysis of this difficult subject (51), points out that there are four bases for making such a distinction, namely, physiological, functional, qualitative, and perceptual. To us, a more attractive choice of words designating these criteria would be anatomical, physiological and perceptual, (making no distinction between "qualitative" and "perceptual").

The criterion "physiological" as used by Boring, refers to the normal anatomical, neurophysiological, and sensory-physiological aspects of the sensation. As regards pain, the histological identification by Weddell and others of specific pain endings appears to be satisfactory. More recently, Woollard confirmed and extended these observations and established the fact that the peripheral neural apparatus subserving pain consists of fine free nerve endings which form networks in the skin, the cornea of the eye, the walls of blood vessels, muscle tissue, viscera, and in the perineural sheaths of the nerves themselves. Other investigators, by using electrophysiological methods, have been able to identify both myelinated and non-myelinated fibers as pathways subserving pain. The fiber pathways in the cord which mediate impulses resulting from noxious peripheral stimulation are found especially in the ventrolateral portion of the cord. These pathways terminate in the posterolateral ventral nucleus of the thalamus (350). Electrical stimulation of the cerebral cortex does not produce pain (338), while tumors in the postcentral portion of the cortex may be associated with paroxysmal pain somewhere in the periphery (311). Thus, although a cortical field-area for pain sense has not as yet been established, the same limitation applies equally to other sensations such as heat and cold. As regards the criterion "anatomical", pain, therefore, fulfills many of the requirements for being an independent sensation.

The physiological characteristics of sensation have to do with their functional relationships to certain stimuli (thresholds, spatial summation, "Weber Ratio" characteristics, etc.) and with the importance of the sensation to the body economy. For example, hearing is evoked by extremely small periodic changes in air pressure. Such stimuli, called "adequate" stimuli, have a low intensity threshold. Further, the body economy is served by the sensation of hearing, as it provides one of the important contacts between the individual and his environment. From the point of view of sensory physiology, pain is a separate entity having its own thresholds, its own Weber-Law characteristics, and its own spatial summation factor, all three being different from those of other senses.

As regards the body economy many stimuli, both internal and external, give rise to pain. Pain serves a useful purpose as being a warning of injury from influences in the external or internal environment. Body tissues can be injured by mechanical, thermal, electrical, or chemical agents, and these are the particular stimuli which evoke pain. However, below certain intensities these stimuli do not elicit pain and cause no tissue damage. For example, thermal radiation evokes pain at a threshold (expressed in millicalories per second per square centimeter) which is 2000 times that of the warmth threshold. The pain threshold (see Chapter IV) as determined by the thermal radiation method lies at a level at which tissue damage first occurs. The close relationship between pain stimulation and tissue damage suggest that the common effect of the variety of stimuli in eliciting pain is tissue damage. From this it would seem that some aspect of tissue injury is the prime factor, i.e., the "adequate stimulus" for pain sensation.

From a physiological point of view, therefore, pain qualifies as a sensation of importance to the self-preservation of the individual. Persons without pain sense must learn to make adjustments to their environment by using other senses.

The perceptual characteristic of pain lies in the fundamental nature of the sensation with its unique esthetic features, causing it to be different qualitatively from other sensations. To distinguish vision clearly from hearing by their different qualities is simple, indeed. There is general agreement that pain, too, can be distinguished qualitatively from other sensations. In contrast, the sensations "wet" and "dry" seem to be compounded of the more basic sensations, touch, heat and cold. As mentioned earlier, one of the difficulties in considerations of the introspectional aspects of pain has been the confusion of the perceptual features of the pain sensation as such with the feeling states that often accompany it. It is the point of view of the present authors that an adequate analysis of the pain experience requires a separation of the two aspects. If this be accepted, pain stands clearly as a sensation from the perceptual point of view.

SUMMARY

In concluding these considerations it might be well to restate briefly the various concepts concerning pain. Until the beginning of the nineteenth century pain was thought to be exclusively a *feeling* state and the normal opposite to pleasure. This concept was countered by the *intensive theory* of pain which came to the fore during the latter half of the century. It considered pain to be the result of excessive intensity of other sensations. This view was replaced by the *sensory theory* which seems now well established.

Recent evidence supports the old view that the feeling state may perchance be the most relevant aspect of pain to the one who suffers. Yet, it supports as well the conclusion that pain is a specific sensation with its own structural, functional, and perceptual properties. It becomes apparent that these two concepts do not oppose each other; both represent attempts to formulate distinct but fundamental aspects of the pain experience. Thus, a fourth theory of pain might be proposed to take into account the complex interaction of the components of the pain experience as well as the counterparts themselves. This concept, which is developed in the following chapters, holds a pain experience to be composed not only of pain sensation but of associated sensations and of emotional and affective states as well. Every sensation of pain (ache, prick, burn) is thus viewed as accompanied by a more or less predictable pattern of associated sensations (such as heat, cold, pressure) and feeling states (i.e., anger, fear, pleasantness, unpleasantness), the sensory resultant being the total pain experience for a particular individual. Such a concept does not fail to take into account the fact that important bodily reactions to noxious stimulation, themselves entirely below the level of conscious activity, may contribute new sources of noxious stimulation and pain. Also, because of the intimate linkage of pain sensation with strong emotions, feelings, and behavior patterns, these may be dominant in the experience. However, since by definition the pain experience must include pain sensation, associated phenomena, although important, are given secondary consideration in this essay.

Chapter II

FORM AND FUNCTIONS OF STRUCTURES SUBSERVING PAIN

A brief survey of the structures which make up the neural apparatus subserving pain is essential to an understanding of the phenomenology of pain. Starting with the peripheral structures, the pain endings in the skin and the fiber tracts, the following outline will include the pathways in the cord, and the organization at the cord level.

Nerve Endings and Fibers Subserving Pain Sensation

Although pain is elicited from deep somatic and visceral structures as well as the skin, the latter has been more carefully studied as regards the sensory nerve fiber terminations. This aspect was first systematically studied by von Frey and later re-investigated by Woollard and Weddell (499, 461). Figure 3 shows a composite drawing of a cross-section of human skin with all identifiable nerve endings. Pain endings are the unspecialized or free nerve endings that form a closely interlocking network of fine fibrils in the most superficial skin layers. The depth of these pain terminals beneath the surface of the forearm is roughly 0.04 mm.; they are the most superficial sensory endings in the skin. As shown in figure 4 the nerve fibers serving these endings are collected into bundles in the superficial subcutaneous tissues. The larger of these fibers have myelin sheaths (so-called "medullated" fibers) and conduct the neural impulse rapidly to the spinal cord. The smallest fibers have no myelin sheaths ("non-medullated") and conduct impulses slowly to the cord.

All fibers carrying impulses experienced as pain enter the spinal cord or brain stem through the dorsal root ganglia. Impulses resulting from noxious stimulation of cutaneous tissue are usually conveyed by the somatic nerves and enter the cord more or less directly through the dorsal roots. Impulses resulting from noxious stimulation of deeper tissue may approach the central nervous system in a number of ways: some are conveyed by afferent nerve

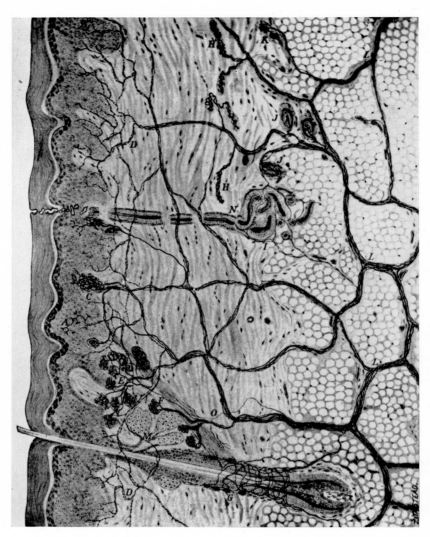

Fig. 3. Composite Diagram Showing the Innervation of the Human Skin
A: Merkel's discs, subserving touch. B: Free endings, subserving pain. C:
Meissner's corpuscles, subserving touch. D: Nerve fibers, subserving pain. E:
Krause's end bulbs, subserving cold. F: Nerve endings, subserving warmth (sometimes called Ruffini's endings). G: Nerve fibers and endings on hair follicle, subserving touch. H: Ruffini's endings, subserving pressure. I: Sympathetic nerve
fibers innervating a sweat gland. J: Pacinian corpuscles, subserving pressure.
K: Golgi-Mazzoni endings, subserving pressure. L: Nerve trunks containing
thick and thin fibers. M: Sebaceous gland. N: Sweat gland. O: Sympathetic
nerve fibers supplying erector pili muscle. Drawing composed from methylene-
blue and reduced silver preparations. The functional interpretations summarized
above are based upon observations by H. H. Woollard, G. Weddell and J. A.
Harpman. (Reprinted from the Journal of Anatomy, **74**: 427, Part IV, July 1940,
Cambridge University Press.)

fibers which attach themselves to blood vessels for part of the way and then join autonomic nerves; other fibers join with somatic nerves. The course they assume in approaching the dorsal root ganglia is irrelevant to a consideration of the quality of pain or the reflexes aroused (460, 121, 72, 255, 467, 231, 274, 6, 133, 280, 314).

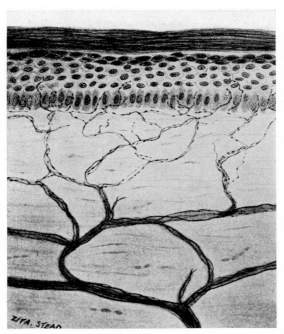

Fig. 4. Drawing Showing the Arrangement in the Skin of the Human Forearm of Nerve Fibers and Nerve Endings Subserving Pain
Composite drawing from methylene-blue and reduced silver preparations. ×1100. (Reprinted from Woollard, H. H.; Weddell, G. and Harpman, J. A.: Observations on the Neurohistological Basis of Cutaneous Pain. Journal of Anatomy, **74**: 426, Part IV, July 1940, Cambridge University Press.)

Although pain endings are usually naked and unmyelinated, with or without slightly swollen twigs, there is no uniformity in the size of fibers which conduct impulses resulting from noxious stimulation to the cord and brain. Fibers conducting such impulses may be roughly grouped as regards speed of conduction of impulses into slow and rapid, involving respectively small and large caliber fibers (83, 143). It has been shown by Gasser (145) that the gamut of size involved in the conduction of impulses giving rise to pain is wide, spreading from the very smallest to large caliber fibers.

27

The relation of the various parts of a neuron may be obtained from the sketch in figure 5 of a myelinated or medullated fiber (58). The nerve impulse is initiated at the peripheral terminations and travels as a wave over the axon to the cell body or soma, and to the dendrites. The myelin sheath and neurilemma afford elec-

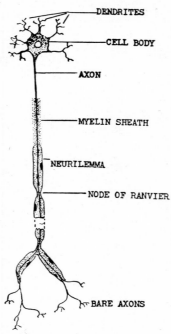

FIG. 5. DIAGRAM SHOWING DIFFERENT PARTS OF THE NEURON
Adapted from Brink (58)

trical insulation to the axon and at the same time increase the speed of travel of the impulse. The dendrites serve to pass the activity in the form of a wave of negativity to adjacent cells through the synaptic junction (33). The synaptic junction is composed of small terminal enlargements in contact with the cell body and dendrites of the receptor cell. This "synaptic scale" (see fig. 6) induces a state of negativity in the neuron which when of threshold value causes it to discharge. This negativity is thus an electrical indicator of a state of excitation even though

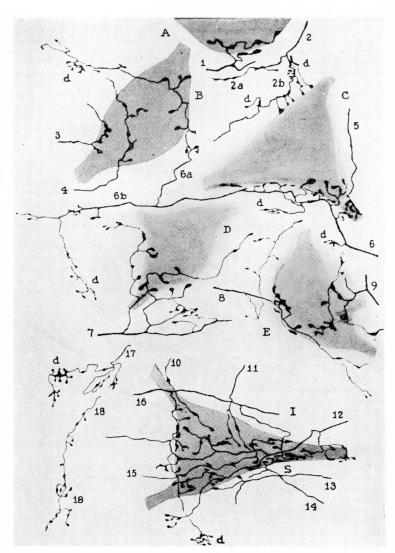

FIG. 6. SYNAPSES ON MOTONEURONS (A TO E) AND ON A LARGE INTERNUNCIAL (I) OF THE SPINAL CORD OF A 15–16-DAY-OLD CAT

Silver-chromate method of Golgi. d: synaptic knobs in contact with dendrites. (Reprinted from p. 200: Lorente de Nò, R.: Synaptic stimulation of motoneurons as a local process. J. Neurophys. **1**: 195, 1938.)

below threshold level; intercellular transmission of excitation is the basis of neural integration and occurs in only one direction—dendrite to soma. A cross-sectional photograph of a peripheral nerve (fig. 7) (97) shows the variations in the diameters of nerve fibers present. The larger fibers, of the "A" group, which subserve pain have diameters of roughly three to eight microns and conduct impulses at 15 to 40 meters per second; the small "C" fibers,

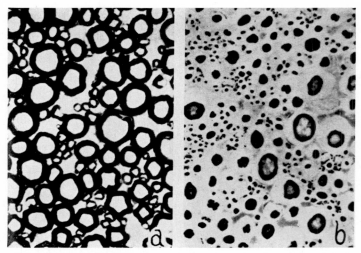

FIG. 7. a) Photomicrograph of a cross-section of a dorsal root of the third sacral nerve in dog. Osmic-acid stain, ×1000. Oil-immersion objective. b) The same, silver stain, ×1400. (Reprinted from p. 205: Davenport, H. A. and Ranson, S. W.: Ratios of cells to fibers and of myelinated to unmyelinated fibers in spinal nerve roots. Am. J. Anat. **49:** 193, 1931.)

also mediating pain, conduct impulses at 0.6 to 2 meters per second (171).

The painful sensations mediated by these fiber groups can be distinguished by stimulating a finger or a toe with a hot object. Two sensations of pain are felt, one after the other; the first due to A fiber impulses, and the second due to the slower C fibers (83).

THE NERVE IMPULSE

The signal conducted along the nerve has an electrical manifestation, termed the impulse. The electrically polarized membrane of the nerve axon is conceived of as being progressively neutralized by the passage of the impulse and of being immediately repolarized after the impulse has passed. A series of such impulses or volleys is the typical signal carried along the nerve fiber from the stimulated sensory organ to the spinal cord. The frequency of the nerve impulse can be measured by the placing of suitable electrodes along the nerve fiber and connecting them to an oscillograph. As nerve fibers obey the "all or none" law (i.e., respond maximally or not at all) each impulse is similar to the next, although the frequency, or number of impulses per second, increases with the intensity of the stimulus. This is demonstrated with remarkable clarity in figure 8 showing the response of a pressure receptor to increasing pressures (60). As noted in Chapter I the relationship between stimulus intensity and impulse frequency is logarithmic, and as is to be expected there is a definite limit to the number of impulses that can be carried by a single fiber. The impulses can crowd together only up to the point which is determined by the time required by the nerve membrane to repolarize.

Peripheral Pathways Subserving Pain Sensation

For purposes of gross orientation concerning those structures that are pain sensitive, and the pathways by which they are subserved, the following general survey is presented.

Erroneous inferences have been drawn that certain structures of the body are not pain sensitive because pain cannot be induced in them by stimuli commonly productive of pain in the skin, such as pricking, cutting and pinching (274). Thus, in the case of the mesentery of the intestines or the visceral peritoneum over the spleen, scratching or cutting may not be painful, while a pull from traction in the one case and rapid distention in the other may be painful. The parenchyma of the lung and liver have been alleged to be devoid of nerves capable of transmitting impulses interpreted as pain because they may be cut and pinched during operations in the conscious patient without inducing pain. This evidence, however, as indicated, does not allow of such a sweeping inference. The adequacy of a stimulus may depend not only on its nature but also on the state of the tissue stimulated.

Among other tissues of ectodermal origin, the skin and cornea are richly supplied with pain endings and are consequently sensi-

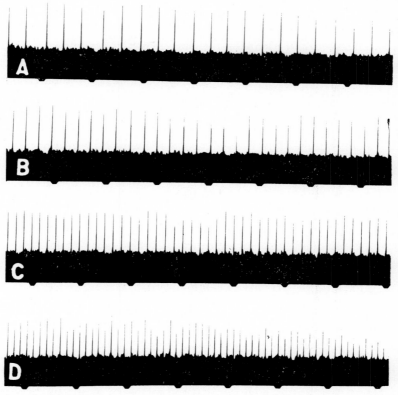

FIG. 8. AFFERENT IMPULSES FROM A SINGLE END ORGAN IN THE CAROTID SINUS STIMULATED BY CONSTANT PRESSURES WITHIN THE SINUS

In A: 40 mm. Hg; B: 80 mm. Hg; C: 140 mm. Hg; D: 200 mm. Hg. Time marker gives ⅕ second. (Reprinted from p. 711: Bronk, D. W. and Stella, G.: The response to steady pressures of single end organs in the isolated carotid sinus. Am. J. Physiol. **110:** 708, 1934–35.)

tive to pain aroused by a variety of stimuli. Similarly the dentine and deeper structures of the teeth are sensitive to pain.

Most tissues of mesodermal origin are supplied with pathways which conduct impulses giving rise to pain sensation; notably the subcutaneous bone is sensitive as is the cancellous portion, but existing evidence indicates that the cortex and marrow cavities of bones are not equipped with receptors for pain. The marrow itself is pain sensitive (107). Stimulation of fascia, ligaments, articular capsules and synoviae has been found to evoke pain, but this is not true of the articular cartilage (271). These structures are often implicated in pains which occur after sudden reduction in atmospheric pressure, as in decompression and altitude sickness. In the latter condition, nitrogen bubbles have been demonstrated about the joints (41, 371). In the case of skeletal muscle, cutting, pricking and pinching are less painful than when applied to the skin. Chemical irritant injected into muscles may give rise to intense pain but usually pain in the intact body arises from muscles in association with stretching and tearing, ischemia, and unduly forceful or sustained contractile activity (275, 298). In both of the latter the nerve endings are, according to recent evidence, probably stimulated by an excessive concentration of potassium (194). It has been shown that a large portion of headaches, especially those accompanied by stiffness or tenderness in the neck and occipital region, are due to unduly sustained contraction of underlying head and neck muscles (403). It is likely that a similar mechanism explains many backaches (221a). Ischemia of muscles induces the pain in the extremities in intermittent claudication and occlusive vascular disease and is the basis of the pain of coronary occlusion (275).

In the chest, the visceral pleura is not pain sensitive, while the parietal pleura is richly supplied through the intercostal nerves with endings sensitive to painful stimuli, and, on the diaphragmatic surface, by the phrenic nerve as well (72). The lower portion of the fibrous pericardium appears to be supplied by fibers from the phrenic nerve which subserve pain. Elsewhere and throughout their serous surfaces the visceral and parietal pericardia are not pain sensitive.

Other mesodermal structures frequently involved in the genesis of pain are the blood vessels. Distortion of cranial vessels by pulling, displacement or distention has been found to be the source of a large proportion of headaches, including the headache of brain tumor, and headache associated with variations in the pressure of the cerebrospinal fluid (488).

Most endodermal structures, when stimulated under appropriate circumstances, are found to be pain sensitive. These include the mucosa and deeper structures of the gut (232) and the mucosal linings of the urethra, bladder, ureters, and kidney pelvis (298).

Below the head, the sites of painful sensations bear a more readily recognizable segmental relationship to the sites stimulated. For the skin and the supporting structures, this distribution is well known and localization of pain from noxious stimulation is sharp. The distribution on the body is in belt-like strips arranged obliquely, higher posteriorly over the spine and lower anteriorly over the chest and abdomen (see figs. 9 and 10). The neck and region above the clavicle are supplied by C3. The slope of the shoulders and the region anteriorly just beneath the clavicle are supplied by C4. Segments C5 to T1 supply the shoulders and upper extremities. This more complex distribution is illustrated in figures 11 and 12 (225). The thoracic segments supply areas on the body below that indicated for C4. There is considerable overlapping of ramifying branches but the following landmarks serve as useful orientation for the distribution of the various segments. T4 supplies the area in which would fall a line drawn along the fifth rib to the midsternum through the nipples. T10 supplies an area in which would fall a line drawn along the twelfth rib and extended through the umbilicus. T12 extends from the flank region in back, anteriorly along Poupart's ligament. Among these various landmarks lie in orderly fashion the areas of distribution of the other thoracic segments. The lumbar and sacral segments are concerned with supplying the lower extremities and perineum. These more complex distributions are illustrated in figures 13 and 14 (225).

The segmental distribution for the deeper structures including muscles, ligaments, and periosteum differs from that in the skin mainly in the extremities and the region of the shoulders and pelvic girdle. Here, in the region of the angle of the scapula, for example, periosteum, tendons, and muscles are innervated by the seventh cervical segment, while the overlying skin is supplied by branches from seven or more segments below, namely T6 to T9 (see figure 10). Elsewhere the segmental innervation is arranged approximately as that in the overlying skin. From most viscera, however, afferent impulses travel into the cord over a large number of roots which may be remote from the viscus itself. Thus, several segments may be involved. Data concerning pathways for noxious impulses from viscera have come mainly from studies involving surgical interruption of pathways either in the sympathetic chains,

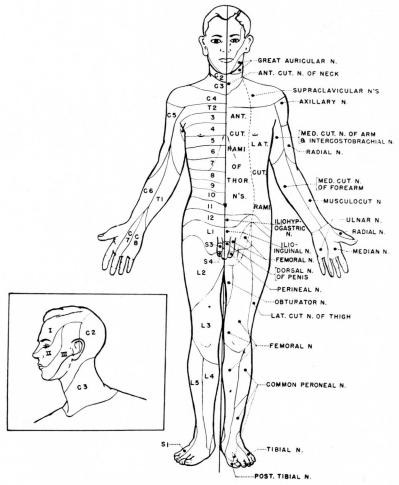

FIG. 9. ANTERIOR VIEW

On left of midline: dermatomes of man. On right of midline: approximate distributions of nerves innervating the skin (Wolf and Wolff, 484a).

the dorsal roots or in the cord. The visceral contents of the abdominal cavity can be deafferented as regards pain by resection

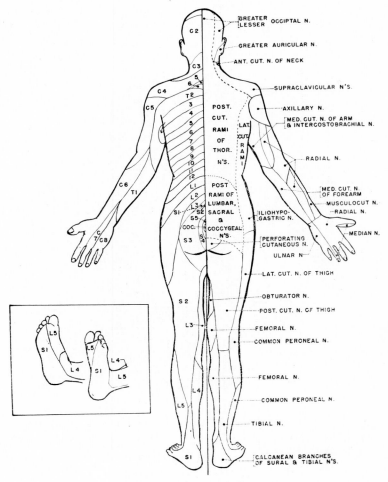

FIG. 10. POSTERIOR VIEW

On left of midline: dermatomes of man. On right of midline: approximate distributions of nerves innervating the skin (Wolf and Wolff, 484a).

of the sympathetic ganglionated chain from the stellate through the third lumbar. These sizeable nerves contain both autonomic (efferent) fibers and sensory (afferent) fibers. Some of the organs are innervated unilaterally but most have bilateral innervation. Much confusion could be eliminated if it were appreciated that "sympathectomy" within the abdominal cavity is always deafferentation as well. Section of the so-called sympathetic nerves for abdominal pain presents the advantage of specific organ analgesia without involving peritoneum, muscle, or skin sensation.

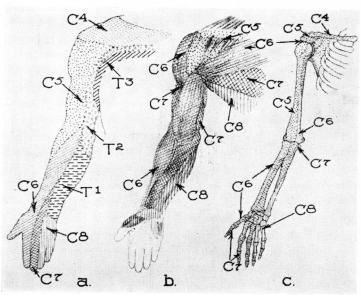

FIG. 11. DERMATOMES AND SCLEROTOMES OF THE UPPER EXTREMITY a) skin, b) muscles and c) skeletal structures in front view (Inman and Saunders, 225).

The emphasis on the referral of deep pain to skin segments has clouded awareness of the fact that deep pain from skeleton or viscera may be felt in situ and may be referred along the distribution of the deep branches of a segmental nerve and not be felt in the skin.

Cutaneous dermatomes, of course, are commonly involved with deep pain. The fact that a referred pain actually involves skin is most readily established by the presence of hyperalgesia.

Also, a referred pain need not involve the whole segment of reference (298), and, in fact, usually does not. Most pains arising from disease in abdominal viscera are felt anteriorly on the abdomen in the ventral part of the dermatomes concerned. Ureteral pain is first felt anteriorly, and posteriorly in the flanks only when the stimulus is intense. Pain resulting from noxious stimulation of the kidney pelvis a few millimeters away, however, is characteristically first felt at the costo-vertebral angle. Pain from noxious

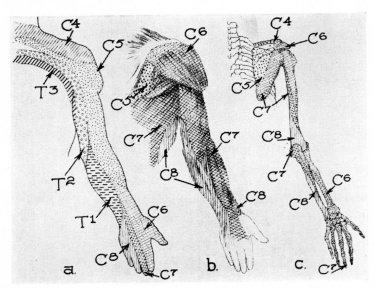

FIG. 12. DERMATOMES AND SCLEROTOMES OF THE UPPER EXTREMITY
a) skin, b) muscles and c) skeletal structures in rear view (Inman and Saunders, 225).

stimulation of the gallbladder may be felt only posteriorly at the angle of the scapula in one portion of the tissue supplied by the ninth thoracic segment. Thus, pains from deep structures may be felt in situ and often fairly well localized. They may be referred along the deep distribution of spinal nerves or along their cutaneous distribution, or both. Reference occurs most readily first to certain other parts supplied by the same segment, next to tissue supplied by adjacent segments higher in the cord, next to adjacent segments lower down, and finally to corresponding segments on the opposite side of the cord, without ever involving the whole of the distribution of the original segment (440). Disease of specific organs of the body often gives rise to a pattern of distribution of pain which is characteristic of that organ. Why noxious stimula-

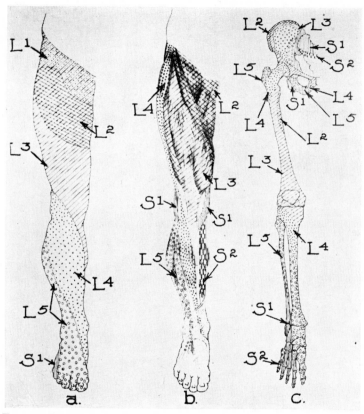

FIG. 13. DERMATOMES AND SCLEROTOMES OF THE LOWER EXTREMITY a) skin, b) muscles and c) skeletal structures in front view (Inman and Saunders, 225).

tion of several structures innervated by the same segments are referred along more or less characteristic pathways involving specific parts of the segments and the tissues so supplied is not clear but is probably related to use and experience. One is generally more conscious of the anterior half of his body than the posterior and is especially conscious of parts which customarily receive noxious stimuli from the outside, such as the precordium and epigastrium. Hence, it is suggested that these parts of the thoracic segments are most involved in painful experiences originating from beneath the surface. Similarly, in the head, the eye is prominently

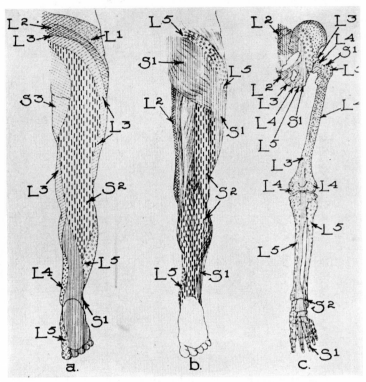

FIG. 14. DERMATOMES AND SCLEROTOMES OF THE LOWER EXTREMITY
a) skin, b) muscles and c) skeletal structures in rear view (Inman and Saunders, 225).

involved in painful syndromes since the eye is a structure which is continually exposed to noxious stimuli resulting from particles of dust and other foreign bodies.

Cardiac Pain

Noxious stimulation of the heart gives rise to impulses that travel in company with sympathetic nerves, entering the sympa-

thetic chains from the middle cervical to the fifth thoracic ganglion. Here the involved afferent fibers are contiguous with the
sympathetic chain, and enter the cord with the upper five thoracic
dorsal roots (218) (see fig. 15). Characteristically, pain from the
heart is felt in situ beneath the sternum. Referred pain to the
surface is localized mainly in the anterior portion of thoracic segments 3–6 with hyperesthesia involving the precordial area, and
the medial aspect of the left shoulder and arm in the distribution
of T1 and 2. The area of reference of cardiac pain may, however,
extend over a wider distribution, i.e., from C3 to T10 (467, 231).
Thus, the pain may be confused with that arising from noxious
stimulation of other structures, innervated from the same segments, notably the biliary passages, diaphragm, mediastinum,
esophagus, apex of the lung, cervical and thoracic spinal cord and
nerve roots, and skeletal and muscular structures about the left
shoulder and chest. When cardiac pain reaches to the lower jaw it
may suggest disease of the teeth.

Pulmonary, Diaphragmatic and Pleuropericardial Pain

The visceral pleura is apparently not a pain sensitive structure.
From the parietal pleura noxious impulses reach the cord via the
intercostal nerves and hence pains are felt in the area of the dermatomes immediately overlying the site of stimulation (467). This
is true also of the portion of the parietal pleura reflected over the
peripheral border of the diaphragm (see fig. 16). Posteriorly, where
a considerable extent of the diaphragm lies against the chest wall,
pain resulting from noxious stimulation of its pleural surface may
be felt in tissue supplied by thoracic segments 7–12 including the
lower thorax, lower back, epigastrium and even lower abdomen.
In patients with diaphragmatic pleurisy associated with pneumo-
nia, occurrence of pain in the right lower quadrant of the abdomen
with localized tenderness, cutaneous hyperesthesia in the region
of McBurney's point and spasm of underlying muscles has been
described (72).

Noxious stimulation of the central portion of the diaphragmatic
pleura which is supplied by branches of the phrenic nerve gives
rise to pain in the region of the trapezius muscle in the neck and

shoulder, the cutaneous distribution of the third and fourth cervical segments of the cord.

Phrenic nerve endings also supply the lower portion of the pari-

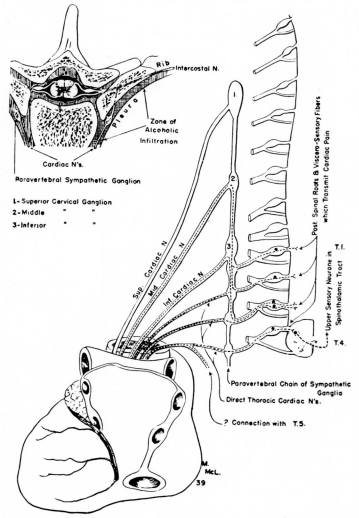

FIG. 15. AFFERENT NERVE PATHWAYS FOR HEART AND LOCATION OF
PARAVERTEBRAL SYMPATHETIC GANGLIA
(J. C. White and R. H. Smithwick, 466)

etal pericardium and thus noxious stimulation of this membrane also causes pain in the trapezius region. Noxious stimulation of the parietal pericardium a few centimeters from the diaphragm, however, does not induce pain. Neither has the visceral pericardium been found to be pain sensitive. The frequent association of pain in the chest with certain types of pericarditis has been ascribed to

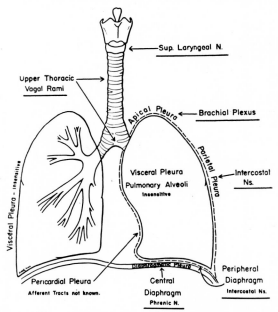

FIG. 16. AFFERENT NERVE PATHWAYS FOR RESPIRATORY TREE AND PLEURAL
SURFACES (J. C. White, 467)

noxious stimulation of the pleural surfaces adjacent to the pericardium.

The lungs and bronchi are innervated by fibers from the third and fourth cervical segments which are carried in the vagal rami to the cord (467). Sensations arising from noxious stimulation of these structures are not necessarily referred to the cervical region, however, and are often correctly localized.

The parenchyma of the lung can be pinched, pulled, cut and cauterized without inducing pain. Traction on any of the attachments of the lung cause pain to be felt substernally (220a). Distention with a balloon (160) as well as electrical stimulation of the tracheobronchial tree (318a) induces aching and burning pain in the homolateral anterior chest. Unilateral vagotomy immediately below the origin of the recurrent laryngeal nerve eliminates pain and cough resulting from stimulation of the homolateral bronchial tree. Reduction of pain and cough in those with bronchogenic carcinoma has been achieved by unilateral vagotomy (318a). Impulses from the diaphragm resulting from noxious stimulation travel mainly in the phrenic nerve, entering the cord in the third, fourth and fifth cervical dorsal roots. The peripheral portion of the diaphragm receives fibers from intercostal nerves and thus, as in the case of the pleural surface, noxious stimulation of the muscle near its insertion will give rise to pain felt in the thoracic dermatomes. Areas of reference for pain in the diaphragm may extend as far down over the abdomen and lumbar region as T12. Indeed, the pain of coronary occlusion has been closely simulated by diaphragmatic spasm (481).

Gastrointestinal Pain

In the gastrointestinal tract impulses from noxious stimulation arise principally from one or more of three sources: 1) local noxious stimulation of an engorged or inflamed mucosa; 2) distortion of pain endings in the muscular elements by distension or spasm of the tube; 3) traction upon mesenteric attachments.

ESOPHAGUS

From the esophagus nerve impulses resulting from noxious stimulation travel in fibers alongside of sympathetic nerves to the chains of sympathetic ganglia. From here they may enter the cord via dorsal root ganglia anywhere from the lowest cervical through the entire thoracic distribution (see fig. 17). Whether or not the vagus participates in carrying visceral efferent fibers involved in pain is still unsettled (467). The commonest pain from noxious stimulation of the esophagus is "heartburn", a burning pain felt substernally over the site of stimulation. Such pain may result from spasm of the cardiac end of the esophagus (232). The spasm may be induced by mechanical, thermal, chemical and electrical stimulation. "Heartburn" may also result either directly or indirectly from the regurgitation of highly acid gastric juices into the esophagus which has already had its pain threshold lowered by the presence of engorgement and inflammation (486).

Not only is the pain of "heartburn" of a burning quality but the pain of peptic ulcer which arises from the stomach and duodenum is also frequently described as burning. It is of special interest that burning pain, ordinarily associated with noxious stimulation of the skin, can be elicited by stimulation of the upper gastrointestinal tract and of other mucous membranes as, for example, in the nose.

STOMACH AND ADJACENT STRUCTURES

The pathways for afferent impulses from the stomach have not been clearly delineated but those which mediate pain appear to be carried in the splanchnic sympathetic trunks and enter the cord via the seventh to ninth thoracic dorsal roots (see fig. 17).

Afferent impulses resulting from noxious stimulation of the pancreas, liver and biliary tracts appear to travel in the same pathways as do those from the stomach. These facts explain in part the difficulties encountered in differential diagnosis of epigastric pain. Not only may it arise from those structures named but also from retroperitoneal tissues, skeletal muscles and from lesions of the nervous system such as posterior poliomyelitis and cord tumors which involve dorsal roots. Epigastric pains may even be the result of reference from the heart or other thoracic structures or from impulses arising in the lower bowel including the transverse colon and appendix. The parenchyma of the liver has not been shown to be pain sensitive but noxious stimulation by rapid distension of its capsule does give rise to pain. The same generalizations apply to other solid organs including the spleen and probably the kidneys. Pain from the gallbladder has been found to be commonly localized in the distribution of T9 (352) either anteriorly beneath the right costal margin or posteriorly at the angle of the scapula.

SMALL AND LARGE INTESTINES

Afferent impulses resulting from noxious stimulation of the small intestine also travel with splanchnic autonomic fibers but enter the cord from T9 to T11. The afferent innervation of the colon subserving pain above the sigmoid and the sympathetic trunks are contiguous. Below this level it is probably mainly supplied by afferent fibers through its mesenteries along with the lower thoracic sympathetic and parasympathetic fibers. The rec-

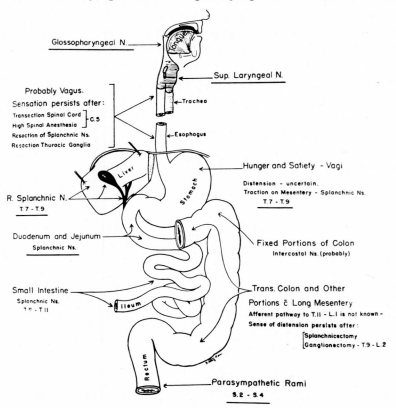

Glossopharyngeal N.

Sup. Laryngeal N.

Probably Vagus.
Sensation persists after:
Transection Spinal Cord ⎱ C.5
High Spinal Anesthesia ⎰
Resection of Splanchnic Ns.
Resection Thoracic Ganglia

←Trachea

←Esophagus

Hunger and Satiety - Vagi

R. Splanchnic N.
T.7 - T.9

Distension - uncertain.
Traction on Mesentery - Splanchnic Ns.
T.7 - T.9

Duodenum and Jejunum
Splanchnic Ns.

Fixed Portions of Colon
Intercostal Ns.(probably)

Small Intestine
Splanchnic Ns.
T.9 - T.11

Ileum

Trans. Colon and Other
Portions c̄ Long Mesentery
Afferent pathway to T.11 - L.1 is not known -
Sense of distension persists after:
Splanchnicectomy
Ganglionectomy - T.9 - L.2

Rectum

Parasympathetic Rami
S.2 - S.4

FIG. 17. AFFERENT NERVE PATHWAYS FOR ALIMENTARY TRACT
(J. C. White, 466)

tum, however, is supplied by afferent nerves through the parasympathetic rami and dorsal roots from S2-S4 (see fig. 17).

Urinary Tract Pain

In the urogenital tract, renal and ureteral pain arises from impulses reaching the cord via the lower splanchnic trunks and the lower two thoracic and first lumbar dorsal roots. Noxious stimulation of the ureter, in addition to pain, often gives rise to secondary painful spasms of lumbo-dorsal muscles which may long outlast the period of noxious stimulation of the ureter or renal pelvis. Noxious stimulation by distension of the detrusor muscles initiates afferent impulses which, like those from the lower colon and rectum appear to travel in segmental nerves in the peritoneum.

From the trigone and structures below the bladder afferent impulses resulting from noxious stimulation reach the cord over the sacral parasympathetic rami and dorsal roots from S2–S4 (see fig. 18). Noxious stimulation of the bladder trigone and region of the urethral origin causes pain to be felt at the distal tip of the urethra. Prostatic pain may be felt in the perineum or referred to the lower lumbar region where it may be confused with skeletal, muscular, nerve or renal pain. Pains resulting from noxious stimulation of the spermatic cords and testicular structures are felt largely in situ but may be referred to the hypogastric region where they may be mistaken for pains emanating from the colon region. Renal colic may be experienced as pain in the testes and along the groin and inner aspects of the thighs and may appear to arise from the spermatic channels or from local vascular lesions such as thrombophlebitis.

In the female, afferent impulses from noxious stimulation of the fundus uteri reach the central nervous system by way of the superior hypogastric plexus entering the cord via dorsal roots from T10 to L1 (272, 273, 85). From the cervix and from the bladder neck, on the other hand, they ascend with the second and fourth sacral nerves and enter the cord via corresponding dorsal roots. Afferent impulses resulting from noxious stimulation of the Fallopian tubes and ovaries reach the cord via the tenth thoracic dorsal root contiguous with the plexus of nerves that accompany ovarian vessels. Closely contiguous structures including the broad ligaments and other mesenteric and retroperitoneal structures are innervated as regards structures subserving pain by branches of the lumbosacral plexus and segmental nerves (see fig. 19). Thus, to relieve the pain of ovarian carcinoma, it is necessary to sever a wide extent of pathways in order to denervate the various structures almost invaded by the growth.

The commonest pains arising from the female genital structures are those of dysmenorrhea and labor. It is likely that most dys-

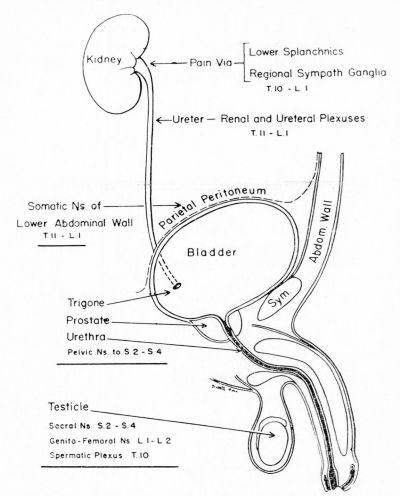

FIG. 18. AFFERENT NERVE PATHWAYS FOR MALE UROGENITAL TRACT
(J. C. White, 466)

menorrheic pains are related to the subject's reaction to contractions of the uterine musculature. Pelvic congestion may also be a factor. Pain may occur during menstruation with certain disease states from traction on adherent structures involved in an inflammatory, fibrotic, or neoplastic process. The pains of labor arise from the vigorous and sustained muscular contraction of the fundus uteri.

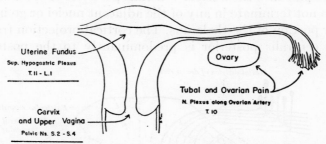

Uterine Fundus
Sup. Hypogastric Plexus
T. II - L. I

Ovary

Tubal and Ovarian Pain
N. Plexus along Ovarian Artery
T. 10

Cervix
and Upper Vagina
Pelvic Ns. S.2 - S.4

Fig. 19. Afferent Nerve Pathways for Female Genital Structures
(J. C. White, 466)

Neural Structures in the Central Nervous System Involved in the Conduction and Integration of Impulses Giving Rise to Pain Sensation

After entering the spinal cord, by way of the dorsal roots, impulses resulting from noxious stimulation of peripheral structures meet their first synaptic relay point (fig. 20). Here, by way of various interneuronal connections the excitation undergoes a first step in integration and thus gives rise to several observable reactions. For example, the withdrawal of a noxiously stimulated hand or foot and the extension of the opposite member indicate that motoneurons have become involved on both sides of the cord. Facilitation, inhibition, summation, and occlusion are only a few of the properties of this integration which can be observed in the simple reflex mentioned. If the noxious stimulation has been sufficiently intense, the spread of the integrated activity in the cord can be observed to include vasomotor and glandular activity. Integration of the activity arising from noxious stimulation within a single cord segment and over segments rostrally and caudally is of so high an order that many of the protective reactions of the body are initiated therein.

Some of the activity is conveyed across the cord to ascending pathways localized in the anterolateral portion of the spinothalamic tract and it is this portion of the initial activity which is responsible for the sensation of pain. The fibers of the spinothalamic tract pass into the nucleus centralis posterior of the thalamus. They do not terminate in any of the adjacent nuclei or go into the anterior portion of the thalamus. The cortical projection from the nucleus centralis posterior is predominantly to the postcentral

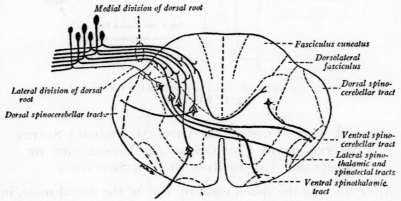

FIG. 20. DIAGRAM OF THE SPINAL CORD IN DORSAL ROOT, SHOWING THE DIVISIONS OF THE DORSAL ROOT, THE COLLATERALS OF THE DORSAL ROOT FIBERS, AND SOME OF THE CONNECTIONS WHICH ARE ESTABLISHED BY THEM)
(Reprinted from p. 106: Ranson, S. W.: The Anatomy of the Nervous System. Philadelphia, W. B. Saunders Co., 1943, 7th ed.)

convolution. There is in this projection a definite topical organization so that those fibers from the medial portion of the nucleus (cephalad parts of the body) end in the lower parts of the gyrus; those from the lateral portion (caudad parts of the body) in the paracentral region; and those from the middle, in the intermediate region (350).

It is probable that the brain structures involved in pain perception occur in both cerebral hemispheres in the region of the central fissure (350, 453, 118, 311). Complete hemianalgesia is rare after destruction of fibers in either hemisphere. More specifically, pain from the face seems to have both homolateral and contralateral cortical representation so that unilateral hemispherectomy does not result in analgesia of the face. Although the thalamus is important in the integration of neural activity having to do with pain, the cortex is essential to discriminations involving localization and intensity. That there is also mid-brain sensory integration is suggested by the survival of pain sensation after destruction of the fibers entering the thalamus and cortex.

Since electrical stimulation of the cerebral cortex arouses no painful sensations, no more precise localization of structures involved has been defined (338).

Chapter III
METHODS FOR THE STUDY OF PAIN THRESHOLDS

Since pain is an esthetic experience its perceptual component can be studied only in conscious man, and its presence is best established through reports given by trained subjects. For this reason the emphasis of this discussion is placed on pain threshold measurements in man. Many reaction patterns associated with pain can be studied profitably in laboratory animals and unconscious man. The distinction between perception of and reaction to pain must be emphasized, as these two components of the pain experience are not always predictably related. A human subject may or may not perceive pain before the effective threshold of a reaction to noxious stimulation is reached (493). Thus, an "alarm" reaction, as measured by changes in electrical skin resistance, may occur in response to a fraction of the stimulus energy necessary to elicit threshold pain; whereas in the same individual under other circumstances such a reaction may not occur until pain well above threshold has been elicited (138).

The threshold sensation of pain may be defined as the least perceptible intensity of pain; the pain threshold stimulus is the amount of stimulus which, on the average, is required to evoke threshold pain, and this measurement should lend itself to expression in standard physical units. The threshold is statistical in concept as threshold pain will be reported for stimuli both above and below the average threshold. The "normal range" of threshold values is taken arbitrarily as the range of stimuli included within two standard deviations of the mean. On this basis 95 per cent of the reports can be expected to fall within this range.

A variety of methods has been devised to evoke a threshold sensation of pain and to ascertain the intensity of the stimulus required. These methods include mechanical, chemical, electrical, and thermal procedures any of which may elicit either superficial or deep pain, or both. Goetzl, Burrill and Ivy (152) have reviewed the literature describing the various methods employed up to 1942 for the investigation of pain threshold. They cite: under "mechanical stimulation" 33 reports, under "chemical stimulation" 5, under "electrical stimulation" 32, and under "thermal stimulation" 12 reports.

All of these stimuli—mechanical, chemical, electrical, and thermal—have been used in our laboratory at some time or other as part of a particular investigation. As a result of this experience, certain impressions have been gained as regards the effect of various stimuli in producing pain. Careful observation of the site of stimulation, by whatever method, commonly revealed the evidence of some local tissue changes, such as, for instance, a transient erythema. This could be observed immediately following a tiny prick, or after minimal electrical, thermal, or chemical stimulation strong enough to evoke pain. In search of some local event that might link together the various means of noxious stimulation of tissue, the occurrence of erythema following such stimulation seemed to be more predictable than any other phenomenon. Further, in contrast with stimulation of other sensations, continued *noxious* stimulation invariably so alters the tissue as to interfere with its integrity and disrupt its function. Thus, a close relation between noxious stimulation and tissue damage can be inferred. This has led us to the hypothesis that the production of tissue damage is the result of that type of stimulation termed "noxious", and that noxious stimulation of tissues innervated by pain fibers evokes pain. The relationship may be represented as follows:

$$\left.\begin{array}{l}\text{Electrical} \\ \text{mechanical} \\ \text{thermal} \\ \text{chemical}\end{array}\right\} \text{energy} \rightarrow \text{tissue injury at a rate sufficiently great (noxious stimulation)} \rightarrow \text{afferent impulses at an adequate frequency in nerve tracts subserving pain} \rightarrow \text{pain sensation.}$$

Viewed in this sense "noxious stimulation" occupies the position of the "adequate stimulus" for pain sensation. Experimental evidence for the support of this concept is also found in the fact that the pricking pain threshold for thermal stimulation is reached when the temperature of the skin is raised from any initial temperature to roughly 45°C. Forty-four to 45 degrees centigrade is the threshold temperature range for the production of skin damage, as shown by the experiments of Moritz and Henriques (316). It is not to be inferred from the above that pain always accompanies tissue injury, for in some parts of the body adequate neural apparatus is absent. Also, during the healing process and in chronic inflammation pain is often absent. It is postulated that in these circumstances the rate of production of tissue injury is insufficient to stimulate the pain endings.

For measuring the threshold sensation of pain by whatever method, the stimulus must meet the following requirements:

a) The measurable aspect of the stimulus should be closely associated with changes causing pain, i.e., with noxious stimulation.

b) The stimulus should be one for which, under the same conditions, reproducible quantitative measurements of the pain threshold are obtained.

c) The intensity of the stimulus should be controllable and measurable to a degree higher than the difference between two stimuli which evoke a just noticeable difference in pain sensation.

d) The stimulus should be one for which the ability of the subject to discriminate differences in pain intensity can be ascertained throughout the effective range of the stimulus, i.e., from threshold to "ceiling" pain.

e) The stimulus should cause minimal tissue damage at pain threshold and should be a minor hazard to the subject even at highest intensities.

f) The stimulus should be capable of evoking separately one of the qualities of pain—burning, pricking, aching.

g) The stimulus should be one which can be conveniently applied.

h) The stimulus should be one for which the perception and identification of pain is clear cut, whether or not other sensations are evoked prior to, concomitant with or following the pain.

Generally speaking, either the intensity of noxious stimulation for a fixed time of application, or the time of application of a fixed stimulus intensity can be used for the determination of the pain threshold. This statement implies that there is a reciprocity between time and intensity. The existence of this relationship should be established if time is to be used as a measure of threshold.

MECHANICAL METHODS OF EVOKING PAIN AS A MEANS FOR STUDYING THE PAIN THRESHOLD

By the use of mechanical devices for production of pain by pressure, the amount of pressure and the pain threshold have been related (360, 336, 257). von Frey, in 1897 (449), described two instruments for measuring the thresholds of pressure in the skin, one of which he later adapted for evoking pain. One instrument, called a limen-gauge, or liminometer, was used for the study of touch. The other instrument, adapted for the study of pain, was the hair-stimulator. von Frey chose hairs of different lengths and diameters ($\pm$ 0.05 to 0.2 mm.) measuring on a balance the maximal force required to bend the hair. He found that the force a hair will exert depends upon its length and diameter. With sharp bristles attached to the ends of hairs he tested skin areas for pain sensation. In 250 tests with a 0.5 gm. pressure stimulus he obtained 57.6 per cent reports of pure sensation of pain. There were 16 per cent reports of "no sensation", 6.4 per cent of "contact" only, and 20 per cent of "contact and pain". In this way he demonstrated that the pain threshold with pressure on the skin by fine hair is lower than the touch threshold, an observation which has been repeatedly confirmed by later investigators (179). von Frey also found definite "pain points" scattered more or less abundantly over different parts of the body, and these points responded to the same stimuli with the same quality and intensity of pain sensation. This method of von Frey was discussed in detail by Kiesow (240) in 1928. Later, in 1936, Seevers and Pfeiffer (396) used von Frey's technique to establish the amount of pressure by such hairs required to elicit threshold pain. In using this method, these authors found that the threshold for pain varied widely in different subjects. Fourteen individuals had thresholds ranging from 0.4 to 6.0 grams. The mean of 64 determinations on eight subjects was 1.44 grams, and the mean deviation of all determinations from the group mean was 0.69 grams. Each of these 64 determinations represented the average on five different regions of the face. Seevers, Bennett, Pohle, and Reinardy (395) subsequently modified this method and described an algesimeter for measuring pain thresholds.

In 1949 Bishop (37), using some modifications of von Frey's technique, mapped out pain sensitive areas on the shaved skin of the forearm and on the palm of the hand. He employed on the ends of hairs small spherical beads of solder of various diameters and reported pain threshold values for the various sizes of bead in terms of grams of force per radius squared. He observed on the dry skin of the arm that the pain threshold was between 10 and 20 gm./mm.² for bead diameters ranging from 0.6 to 1.0 mm. On the moist skin of the arm thresholds were 8 to 22 gm./mm.² for stimulator diameters from 0.2 to 1.5 mm. in diameter. The thicker skin of the palm required a greater stimulus, 25 to 100 gm./mm.², to elicit pain. Bishop infers that the constant factor of stimulation at pain threshold elicited by this means is the lateral stretch of the subepithelial nerve net. Perusal of Bishop's data justifies the inference that the pain threshold does not depend on the size of the area stimulated. This supports the view that there is no spatial summation of pain, as previously stated by Hardy et al. (185) on the basis of their studies of pain threshold with thermal radiation (see next chapter).

Kellgren, McGowan and Wood (238), in 1946, tested skin pain thresholds with needles mounted on von Frey hairs. They also studied deep pain thresholds by pressure over the tibia with an algesimeter. With the latter calibrated in pounds the force at which pain was just being felt could be ascertained. It was found to be from 12 to 15 pounds (5.4 to 6.8 kg.). The size of the area stimulated was not given. These investigators found that after the administration of 11 mg. of morphine sulfate the deep pain threshold was raised from an average of 12 lbs. (5.4 kg.) to 24 lbs. (10.8 kg.).

Libman (284), in 1934, in attempting a rough estimate of pain sensitivity grouped individuals according to their reports of pain experienced, as having 0, 1+ and 3+ pain sensitivity. The test consisted of pressing the thumb against the tip of the mastoid bone and the index finger against the styloid process.

Hollander described in 1939 (220) his method for gauging an individual's sensitivity to pain. He placed an elliptical metal grater 3 by 4 in. under a blood pressure cuff around the upper arm, inflated the cuff and noted the pressure at which the subject "winced".

Gluzek, in 1944, (150) devised a "dolorimeter" to measure pain threshold on the flat surface of the middle third of the tibia. With the subject's leg placed on a leg rest, a plunger surrounded by a metal sleeve ending in a rubber ring was rested lightly against the tibia and fixed in position by an adjusting screw. Air was pumped through a gauge into the sleeve cylinder, which forced the plunger against the tibia. Pain threshold was estimated as the amount of air pressure which first elicited pain by this force. In 16,000 tests the normal range of pain threshold extended from 500 to 2700 grams. Age of the persons tested ranged from 6 to 82 years. Most individuals were found to have "a fairly stable pain threshold".

Lewis, Pickering and Rothschild (281) occluded the vessels of a subject's arm by means of a sphygmomanometer cuff. The subject grasped a metal bar, and performed isometric contractions at a constant rhythmic rate until pain occurred. The flexor muscles of the forearm and hand were exercised by vigorous gripping movements at a rate of one per second, each grip developing a tension of from 20 to 28 lbs. To record the force of these regular contractions, the subject grasped the edge of a small table top, on the underside of which was fastened a metal bar with an index finger-rest attached to it. With each grasp of the subject one end of the metal bar pressed upon a thick-walled rubber bulb from which a tube led to a recording stylus. Pain began between the 24th and 45th second.

Harrison and Bigelow (195), for purposes of simplicity, used a modification of the Lewis, Pickering and Rothschild technique. Their method also studied the pain produced by contractions of an ischemic muscle, however, with isotonic rather than isometric contractions. A sphygmomanometer cuff was applied to the arm and inflated to a pressure of 250 mm. Hg. The subject alternately flexed his fingers, forming a tight fist, and extended them fully, performing the entire action rhythmically at the rate of one per second. The number of contractions performed until the subject first experienced pain was noted as the pain threshold, and was found to vary from 30 to 80. Following the intramuscular administration of 15 mg. of morphine sulfate this deep pain threshold was raised by approximately 60 per cent; 25 to 35 per cent following the ingestion of 15 to 30 cc. of 95 per cent ethyl alcohol; and by 20 to 50 per cent following the ingestion of 0.3 gm. of acetylsalicylic acid. In some subjects the threshold was raised by about 20 per cent following the administration of placebos.

A method of inducing pain in the gastrointestinal tract is that of distending the viscus by the inflation of a swallowed balloon. This method, the results of which are not very accurate, was employed by Boring (50) to elicit pain from the gut. It has also been described in detail by Chapman et al (79, 77) who studied pain initiated by this means in the esophagus. The apparatus consisted of a rubber balloon about 3 cm. long attached by a stomach tube to a U-shaped water manometer. The balloon was introduced through the nose and secured in a position from 5 to 10 cm. above the cardiac end of the esophagus. Air was passed into the balloon by a syringe at a rate of rise of water pressure of 2 cm. per second. The subject was taught to point to the location where a sensation of substernal fullness first occurred. When it was thought that the instructions had been understood, ten observations at one-minute intervals were made on each subject.

The results of visceral sensory threshold measurements on 29 normal subjects, as reported by Chapman and Jones (79), showed values ranging from a level of 15 cm. of water pressure for the most sensitive subject, to 89 cm. for the least sensitive. The mean average value of all the thresholds was 37 cm. water pressure with extreme variations of from −60 per cent to +58 per cent. For individual subjects, tested under standard conditions, the variation was from ±5 per cent to ±18 per cent of the particular threshold. In each case the visceral sensory threshold was compared with the cutaneous pain-perception threshold. The rank coefficient of correlation of the two measurements for the group of

29 was 0.57 with a probable error of 0.9. Excepting one subject who had an extremely high cutaneous pain-perception threshold but a low threshold for visceral perception, the figures indicate for this group a significant correlation between cutaneous and visceral sensitivities.

By this method Gaensler (140) measured the pressure needed to evoke pain in the common bile duct. He established a pain threshold and studied the effect upon it of various analgesics. As subjects he used 40 patients who had had surgical exploration and intubation of the common bile duct, with a T tube emerging from the abdomen. The tube was connected by rubber tubing to a three-way manometric system, one limb to an infusion bottle containing sterile saline solution, the second limb to a short manometer containing a glass bubble float to record pressure on a revolving smoked drum, the third limb to a long manometer, graduated in mm., which permitted reading of hydrostatic pressures when the infusion bottle was connected to the system and elevated. The level of the xyphoid process was chosen arbitrarily as the reference zero point for measuring pressure.

The resting patient was connected to the manometer, and the infusion bottle was slowly raised behind a screen (to prevent the patient's observing its elevation). The patient was asked to call out as soon as "discomfort" was being felt, and to describe the character and location of the sensation experienced.

In six patients measured 17 times during 12 hours the pain thresholds varied from 146.7 to 705.6 mm. of water pressure. In 32 of the 40 patients studied at various times the thresholds varied from 90 to 800 mm. water pressure; all measurements made on the same patient on the same day were found to be within ±10 per cent of his respective average. In general, lower thresholds appeared to be associated with inflammation.

It was found that the pain thresholds ascertained by this method were elevated by analgesics.

In 1947, Wells (465) demonstrated the effect of tissue temperature on the pain threshold as measured with a percussion type of algesimeter. A metal rod weighing 12.5 gm. was dropped from varying heights onto the dorsum of a finger held firmly in a groove cut into a large cork stopper. Pain threshold was expressed in terms of the height from which the metal rod had to be dropped to first produce pain. The thresholds were observed to be lowered when the finger temperature at 36°C. was either increased or decreased. Wells also called attention to the fact that the pain elicited by applying a clamp to the web between thumb and forefinger was intensified when the web temperature was decreased below or increased above 36°C.

A new, and as yet only partially investigated method for stimulating pain by mechanical means is that recently described by Huetter (15, 223). It consists of the application of a supersonic oscillator to the skin and the ensuing transmission into the tissues of high frequency sound waves. This energy is absorbed particularly well at a bony interface. It results in the production of aching pain.

An appraisal of the mechanical methods for evoking pain indicates that:

1) Mechanical stimuli seem to be particularly suited for evoking pain. The variability in pain thresholds observed by such methods may be due to the choice of the particular physical property of the stimulus used for threshold measurement. In other words, usually force (grams, cm. of water, etc.) or pressure (gm./cm.^{2}) is used as the criterion for determining the magnitude of mechanical stimulation. However, the reactivity of tissue to pressure is a variable factor, and from this it can be inferred that noxious stimulation is variably related to pressure. If the rate of change of pressure upon the tissue and the rate of deformation of the tissue were also observed more reliable pain threshold measurements might be obtained.

2) As regards the second and third requirements, mechanical methods of stimulation are not as satisfactory, since the range of measureable stimulus values between threshold pain and maximal discernable pain is relatively small and highly variable. Further, in the case of distensible hollow organs the range of variability of normal threshold values may include stimuli which in the same individual at some other time, may produce pain of high intensity. Under the circumstances in which the measurements of pain

threshold were made on viscera no relationship between stimulus intensity and pain intensity could be established. Aside from the difficulties of threshold variability and inability to relate stimulus strength to pain intensity, mechanical methods are satisfactory as regards the other requirements for suitable stimulus, for the experimental study of pain.

CHEMICAL METHODS OF INDUCING PAIN AS A MEANS FOR STUDYING THE PAIN THRESHOLD

Little of a quantitative nature has been done using injurious chemicals to evoke pain. An approach, however, has been made by Revici and Ravich (358–9) who made studies of the pain from gastric ulcer as affected by the concentration of acid in the stomach. Palmer (331), Wolf and Wolff (486), and others have also employed chemicals to evoke pain from the gastric and intestinal mucosa. Stimulation of the nasal mucosa with epinephrine packs (296) and intramuscular injection of hypertonic saline (488, 403) are other methods of inducing pain by chemical means. The introduction of corrosive mixtures onto and into the skin has been used in some investigations (372). Thus, whereas chemical means of evoking pain are in current use, there is available at present no quantitative chemical method of study of pain threshold or pain intensity. However, as the stimulation of the pain fibers is probably a chemical process, it can be anticipated that the chemical methods may be most important in the future studies of pain (12a).

ELECTRICAL STIMULATION AS A METHOD FOR STUDYING PAIN THRESHOLD

The method of stimulation of pain by a faradic current was first introduced in 1851 by von Helmholtz (207), who established the principles of break-induction shocks. A more detailed discussion of this method was presented by Fleming in 1892 (124).

Martin and co-workers in 1908 (307, 308, 164), studied sensation in humans by the method of faradic stimulation. These authors observed a diurnal rhythmic variation in the level of the sensory threshold for faradic stimulation. The individual studied dipped two fingers into liquid electrodes which consisted of two glass tubes containing an NaCl solution. Wires from the secondary coil of the inductorium were sealed into the bottom of these tubes. The subject was instructed to press a signal key with the other hand when any sensation became noticeable. Such "sensory thresholds", expressed in arbitrary units varied in sixteen subjects from a mean of 85 at 8:30 in the morning to 103 at 4:30 in the afternoon, to 57 at 8:30 in the evening. As there is doubt as to the quality of sensation evoked it is questionable whether this actually was a measure of pain threshold. Using this same method these authors demonstrated that in humans this "sensory threshold" for faradic stimulation was raised after the administration of analgesic agents.

Fender (122), in 1939, improved the faradic stimulator and made it possible thereby to deliver graded, predetermined intensities of current. Voltage, he maintained, had little descriptive value for faradic stimulation, while current, frequency, and wave form were suitable criteria. Fender himself does not report using faradic stimulation for eliciting pain.

Extensive quantitative studies of the "pain threshold" in rats after the administration of various analgesic agents were reported by Macht and Macht in 1940 (301). These observers applied faradic stimulation from a standardized induction coil (Harvard inductorium) to sensitive areas of the scrotum of tame adult male rats, and measured the "minimal energy" required to elicit a "painful squeal". They designated this point as the pain threshold. In one of their series of 20 rats the voltage required to elicit threshold pain varied from 100 to 445 volts. Still, they considered the method useful for detecting analgesic properties of new compounds on which investigative work had not yet progressed enough to warrant trials on humans.

Weitz (464), in 1942, using the method of Fleming as well as that of Martin concerned himself with the effect of skin temperature on pain thresholds. He tested the latter on the arms with single break shocks from a Harvard inductorium and measured intensity of stimuli in terms of the position of the secondary coil. After establishing a control threshold stimulus, he heated the arm with radiant heat and found that with increasing skin temperature the pain threshold decreased. After it had reached a certain minimum, it began to rise again.

In 1943, Goetzl, Burrill and Ivy (152) described their method for ascertaining pain thresholds by applying an electric current through a metal filling in a tooth and noting the voltage at which the subject first experienced a painful sensation. Their pain threshold measuring apparatus is described as follows: It consists of 2 coils. The primary coil is mounted on a pivoted arm so as to swing in a plane parallel to its windings, and is rotated in the plane by an electric phonograph motor. The secondary coil is mounted parallel to the primary and on a second arm arranged to swing in a plane parallel with and just above the plane of motion of the primary coil. When the primary coil passes close to the secondary coil there is generated in the secondary coil a sudden peak voltage. This peak voltage generated in the secondary coil is varied by moving the secondary coil toward or away from the path of the primary coil. Between peaks no current can be detected in the secondary coil by means of a standard oscilloscope. The arm carrying the secondary coil passes over a scale calibrated to show the voltage delivered. One side of the secondary coil is connected by a gold electrode to a metal filling in a subject's tooth. The same tooth and filling is used in all tests for any one subject. The other side of the secondary coil is connected to a salt water bath into which the subject places one hand.

It was found that a sensation of pain was the only definite sensation that could be produced in a tooth by this stimulus. At each determination, the pain threshold value accepted for the subject was the lowest voltage which produced a painful sensation three times in succession. Barring interfering factors, each subject at the same time of day responded initially at approximately the same voltage. The authors did not report numerical measurements of pain threshold in their subjects.

This method was also adapted to the study of effects of noxious stimulation in dogs. Two silver amalgam pit fillings were placed in each cuspid tooth in opposite positions so that pincer-like electrodes would engage pits in the two fillings. The electrodes had platinum points. The cavities for the fillings were cut as deeply as possible without opening into the pulp chamber. The first distinctly perceptible twitch of an isolated muscle or group of muscles was regarded as the "standard pain threshold" response. In a group of five dogs observed over a period of 16 weeks these authors reported an average threshold of 1.09 volts with an "average deviation" of ±0.14 volts.

In 1943 Bishop (36) described a method for effectively stimulating single sensory receptors in human skin, without mechanically deforming the skin. He used repetitive electric sparks to the skin and "adjusted the strength to give threshold prick sensation". Such a stimulus excited touch endings at many points, which sensation could be readily differentiated from prick. In general, prick had a lower electrical threshold than touch. Bishop does not report on quantitative measurements of pain thresholds in any units of stimulus.

Robertson, Goodell and Wolff (370), in 1947, studied the distribution and mechanism of headache and other pain in the face and head, which resulted from noxious stimulation of the teeth. Using an adaptation of the method of Goetzl et al. as described by Ziskin and Wald (503), they ascertained pain thresholds in the teeth of four subjects. Considerable variation in the pain threshold could be observed from tooth to tooth and at various sites on the same tooth. There was no uniformity of pain thresholds in the teeth of the same subject nor in corresponding teeth of different individuals. This lack of uniformity of the pain thresholds might have been due to variations in the structure of the teeth, such as thickness and intactness of the enamel, or the presence of metal fillings at varying distances from the nerve endings.

An evaluation of electrical methods as procedures for studying the pain experience is difficult, for, none of them meets the first requirement of a satisfactory method, i.e., that the stimulus be closely associated with tissue changes causing pain. In consequence there is no agreement among investigators as to which aspect of the stimulus should be measured as indicative of "stimulus intensity". It has been variously suggested that electromotive force rather than current is the important measurable component; or that frequency of stimulation rather than voltage or current is the proper measurable factor. Even wave form has been mentioned in this connection. As a result, confusion exists as to what is the pertinent quantitative factor in measurements of pain threshold by electrical methods. Further, so far no studies have been made as to the relationship of stimulus intensity to pain intensity. Even so, electrical methods do fulfill important requirements in that all qualities of pain can be evoked by electrical stimulation and reproducible threshold values can be obtained for any particular property of the stimulus. Measurable aspects of the stimulus can be expressed in standard physical units, stimulation is easily applied to the subject, and identification of pain by the subject is readily accomplished. From the teeth, for instance, no sensation except pain is evoked. However, in the latter instance the method suffers from a grave defect since it is hazardous to the tooth stimulated. Prolonged stimulation at high intensities results in irreversible damage to the tooth.

THERMAL METHODS OF EVOKING PAIN AS A MEANS FOR STUDYING PAIN THRESHOLD

These methods are among the oldest and were first introduced by Goldscheider in 1884 (157). The older thermal methods involved immersion of an extremity in hot water or the application of hot objects to the skin (69, 386). Later, Boring (50) introduced hot and cold water into the alimentary canal, thereby evoking pain. None of these studies was particularly concerned with measurement of pain threshold. One of the first attempts to measure pain threshold by the application of a hot object to the skin was the method of Elo and Nikula (116) in 1910. A thermometer was used, the bulb of which was flattened to a surface of about 0.5 cm.² Just above this flattened end the bulb was covered with insulating wire connected with resistances and a source of electrical energy. Any desired temperature could be obtained and easily read from the thermometer itself. The temperature at which pain was elicited was called the pain threshold.

Wolf and Hardy (483) used lowered tissue temperature to induce pain. The subject's hand was immersed in well-stirred cold water and threshold aching pain was induced at a temperature of 18°C.

In 1897 Alrutz (5) pointed out that thermal radiation had the advantage of dispensing with sensations of contact and pressure and posed it as a method for studying skin sensation. In 1921, Sonne (413) studied the effect of sun-rays focused onto the skin, being interested not in pain threshold, but in how much radiation the skin could "bear". He found that white human skin could tolerate more penetrating than non-penetrating radiation.

von Frey (posthumous publication (445)), in order to avoid the pressure sensation which is apt to arise when an object is brought in contact with the skin, was successful in eliciting pain by focusing the sun's rays upon the skin. He demonstrated that pain could be elicited independently of touch. von Frey did not measure the pain threshold.

In 1934 Stone and Dallenbach (425) studied "adaptation to pain" from radiant heat. They stimulated shaved skin on the dorsal surface of the forearm with thermal radiation. The intensity of the stimulus was not measured. Its duration varied between 5 and 212 seconds. The stimulator consisted of a coil of 20 gauge resistance wire placed 2.5 cm. from the lower end of a pyrex glass tube (15 x 1.2 cm.) wrapped in asbestos. The lower opening of the tube was reduced to 2 mm. in diameter by inserting in it an asbestos plug. A mica shield was placed inside the tube just above the coil which was heated by an electric current. The apparatus was held by a clamp and could be lowered into position by a rack and pinion gear to a point 1 mm. above the skin surface. The arm to be tested was held securely in an open plaster cast. The time required for pain to be evoked was recorded by a stopwatch. Stimulation was continued until the pain gradually declined and disappeared. This was followed by the reappearance of sensations of heat and warmth, the latter frequently persisting after the removal of the stimulus. Dallenbach was not primarily concerned with measurements of pain threshold, but rather with the fact that following disappearance of pain, no sensation of pressure was experienced. He presented his observations as evidence against Goldscheider's theory that pain results from intensive stimulation of structures responsible for pressure sensation, and in support of von Frey's contention that pain is a separate sensory experience.

Lloyd-Smith and Mendelssohn (289), in 1948, in studying the "tolerance limit" of the human skin to radiant heat, exposed areas of skin measuring 12 x 12 cm. over the epigastrium and interscapular region, to radiation from a 1000 watt tungsten filament bulb set in a concave mirror. The "tolerance limit" was defined as "the maximal amount of radiant heat that could be tolerated with comfort" and "without hazard of burn". They devised a skin thermometer of fine copper and constantan wires threaded through a hypodermic needle and soldered together at the tip to form a thermojunction. In order to measure skin temperature this thermometer was laid on the skin, and connected in circuit to a galvanometer and to a constant temperature reference junction maintained at 37°C. It was found that at a skin temperature of 44.6°C. $\pm$ 0.7°C. there is a sharp and well-defined transition from a sensation of heat to one of burning or sharp prick. These authors estimated that human skin could "tolerate" approximately 2.5 gm.cal./cm.²/min.

In 1936 the methods of Oppel and Hardy (330), who demonstrated that the radiation technique could be applied quantitatively to the study of temperature sense, were adapted to measuring the intensity of the thermal stimulus required to evoke a painful sensation in the skin. This new method for measuring pain threshold was first described in 1940 (185), and the investigations involving its use form the basis of this book. Because of this and because of the widespread use of the method by others the construction, adjustment, calibration and use of the thermal radiation equipment is described in detail in the following paragraphs.

CONSTRUCTION OF THE DOLORIMETER

The arrangement of the essential parts of the apparatus for measuring pain threshold by means of thermal radiation is shown schematically in figure 21. Modifications of the apparatus, designed to increase the ease of operation have been made since its first description in 1940. However, these changes have not altered the essential principles as first explained.

The surface of the skin to be tested was always thoroughly blackened with India ink. This measure insured a high degree of absorption of the radiation, independent of the degree of natural pigmentation of the skin, and eliminated all effects which could arise from any possible penetration of the rays below the skin surface. The stimulus could thus be considered purely thermal. The light from an incandescent lamp, L, was focussed by a condensing lens, S, through a fixed aperture onto the blackened forehead of the subject. The aperture, circular in shape, was cut through a non-heat-conducting material, with a diameter of 1 to 2 cm. In back of the aperture, between the lamp and the lens, was interposed a shutter, SH, which could be opened and closed to regulate accu-

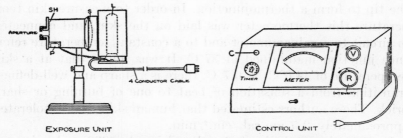

EXPOSURE UNIT   CONTROL UNIT

FIG. 21. THE HARDY-WOLFF-GOODELL DOLORIMETER

SH, shutter; P, electronically controlled relay for actuating shutter; S, corrugated biconvex lens; L, 500 watt projection lamp; C, timer button starting exposure; R, rough intensity control; V, fine intensity control.

rately the duration of exposure to the stimulus. A three-second exposure was chosen as standard.

As will be shown in the next chapter, the average thermal pain threshold is reached when the skin temperature has been raised to roughly 44.5°C. The number of mc./sec./cm.^{2} of thermal radiation which is required to heat the skin to this critical level depends upon a) the absorbing power of the skin, (a function of the skin's transmittance and reflectance), b) the time of exposure to the radiation, and c) the initial skin temperature. By painting the skin with India ink (absorptive power = 90%) and by setting the exposure time to a constant value of three seconds, all the variables except the initial skin temperature are taken into account. For precise measurements of pain threshold, initial skin temperature must be measured. However, if, in a room at comfortable temperature, the forehead be used as the testing area, only minor errors are introduced by omitting the skin temperature measurement, because the forehead maintains itself at a remarkably constant temperature, $34 \pm 0.5°C$. On the other hand, if the room temperature be noticeably hot or cold, and if other body areas, such as the hands, be used as test areas, errors as great as 100 per cent can be made if the initial skin temperature is not taken into account.

The size of the incandescent lamp to be used in the dolorimeter is chosen according to the size of the area of skin to be stimulated. A 500 watt lamp proves adequate for stimulating an area of 1–2 cm.², whereas a 1500 watt lamp is required for areas up to 10 cm.² Originally, an area of 3.5 cm.² was used and predictable results could be obtained thereby; with further experience smaller areas, between 0.5 and 1.0 cm.² were found optimal for pain threshold measurements as these minimized the stimulation of warmth sense and gave, thus, a more clearly defined transition from heat to pain. However, the size of the stimulated area may not be reduced to below 0.1 cm.² as then the conduction of heat from the edges of the irradiated skin areas becomes great enough to affect the rise in skin temperature for a given intensity of radiation. This effect is shown in figure 22. A substance (rubber) with thermal constants similar to those of skin was irradiated at a constant intensity through various sized apertures, and the surface temperatures measured. The temperature rise was ascertained by a tiny bead thermistor less than 0.5 mm. in diameter, imbedded in the surface of a large rubber stopper at the center of the field to be irradiated. The pain threshold measuring apparatus was set at an intensity of 100 mc./sec./cm.² and the rubber surface exposed to radiation for three seconds through apertures of 1, 2.2, 3, 3.5, 4.5, 10 and 15 mm. diameter. The rises in temperature were recorded with a rapid galvanometer. Although the radiation remained constant throughout the measurements, the smallest rise in temperature was recorded with the aperture of 0.01 cm.² As the size of the aperture was increased, the rise in temperature of the center of the irradiated area increased so that between 0.1 and 0.5 cm.² 95 to 100 per cent of the maximal temperature elevation was attained. The reason for smaller rises of surface temperature observed with areas smaller than 0.1 cm.² is that the lateral heat flow from the edges of the exposed small areas (fig. 22, lower left) does not permit the temperature to rise as high as in larger areas in which lateral conduction of heat from the center is negligible. Figure 22 (lower right) illustrates the situation with the larger areas for which the conduction of heat at the center is perpendicular to the surface, thus giving a maximal change of temperature. It will be seen in the next chapter that the pain threshold when measured with apertures smaller than 0.1 cm.² rises while through larger apertures it remains constant. This rise in pain threshold is due solely to rapid cooling of the stimulated area by lateral conduction of heat.

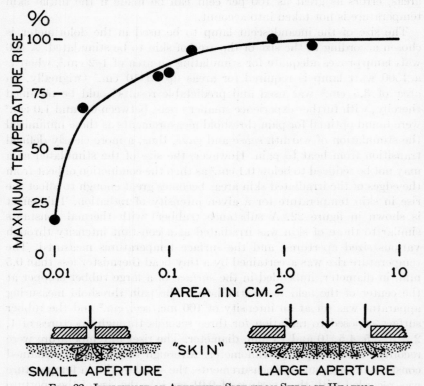

FIG. 22. INFLUENCE OF APERTURE SIZE UPON SURFACE HEATING

Upper curve: per cent of maximum temperature rise produced by a three-second exposure to a constant radiation intensity passing through various sizes of apertures. Diagram at lower left: heat flow into surface through small aperture, showing cooling due to lateral heat flow at edges. Diagram at lower right: perpendicular heat flow in center of large aperture.

The lens used in this type of stimulator should have a short focal length (15 to 20 cm.) and a large aperture. A biconvex lens of 10 to 20 cm. diameter collects sufficient energy to furnish intensities of radiation up to 500 mc./sec./cm.² from a 500 watt lamp. The lens need not be especially good from an optical standpoint. It is necessary in any event to "fuzz" the image of the lamp filaments so that a uniform area of illumination is obtained. Thus, in some instruments a corrugated lens, such as is used in traffic lights, has been found satisfactory. The lens should be arranged to bring the filament image to a focus 2 cm. behind the plane of the fixed aperture. This results in the production of a uniform field of radiation in the plane occupied by the subject's skin. Tests of uniformity provided by a 500 watt lamp have been made with a radiometer exposed through various size apertures. With apertures ranging from 0.1 to 4 cm.² the intensity of radiation measured in milli-calories per second per square centimeter exposed was found to be of the same value within ±5 per cent, regardless of size of aperture.

Adjustment

Lamp, lens and aperture must be rigidly mounted in order to preserve the calibration of the instrument. An optical bench, such as served in the first design, or rigid tubular mounting, as used in later instruments, is satisfactory. If there be the slightest relative displacement of the three components the calibration of the instrument is altered. The correctness of the alignment can be tested by holding a translucent white card 2 cm. in front of the aperture of the stimulator. When in proper adjustment, an image of the filament is seen, *centrally located* within the circular illumination formed by the aperture.

It is important that no metal surface come into contact with the skin in the neighborhood of the area to be tested. By increasing the "edge effect" mentioned above, metal will cause disturbing thermal sensations which will interfere with the accuracy of the threshold measurements. The aperture should be surrounded by some non-conducting material such as fiber overlaid with cork. Barmack (17) has tested such non-conducting materials and found that more uniform pain thresholds can be obtained with their use than with metals or rubber.

As mentioned above, a shutter must be interposed between the subject and the source of radiation to permit the stimulation of the subject for accurately measured periods of time. The original design of the stimulator included a shutter attached to a heavy pendulum for timing the pulse of radiation, but difficulty in adjustment and transportability made this an unsatisfactory arrangement for some purposes. Other investigators have employed sectored discs attached to a constant speed motor. A light metal shutter serves best for this purpose as it can be opened and closed quickly by an electronic device and can withstand the high temperature developed in the beam of radiation. Polished metal will absorb less of the radiation and will irradiate less to the skin; therefore, polished aluminum or stainless steel are desirable. The most satisfactory position for the shutter is immediately in front of the lamp, as this prevents heating of the lens and the walls of the aperture when the subject is not being stimulated. However, placing the shutter immediately behind the aperture is also practical if the intensity of the lamp is turned down to low

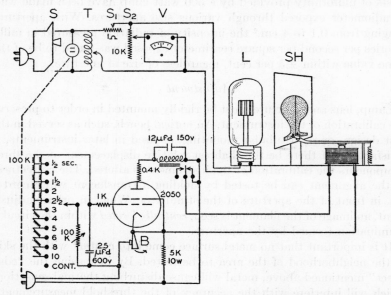

FIG. 23. DIAGRAM OF LAMP AND SHUTTER ARRANGEMENTS WITH ELECTRIC
CIRCUITS AS USED IN THE DOLORIMETER

At top—lamp circuit: S, power switch; T, variac transformer, 500 watt; S_1, fine control for intensity, one ohm, 20 watt rheostat; S_2, calibrating resistance, precision wire-wound 10,000 ohm variable resistor; V, AC voltmeter; L, lamp. Below— electronic circuit for shutter timing: B, push button for starting exposure; SH, shutter.

values between readings. The simplest and most satisfactory shutter of this type opens and closes rapidly and its timing can be set accurately by altering a resistance in the electronic circuit. A diagram of the circuit is shown in figure 23 with a sketch of the shutter mechanism. The operation of the shutter should be checked from time to time with a stopwatch. The three-second time interval of stimulation commonly used for pain threshold measurement should not vary more than ±0.1 second. As mentioned above, some observers use a constant intensity of radiation and measure the time of exposure as an expression of pain threshold. The shutter arrangement shown in figure 23 can be adapted to this method. However, this procedure is less desirable because variability caused by changes in blood flow and conduction of heat away from the edges of the stimulated area are enhanced by prolonged periods of exposure.

To control the intensity of the thermal stimulus either a resistance or a variable transformer can be used to vary the current to the lamp. The latter method is preferable as the heat which develops in the rheostat is avoided. The variable transformer, however, can be used only on alternating current circuits. A convenient lamp circuit is one employing both the variable transformer and the resistance to give an accurate adjustment of stimulus intensity. A diagram of such a lamp circuit is shown in figure 23. In localities in which the voltage of the AC supply mains fluctuates appreciably, a voltage regulating transformer should be added to the circuit. The regulation of a direct current supply is more difficult, but can be accomplished by suitable electronic circuits. The intensity of the thermal stimulus is most conveniently indicated by means of a voltmeter or wattmeter calibrated with a radiometer in terms of mc. (0.001 gm.cal.)/sec./cm.² It is convenient to have the instrument scale marked off in mc./sec./cm.²

The Radiometer

An essential accessory to an instrument for measuring pain threshold by the thermal radiation method is a calibrated radiometer for measuring the intensity of radiant flux per unit area passing through the aperture per unit of time. It has been suggested from time to time that a photoelectric cell would be more convenient to use for such a purpose than a radiometer. However, as by far the larger part of the energy from the dolorimeter lamp is in the infrared spectral region, in which photoelectric cells are not uniformly sensitive, these cells are not suited to energy measurements. Also, as the intensity of the stimulus from the dolorimeter is increased from 100 to 400 mc./sec./cm.², there is a significant shift in the spectral distribution of the energy to shorter wave lengths. For example, at 100 mc./sec./cm.² intensity there is practically no visible radiation (visible spectrum lies between 0.4μ and 0.7μ), whereas, with 400 mc./sec./cm.² there is a brilliant illumination more than 500 times as great. In the infrared spectrum, the ratio of the energies is roughly one to four. Thus, photoelectric cells can be used to monitor the intensity of a dolorimeter lamp but cannot be depended upon for intensity measurements. A radiometer which is uniformly sensitive to radiation throughout the spectral range from 0.4μ to 3μ is required for such measurements.

Noxious stimulation of the skin depends upon the skin temperature being raised to 44 to 45°C. regardless of the initial level of such temperature (189). Thus, it is necessary either to measure the skin temperature while the skin is being heated, or to measure some other stimulus factor to which the change in skin temperature is proportional. As measurement of skin temperature while the skin is being irradiated is difficult, and as changes in skin temperature induced by radiation are directly proportional to the conveniently measureable intensity of radiation, the latter serves as the most conveniently measurable aspect of a thermal stimulus to be used for inducing pain.

The original design of the pain stimulator necessitated the direct measurement with a radiometer, of the intensity of each stimulus. This was an awkward and time-consuming procedure and has been superseded by the use of a standardized voltmeter. Also, the constant use of a radiometer causes changes in its calibration, and accurate results are obtained if the direct-reading voltmeter or wattmeter is standardized before each experimental session.

The radiometer found to be satisfactory for calibrating pain stimulators consists of a 16-junction thermopile contained in a brass shell which is adapted to fit over the aperture of the pain stimulator so that the thermopile occupies the same position as would the stimulated skin. A diagram of this instrument is shown in figure 24.

The support for the thermopile is an aluminum block turned down to form two concentric cylinders, as shown. Two insulated binding posts are led through the outer shell to make contact with the thermopile. A thin sheet of mica is laid over the support and cemented to it with cellulose acetate cement. On top of this sheet is laid the 16-junction copper-constantan thermopile. The thermopile is constructed of ≠ 40 gauge copper and constantan wires and the radiation receivers are one-eighth sections of silver foil disc 15 mm. in diameter and 0.1 mm. thick. The receivers are soldered to the eight warm junctions of the thermopile. The cold junctions of the thermopile which serve as compensating junctions are cemented to the mica along the edge of the outer ring. The radiation receivers are blackened with a dull black paint. After this a second thin sheet of mica (0.005 mm.) is placed over the thermopile and cemented tightly to the first mica sheet at the points of contact of the inner and outer rings. The two mica sheets give the necessary rigidity to the radiation junctions of the thermopile.

Two methods have been used to calibrate the radiometer. The first is that of employing a black body of known temperature such as a muffle furnace of 1000°C. which will provide a calibration of the radiometer at intensities from 0–50 mc./sec./cm.² A simpler method is that of employing a National Bureau of Standards radiation standard which provides calibration at intensities of 0–1 mc./sec./cm.² A diagram of a muffle furnace with the radiometer in place for calibration is shown in figure 25.

Originally, the muffle furnace method was employed to calibrate the

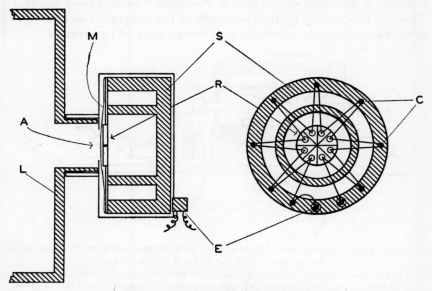

FIG. 24. DIAGRAM OF RADIOMETER

At left in vertical section, in place on dolorimeter for calibrating; at right, plane view showing radiation junctions, R, and compensating junctions, C. L, shell of dolorimeter; A, aperture of radiometer; M, protecting sheet of thin mica; S, aluminum support for junctions; E, leads from radiometer to galvanometer.

radiometer to insure the correctness of the radiometer in the range of intensities for which it was to be used in measuring pain thresholds. Repeated comparisons of calibration made by this method with those made by the Bureau of Standards radiation standard have shown that the latter calibrations yield identical radiometer constants, i.e., number of mc./sec./cm.² for each mv. of emf. Thus, the latter method is suitable for routine calibration of radiometers. The temperature of the furnace must be accurately regulated. An iron-constantan thermocouple designed to operate at high temperatures is used to measure the furnace temperature. An automatic on-off regulator may be employed during an experiment to keep the temperature constant within $\pm 1°C$. An adaptor is placed in front of the radiometer with a known distance, R (4.00 cm.), between the aperture of the radiometer, a, and the aperture of the adaptor, A. When the furnace has reached a constant temperature of roughly 1000°C. as indicated by the thermocouple, the radiometer and adaptor are put in place. The emf developed at the end of a 30-second exposure is measured on a Leeds & Northrup type K-2 potentiometer. This emf is produced by the thermopile of the radiometer as a result of reception through the aperture, a, of energy emitted by aperture A.

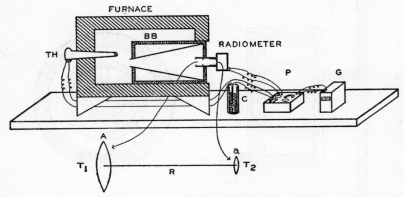

FIG. 25. ARRANGEMENT FOR CALIBRATING THE RADIOMETER BY MEANS OF A BLACK BODY (BB) AT HIGH TEMPERATURE

Th, thermocouple for measuring black body temperature; C, constant temperature junction; P, potentiometer; G, galvanometer. A, aperture at high temperature, T_1; a, aperture at radiometer temperature, T_2; R, distance between apertures.

The equation relating this energy to the absolute temperatures of the furnace, T_1, and the radiometer, T_2, is

$$E = \frac{S_0 A^2}{\pi R^2} (T_1^4 - T_2^4) \left(1 - \frac{a^2 + A^2}{R^2}\right)$$

where E = energy in mc./sec./cm.² and S_0 = Stephan-Boltzmann constant = 1.37×10^{-9} mc./sec./cm.²/°4 (52).

The simpler method for calibrating the radiometer involves the use of 50-500 watt lamps which have been standardized by the National Bureau of Standards as radiation standards. An accurately standardized ammeter is essential for this calibration. The arrangement of apparatus for the calibration is shown in figure 26. The lamp is mounted on a stand, with base down, 50 cm. from a perpendicular black surface one meter square; for this a black cloth or cardboard serves well. The radiometer is clamped in position at a distance of exactly one meter from the lamp as measured from the filament of the lamp to the aperture of the radiometer (see fig. 26). Between the radiometer and the lamp, at a distance of 20 cm. from the latter is set a screen which has a rectangular aperture 10 by 20 cm. This aperture is carefully aligned so that the filament of the lamp is level with its center, as viewed from the position of the radiometer which must face the exact center of the filament. A shutter of highly polished aluminum is fixed in the aperture of the screen so as to

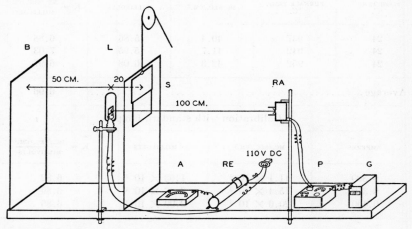

Fig. 26. Arrangement for Calibrating Radiometer with a Bureau of Standards "Radiation Standard"

B, black background; L, "radiation standard" 500 watt lamp; S, shutter; A, ammeter; RE, rheostat; RA, radiometer; P, potentiometer; G, galvanometer.

shut the radiation off from the radiometer between measurements. Once the positions of the lamp and radiometer have been fixed, slight adjustment in the orientation of the radiometer so as to give maximum deflection of the galvanometer is the final step of the alignment. Prior to its use the lamp should be allowed to burn for about 20 minutes at standard current rating.

The procedure of calibration is as follows: The potentiometer is standardized against a standard cell and the zero voltage from the radiometer is noted. This reading usually is not "zero" since the radiometer is "seeing" the warm screen and shutter. The shutter is then opened for a standard period of exactly 60 seconds (for some radiometers 30 seconds may be used as the standard period), and the emf developed by the radiometer at the end of the exposure is measured. Sixty seconds after closing the shutter the potentiometer reading from the radiometer is again checked to determine whether or not there has been a shift in the "zero" position. The measured emf is corrected for zero shift on the assumption that the shift takes place uniformly for the period of the measurement

TABLE 2

A comparison of two methods of radiometer calibration

Calibration with furnace

ROOM TEMP. °C.	FURNACE TEMP. °C.	MC/SEC./CM.²	MILLIVOLTS	$K = \dfrac{\text{MC./SEC./CM.}^2}{\text{MILLIVOLTS}}$
24	937	40.4	5.86	6.88
24	942	41.7	5.95	7.03
24	952	42.3	6.08	6.97
Average..				6.96

Calibration with standard lamp

AMPERES	MC./SEC./CM.²	MILLIVOLTS	$K = \dfrac{\text{MC./SEC./CM.}^2}{\text{MILLIVOLTS}}$
0.300	11.1×10^{-3}	1.63×10^{-3}	6.82
0.350	15.4×10^{-3}	2.23×10^{-3}	6.89
0.400	20.6×10^{-3}	2.99×10^{-3}	6.86
Average..			6.89

(120 seconds). Thus, if R = the measured emf, r_1 = zero position at the start, and r_2 = zero position 120 seconds later, then

$$\text{emf corrected} = R - \left(\frac{r_1 + r_2}{2}\right)$$

These corrections are necessary if a calibration precision of two per cent is to be attained. A comparison of typical calibrations done with the furnace and with a standard lamp is shown in table 2. The radiometer constants as determined by the two methods agree within one to two per cent.

The radiometer constant is determined by these procedures in terms of mc./sec./cm.²/mv. To determine the intensity of a stimulus from the pain stimulator it is necessary to measure the millivolts developed by the radiometer when exposed for a standard period (usually 60 seconds) to the radiation from the stimulator. Multiplying this value by the constant gives the stimulus intensity, thus:

$$I = K \times MV$$

where I = intensity of stimulus in mc./sec./cm.^{2}

  K = radiometer constant

  MV = millivolts read at end of exposure.

Calibration: The Dolorimeter

If a pain stimulator be mounted permanently in one place and carefully handled, its calibration will be maintained for many months. However, if it be used as a portable instrument frequent recalibration is desirable. Having on hand a calibrated radiometer, a potentiometer, and a stop watch, the recalibration can be carried out in a few minutes. To read conveniently the emf developed by the radiometer when exposed, a portable potentiometer with a built-in galvanometer is desirable. The following steps have been found necessary to calibrate the pain stimulator:

1. With the timer indicator set at "3 seconds" measure time between opening and closing of the shutter with a stop watch and if necessary adjust the resistor in the electronic timer from the back of the control box until the exposure time is exactly three seconds.

2. Put timer indicator on "continuous" and open shutter. Then, with a piece of white paper held near the aperture, have the filaments focussed about 2 cm. from the aperture and in the *center* of the aperture. A slight movement of the lamp will correct any defect in alignment. For instruments which are moved about frequently these precautions are particularly important.

3. Put timer indicator on "½ second" and close shutter. Set intensity at 250 mc./sec./cm.^{2} After 15 minutes the instrument is warm and ready for calibration.

4. Set intensity at 150 mc./sec./cm.^{2} as read by the indicating voltmeter or wattmeter. Remove the fiber insulator from the aperture and slip the radiometer over the aperture sleeve until it presses firmly against the base of the aperture. The diaphragm of the radiometer will then be in the same plane as that occupied by the skin in a threshold measurement. Put timer on "continuous", open shutter, and start stop watch.

5. Read millivolts on potentiometer exactly at the end of standard time, usually 60 seconds.

6. Calculate the intensity of radiation by multiplying the number of

millivolts by the radiometer constant. Compare this with the reading of the voltmeter in mc./sec./cm.^{2}

If the stimulator is out of calibration by more than two per cent, it is necessary to make adjustments in the voltmeter as outlined below.

Figure 23 shows an alternating current voltmeter as the indicating instrument together with the "span" adjusting resistance. The scale of the voltmeter is in terms of mc./sec./cm.^{2} and is not linear with the needle deflection.* To adjust the voltmeter so as to indicate the stimulus intensity accurately, the following procedure is suggested:

1. The variable transformer and resistance, S_1 (see fig. 23), are set so that the lamp gives a radiant flux of 150 mc./sec./cm.^{2} through the aperture, as measured by the radiometer and potentiometer.

2. The resistance, S_2, is adjusted so that the voltmeter usually mounted on the face of the stimulator control box indicates 150 mc./sec./cm.^{2}

3. The variable transformer is now reset, with the radiometer and potentiometer so that the lamp gives a radiant flux of 300 mc./sec./cm.^{2} through the aperture. The meter on the face of the stimulator control box should indicate 300 mc./sec./cm.^{2}, but if it does not, the resistance, S_2, is again adjusted until it does.

4. Reduce the lamp intensity to 150 mc./sec./cm.^{2} as measured by the radiometer and potentiometer and adjust the needle of the stimulator meter so that 150 mc./sec./cm.^{2} is indicated. This is accomplished by moving the needle positioner on the face of the meter.

5. Increase the lamp intensity again to 300 mc./sec./cm.^{2} using the radiometer for measurement. Again adjust the resistance, S_2, until the meter reading is 300 mc./sec./cm.^{2}

6. Steps 4 and 5 are repeated alternately until the readings agree with the radiometer readings both at 150 and at 300 mc. settings.

7. The calibration of the meter should then be checked from 100 mc./sec./cm.^{2} to 450 mc./sec/.cm.^{2} at intervals of 50-100 mc.

USING THE DOLORIMETER

Since the report of a conscious individual is taken as the index of the pain threshold sensation, it is necessary to define accurately this endpoint of esthetic experience. Most methods for evoking pain also elicit other sensations before the onset of pain. In the case of thermal radiation these sensations are warmth and heat.

* The voltmeter and special scale can be obtained from the Calidyne Corp., 451 Main St., Winchester, Mass.

The threshold sensation of pricking pain as evoked by the thermal radiation method is recognizable as a distinct, sharp, very small stab of pain experienced at the *exact end* of the three-second exposure to the stimulus. This prick is preceded by a sensation of warmth, heat, and burning which seems to "swell" and then "draw together" into a prick at the end of the third second. Minimal after-sensations of heat and burning pain are common but not predictable. Thus, for identifying the pricking pain threshold sensation it is necessary to focus attention upon the barely perceptible prick.

Other investigators, in searching for a satisfactory threshold pain, have come to adopt this endpoint. However, Chapman and Jones (79), using a group of uninstructed subjects and questioning them about their experiences as the stimulus was increased, found a stimulus intensity at which the majority of the subjects, complained, winced, or withdrew. In their early publications they termed this the "pain threshold" but in later papers they used the term "reaction threshold" to refer to this endpoint which occurs at a stimulus intensity of about 300 to 350 mc./sec./cm.² Experiments indicate that at about this stimulus intensity there is a definite change in pain quality, and also an alteration in the ability to discriminate. An introspectional analysis of the sensation experienced at this level supports the view that deeper pain endings which give rise to aching pain are being stimulated. If the stimulus is increased still further, the aching component of the resultant sensation is much enhanced, and a spread of this pain from the site of stimulus is noticed. Spread of pain is characteristic of deep rather than of cutaneous pain.

Bigelow, Harrison, Goodell and Wolff (32) succeeded in identifying a third threshold which they termed the "burning pain" threshold. On the forehead, this threshold is about 20 to 30 millicalories lower than the pricking pain threshold. Its identification was easier on the extremities where it could be correlated with sensations which are mediated by the smaller "C" fibers. The properties of this endpoint will be more fully discussed in Chapter VI.

Pfeiffer (340) distinguished between the threshold measured on the finger pad, which he called "superficial pain", and the threshold measured on the fingernail, called "sympathetic pain".

It is evident that in studies of pain threshold one must specify clearly which sensation of threshold pain is under investigation. Undoubtedly, much of the reported variation in the level of the cutaneous pain threshold can be attributed to the selection by different investigators of one or another of the three cutaneous pain thresholds. Most observers use the pricking pain threshold and instruct their subjects in its identification. Except as noted specifically, the pricking pain threshold is the one with which the present discussions are dealing.

Subject Instruction

The use of trained and instructed subjects has been found satisfactory. However, such procedure has been criticized from the point of view that training and instruction leads to stereotyped reports and obliges the subject to omit certain features of the pain experience. Certainly, this objection is a valid one. The justification for the selection of one particular pain threshold and of subjects trained to recognize it is that this provides a more uniform index for observing the changes brought about by experimemtal procedures. Ivy and his group (152) have attempted to avoid this difficulty by using a stimulus which is believed to evoke only one type of pain, and no other sensation. However, careful observation has revealed that there are some additional sensations which may be evoked by their procedure.

The "instructed" subject is one who has been told what to expect and what the endpoint should feel like. The "trained" subject is one who has been tested sufficiently to establish his confidence in his ability to recognize the pain threshold under a variety of conditions. Chapman and Jones (79), in their earlier work, used uninstructed and untrained subjects. Potelunas, Meixner and Hardy (345) used untrained but instructed subjects, whereas the major portion of our work (388) has been done with trained subjects. Clausen and King (84) who recently reviewed the literature as regards level of pain threshold and subject training, point out the usefulness of careful instruction of the subject.

The procedure for instructing the subject, used in our laboratory is as follows: It is explained to the subject that the procedure is not a test of his ability to *endure* pain, but rather of his capacity to perceive the *first trace* of pain. The subject's cooperation in concentrating closely on the sensation at the *exact* end of the exposure is requested. The subject is then given a first exposure which results only in a mild sensation of warmth; that is, at the signal "Ready" a stimulus of 100 to 120 mc./sec./cm.² is presented to the subject and he is asked to report on his sensations. Then a second stimulus, at the level of 250 to 270 mc./sec./cm.² is presented on an adjacent spot and the subject again reports his sensations. In nearly all instances the subjects report a definite pricking pain at this higher intensity. The intensity of the stimulus is then lowered to about 150 mc./sec./cm.² for the next exposure. If no pricking pain is reported, the intensity is increased again by 20 mc./sec./cm.², and another stimulus given on *an adjacent spot* of skin. The intensity is increased in steps of this magnitude at suitable time intervals, until the subject first reports pain. In order to avoid, on the one hand, mounting tension and fatigue, with too frequent stimulation and, on the other hand, boredom with unnecessarily long intervals between stimulations, intervals of fifteen to twenty seconds are desirable if adjacent skin areas be used. The entire procedure is repeated once or twice, or until the operator is sure that the subject understands. After this, a series of measurements is made without further instruction to the subject. The instruction given is in the same category as that given to a student to enable him to read an endpoint in a titration, or on a colorimeter, or to read a Vernier Scale. In other words, it is the aim to instruct the subject as to what is the exact target he is expected to hit.

Once the instruction is presented and the observation begun, further instruction and suggestion are scrupulously avoided. The subject is not told by the operator during the tests that at this or that stage of the procedure he will experience pain, or that "now you will feel pain". In fact, no suggestion whatever is made during the period of the readings.

The instructed subject can be considered trained when his estimates of pain threshold are consistent under various circumstances. Thus, as the basic criterion of his report, the subject must have learned to keep attention focused on the sensation experienced at the end of each exposure. He must be sufficiently experienced with the sensation of threshold pain in order to report it confidently, and must not be concerned with the attitude of the operator; for, if he attempt to please or displease the operator, he ceases to be a dependable witness. Further, the subject must be able to maintain the necessary degree of concentration on the threshold pain even during some distracting aspects of various experimental procedures, including the side-actions of analgesics. Changes of from 5 to 10 per cent in pain threshold levels usually are significant when reported by trained subjects, whereas changes of 20 per cent or more may be required before significance can be attributed to reports from instructed but inexperienced subjects.

A critical evaluation of thermal methods of evoking pain for measurement of pain threshold should be focused upon the thermal radiation technique, since this method is in common use. Citing in their order the criteria set up at the beginning of this chapter it can be seen that "a" and "b" are satisfied. As, for "a", the measurable aspect of the stimulus is closely associated with the degree of noxious stimulation; and, for "b", under standard conditions, the pain thresholds are reproducible to the extent of the subject's ability to discriminate. As regards criterion "c", controllability and measurability of the stimulus, the stimulus intensity is precisely controllable, but it can be measured only with a radiometer and potentiometer, two delicate and expensive instruments. This is a handicap in the method. Criterion "d" is satisfied, that is, the ability of the subject to discriminate differences in pain intensity from the threshold pain to the ceiling pain has been ascertained (see also Chapter VI). Criterion "e", calling for minimal tissue damage, is met provided that not too large areas of skin are subjected to high intensity stimuli. Criterion "f", that the stimulus evoke burning, pricking, and aching pain; and criterion "g", that the stimulus be conveniently applied to the subject's skin are also met. However, thermal radiation is not well suited for direct stimulation of nerves or for evoking pain from internal organs. The difficulties associated with criterion "h", the definiteness of the endpoint, have been discussed above. We need only add that the pricking pain threshold is the one most sharply defined, although overlap with burning, and occasionally, with aching pain, occurs. The sensations of warmth and heat which precede the sensation of pain do not appreciably affect the recognition of the pain threshold. However, in this respect, certain analgesics (antipyretic agents) which differentially alter the heat and pain thresholds, add to the difficulty of discrimination.

Chapter IV

THE PRICKING PAIN THRESHOLD IN MAN AS ASCERTAINED BY THE THERMAL RADIATION METHOD

Of the three qualities of pain—burning, pricking, and aching—pricking pain has received the widest attention as regards the measurement of pain thresholds. The reason for this is that of the three qualities, the threshold sensation of pricking pain is most clearcut as an endpoint and thus most easily identified. Some of the properties of burning and aching pain as compared with pricking pain will be discussed in the following two chapters. As mentioned in Chapter III, the methods of ascertaining the threshold for these important qualities are not developed sufficiently to provide data upon which to base as full a discussion as that for pricking pain.

THE PRICKING PAIN THRESHOLD ON THE FOREHEAD

The reports by various observers (382, 409, 263) of measurement of the pain threshold on the forehead, show a wide range of average values, 182 to 305 mc./sec./cm.^{2} Usually, the reports contain no information as to which pain threshold has been measured, although a study of the data shows that some authors have used mostly the aching pain and others the pricking or the burning pain threshold. For example, Chapman and Jones (79) refrained from instruction and simply analyzed the comments of their 200 subjects on the sensations experienced. Thus, the degree of alertness, introspectional insight, and understanding on the part of the subjects, all were uncontrollable variables. The average of all pain thresholds obtained on the forehead of these subjects was 305 mc./sec./cm.^{2}, with a range of 175 to 462 mc./sec./cm.^{2} These results can be compared with those of Clausen and King (84) who studied 31 instructed subjects whose pain thresholds on the forehead had a value of 182 ± 22.9 mc./sec./cm.^{2}

Schumacher et al. (388) reported pain threshold measurements on the forehead obtained on 150 instructed but untrained subjects of both sexes and of ages between 10 and 72 years. The average of the pain thresholds obtained was 206 mc./sec./cm.^{2}, with a standard deviation of ±21 mc./sec./cm.^{2} This group is comparable to that of Clausen and King, and the difference in reported levels

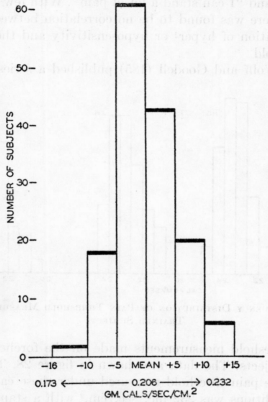

Fig. 27. The Distribution of Pain Thresholds in a Group of 150 Men and Women from 14 to 70 Years of Age

of pain threshold is most likely due to differences in selection of threshold pain sensation. The distribution of the results of Schumacher's study is shown in figure 27, as representing the performance of the method with instructed subjects under laboratory conditions. There were 324 measurements and the data were considered on the basis of one value for each subject, this value being the average of all observations made on the individual. Each subject was asked to express an opinion about his own pain sensitivity. There were wide variations in the expression of personal estimates of pain sensitivity, such as, "exquisitely sensitive", "average", and "I can stand a lot of pain". With few exceptions, however, there was found to be no correlation between the personal estimation of hyper- or hyposensitivity and the measured pain threshold.

Hardy, Wolff and Goodell (185) published a series of studies

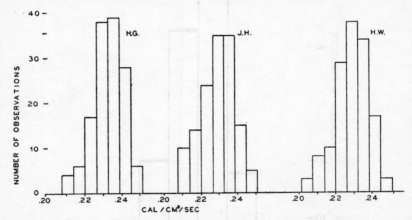

FIG. 28. FREQUENCY DISTRIBUTION OF PAIN THRESHOLD MEASUREMENTS ON 3 TRAINED SUBJECTS

of pain threshold measurements made on the forehead of three trained subjects. The data are shown in figure 28. The average value of the pain threshold measured under these carefully controlled conditions was 232 mc./sec./cm.^{2} with a standard deviation of ±9 mc./sec./cm.^{2} A marked degree of concentration on the part of the subject, and careful attention to laboratory conditions are necessary to obtain results within so narrow a range. Hazouri and Mueller (199) have recently reported a series of pain threshold measurements on 100 paraplegic patients. The average of the pain thresholds was 230 ± 10 mc./sec./cm.^{2}

A summary of the pain threshold measurements made by various investigators is shown in table 3. It seems reasonable to infer from these results that the level of pain threshold reported depended upon the selection of the particular endpoint. Instruction of subjects decreases the variability of reports under standard conditions. For example, average pain threshold levels in the neighborhood of 300 mc./sec./cm.^{2} (1, 2, table 3) indicate that the subjects were reporting for the most part the aching pain threshold sensation, although some were reporting the burning and pricking pain threshold sensations. A second group of observations (3 and 4) with thresholds in the neighborhood of 230 mc./sec./cm.^{2} with a spread from 200 to 250 mc./sec./cm.^{2} was ob-

TABLE 3

Pricking pain threshold measurements on the forehead by various investigators, using the thermal radiation technique

INVESTIGATOR	NUMBER OF SUBJECTS	MEAN PAIN THRESHOLD	STANDARD DEVIATION	MAXIMAL RANGE
		mc./sec./cm.^{2}	mc./sec./cm.^{2}	mc./sec./cm.^{2}
1) Chapman & Jones.............	200 U	305	±45	175–462
2) Schilling & Musser...........	138	348		
3) Hardy, Wolff, Goodell........	3 T	232	±9	202–252
4) Hazouri & Mueller...........	100 I	230	±10	220–240
5) Bigelow et al................	23 I	210		170–240
6) Schumacher et al............	150 I	206	±21	173–232
7) Clausen & King..............	31 I	182	±22.9	

U = Untrained, T = Trained, I = Instructed.

tained from subjects who were instructed in the recognition of the pricking pain threshold. A third group of observations (5, 6 and 7) with average levels ranging from 170 to 240 mc./sec./cm.^{2} probably comprised a majority of reports of burning and pricking pain threshold sensation.

The high degree of uniformity which was observed for the pricking pain threshold was attained by use of the forehead as a test area with the subjects being instructed in the identification of the pricking pain threshold sensation. However, it cannot be inferred from this that the pain threshold is uniform over the entire body surface, or that it is unaffected by such factors as skin temperature, wetness, injury, or by distraction, suggestion, and hypnosis.

MEASUREMENT OF PRICKING PAIN THRESHOLD ON DIFFERENT AREAS OF THE BODY

Using the standard technique for measuring the pricking pain threshold, a survey was made of the pain threshold over the entire body surface (189a). To make data comparable it was necessary to measure the skin temperature of each area prior to testing (see

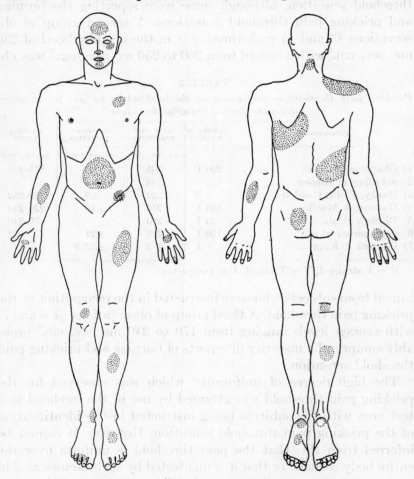

FIG. 29. SURVEY OF SENSITIVITY OF VARIOUS BODY REGIONS
Stippled areas indicate regions of body surface on which pain threshold measurements were made.

TABLE 4

Pricking pain threshold measurements on various parts of the body

SKIN AREA	FINAL SKIN TEMPERATURE	AVERAGE PAIN THRESHOLD	REMARKS
	°C.	mc./sec./cm.²	
Forehead	45.7 ±1.3	235 ±27	
Cheek (zygoma)	44.6 ±1.3	210 ±27	
Nose	44.8 ±1.6	215 ±32	
Lips	44.1 ±1.9	200 ±38	
Chin	45.0 ±1.3	220 ±27	
Chest	44.8 ±2.2	215 ±44	
Nipple	43.8 ±1.6	200 ±32	
Abdomen	43.9 ±0.9	200 ±18	
Groin	43.3 ±1.2	185 ±24	
Thigh (back)	42.8 ±1.4	175 ±28	
Thigh (front)	42.6 ±1.4	170 ±28	
Knee cap	42.7 ±0.9	175 ±18	
Popliteal space	43.5 ±1.0	190 ±20	
Calf	43.0 ±1.4	185 ±28	
Shin	43.9 ±1.1	190 ±22	
Ankle	44.0 ±1.1	190 ±22	
Dorsum of foot	43.2 ±1.4	180 ±28	
Dorsum of toes	43.4 ±1.7	185 ±34	Pain seems delayed
Arch	44.3 ±1.4	200 ±28	
Heel	53.7 ±2.2	390 ±44	Pain delayed more
Heel, corneal layer shaved off		250 ±20	than one second
Shoulder	44.8 ±1.8	215 ±36	
Nape of neck	43.8 ±1.2	195 ±24	
Upper back	43.5 ±1.6	185 ±32	
Middle back	43.8 ±1.2	195 ±24	
Lower back	42.2 ±1.4	160 ±28	
Buttock	42.4 ±1.9	165 ±38	
Upper arm	43.4 ±1.7	185 ±34	
Forearm, volar surface	44.4 ±1.6	210 ±32	
Forearm, outer surface	44.0 ±1.2	200 ±24	
Back of hand	43.8 ±1.6	195 ±32	
Finger pad	47.1 ±2.0	260 ±40	
Finger nail		215 ±15	
Palm (center)	45.1 ±1.7	220 ±34	
Palm over callus	45.6 ±1.8	230 ±36	

below for effect of skin temperature on pain threshold). Correction was applied to bring all measurements to the same basis, i.e., an initial skin temperature before stimulation of 34°C. Seven healthy subjects were used for the measurements, five male and two female, all of whom were trained in the recognition of the pricking pain threshold. There was no sex difference in pain threshold that could be determined with certainty.

Figure 29 shows a topographical representation of the areas on which the pain threshold was measured. Three test sites were selected in each area and three measurements were made on each test site. The results of the survey are shown in table 4 in which are shown the average skin temperature to which the part must be raised to reach the pain threshold and the intensity of radiation necessary to evoke threshold pain in each skin area, with an initial skin temperature of 34°C. The plantar surface of the heel with its thick layer of stratum corneum was the area of highest pain threshold, and the lower back, buttocks, and thighs were areas of lowest pain threshold. In general, however, the sensitivity to pricking pain is roughly uniform over the body surface.

THE LACK OF DEPENDENCE OF THE PRICKING PAIN THRESHOLD ON THE SIZE OF SKIN AREA STIMULATED

When the size of the skin area stimulated is increased at least three factors may operate to lower the pain threshold, viz., 1) a large area would have statistically a better chance to include the most sensitive pain endings; 2) the stimulus might be more effective in a large area than in a small one; 3) spatial summation of subliminal responses by neural interaction might cause a larger area to be more sensitive. As regards the first possibility, the pain sensitivity of the skin to thermal radiation stimulus is practically uniform over the surface of the forehead. This is evidenced by the constant values of pain threshold found in the number of measurements just discussed. The second and third possibilities were tested experimentally on the forehead with special attention to the latter as Hardy and his associates (181) had shown that the threshold for warmth and cold sensation decreases when progressively larger areas of the forehead are stimulated. Thus, the question arose as to the dependence of the pain threshold upon the size of the skin area stimulated. Experiments were carried out with the thermal radiation method by exposing areas of various sizes on the forehead and determining the pain threshold for each area. The data for two subjects are shown in table 5. As can be

TABLE 5

Intensity of radiation required to evoke pain, with three seconds' exposure, for various sized areas of skin on the forehead

AREA	SUBJECT G	SUBJECT H	AVERAGE
cm.²	gm.cal./sec./cm.²	gm.cal./sec./cm.²	gm.cal./sec./cm.²
0.07	0.287	0.247	0.277
	0.314	0.265	
0.13	0.262	0.245	0.258
	0.264	0.257	
	0.269	0.252	
0.19	0.259	0.257	0.258
	0.254	0.255	
	0.265	0.255	
0.95	0.258	0.228	0.243
3.46	0.249	0.228	0.236
7.10	0.240	0.242	0.242
10.00	0.240	0.225	0.233
28.30	0.256	0.241	0.245
		0.241	

seen, the pain threshold for the smallest area is slightly higher than that for larger areas. This difference in pain threshold may have been due to a slight spatial summation of subthreshold stimuli by a greater number of pain endings in the larger areas, or it may have resulted from the conduction of heat away from the edges of the smaller areas as mentioned in Chapter II.

In order to test this latter hypothesis measurements of pain threshold were made on areas of skin 0.01 to 30 cm.² exposed to the radiation. The results of this test on two subjects are shown in figure 30. The pain threshold was constant at the usual level for areas larger than 0.15 cm.², but for progressively smaller areas it increased rapidly. In this figure there is also plotted the heating effect of the radiation stimulus through apertures varying

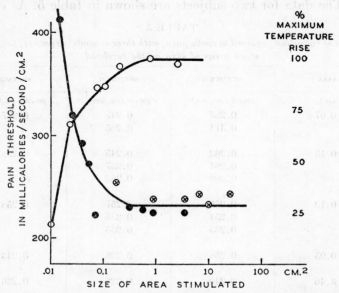

FIG. 30. RELATIONSHIP OF SIZE OF SKIN AREA STIMULATED TO INTENSITY OF STIMULUS INDUCING THRESHOLD PAIN

⊕ and ●, pain thresholds for various sized areas. ○, heating of skin for different sized areas expressed in terms of per cent of maximum temperature rise. The artifact of apparent spatial summation seen for areas smaller than 0.3 cm.² is due to the cooling of the skin by lateral conduction at the edges of the small apertures, preventing maximum heating of the skin.

in size from 0.01 to 4 cm.² as measured by the method described in Chapter II. It is seen that the heating effect of the radiation reaches 100 per cent for exposed areas between 0.15 and 1.0 cm.² In fact, the curve for the heating effect is almost the inverse of the threshold curve, and thus it can be inferred that the observed rise in pain threshold in the smaller areas was entirely due to the failure of the stimulus to heat the skin through smaller apertures.

In figure 31 the data for pain contained in table 5 are compared with similar data obtained for the sense of warmth. The threshold for warmth was determined on the forehead in a similar manner as that for pain. It was found that this threshold increased more than 200-fold as the area of skin stimulated was diminished from 200 to 0.2 cm.^{2} Such a change in threshold with size of area stimulated demonstrated the great effect of spatial summation upon the measured threshold value. On the other hand, the pain threshold when ascertained on areas of the forehead from 0.95 to 28 cm.^{2} is constant, showing a lack of spatial summation.

The change in the sensory threshold with any change in size of area (i.e., number of sensory endings) stimulated is due to the additive effects of the stimulation of the individual endings. This has been termed "spatial summation" and is interpreted as a fundamental characteristic of integration in the central nervous system; that is, the neurons innervating a given skin area may add their effects to those innervating another area, thus causing a summation of effects.

In figure 31, it can be seen from the relationship between pain threshold and size of skin areas stimulated, that cutaneous pain does not have the property of spatial summation. Experiments with other types of noxious stimulation eliciting cutaneous pain also demonstrate a lack of spatial summation. For example, von Frey (449) has shown that the pain threshold of the skin when stimulated by pressure (measured in gm./mm.^{2}) is the same for large and small areas of skin. Touch on the other hand showed spatial summation effects to a marked extent, the touch threshold being higher for the smallest skin areas and decreasing as the size of the area stimulated was increased. As spatial summation has also been demonstrated (182) for cold sensation, the only cutaneous sensation which does not possess this property is pain. This distinguishes pain functionally from other sensations, and lends support to the thesis proposed in Chapter I, viz., that pain is a sensory modality subserved by a special neural equipment.

Although enlarging the area of skin (i.e., increasing the number of sensory endings) stimulated does not result in a lowering of the pain threshold, there is the possibility that suprathreshold stimulation of individual pain endings causes an increase in pain intensity due to the additive effects from the various fibers. In order to investigate this possibility of spatial summation and, at the same time, to use the method of threshold measurement, the following experiment was performed on two subjects. The stimuli were measured on each for areas 0.3 cm.^{2} and 3.46 cm.^{2}, the latter representing a more than 11-fold increase in area over the former.

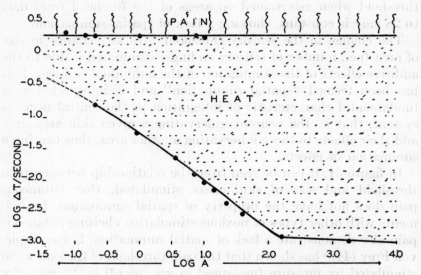

FIG. 31. A COMPARISON OF THE EFFECTS OF SPATIAL SUMMATION FOR WARMTH UPON THE WARMTH THRESHOLD (LOWER CURVE) WITH THE ABSENCE OF SUCH SUMMATION FOR THE PAIN THRESHOLD (UPPER CURVE)

This area ratio, chosen on the basis of the summative effects found in temperature sensation, would have been ample to show spatial summation of pain if it really existed. After obtaining normal thresholds, morphine sulfate (8 mg.) was administered to the subjects subcutaneously, and the change in threshold in the two areas was followed for six hours. Since morphine has central rather than peripheral action it can be assumed that in the fibers subserving pain, impulses were being set up by the suprathreshold noxious stimulation of the skin in both the small and large areas.

On the assumption that the intensity of pain elicited from the larger area is appreciably greater than that evoked from the smaller one, it would be anticipated that the morphine would have less effect in raising the pain threshold in the former than in the latter. The results of this experiment are shown in figure 32. It is seen that morphine caused the same rise in threshold in both areas.

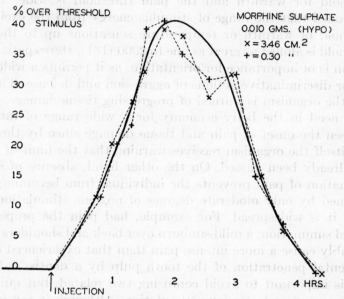

FIG. 32. EFFECT OF MORPHINE SULFATE (10 MG.) UPON THE PAIN THRESHOLD AS MEASURED BY EXPOSING A SMALL AND A LARGE AREA OF THE FOREHEAD TO THERMAL RADIATION

Because the central acting analgesic has the same relative and absolute effect for both sizes of skin areas, it is inferred that spatial summation for pain above the threshold does not exist.

From this it is inferred that spatial summation for suprathreshold noxious stimulation does not exist.

The importance of the absence of spatial summation for pain is two-fold: first, it distinguishes physiologically cutaneous pain from cutaneous temperature sense; second, it implies that the intensity of a given pain is dependent upon the intensity of the noxious stimulus and not upon the size of the area involved. Moreover, associated with this lack of spatial summation for pain the range of thermal stimuli, from that evoking threshold pain to that causing irreversible tissue damage, is small (188). It has been repeatedly demonstrated on the skin that a thermal radiation stimulus of twice the pain threshold value causes irreversible tissue destruction. In contrast with this the range of stimuli between the threshold for warmth and the pain threshold is wide. It was mentioned that the range of stimulus energy from the excitation threshold of warmth or temperature sensations up to the pain threshold is almost as great as one to 2000 (181). Here spatial summation is of importance for orientation, as it permits a wide margin for discriminative actions of aggression and defense. Through pain the organism is warned of progressing tissue damage. There is no need in the body economy for a wide range of intensity between the onset of pain and tissue damage since by threshold pain itself the organism receives warning that the limit of safety has already been passed. On the other hand, absence of spatial summation of pain prevents the individual from becoming overwhelmed by only moderate degrees of noxious stimulation even when it is widespread. For example, had pain the property of spatial summation, a mild sunburn over back and shoulders would probably cause a more intense pain than that experienced during accidental penetration of the tooth pulp by a dentist's drill.

It is important to avoid confusing two related, but quite different responses to noxious stimulation. Although it can be concluded that spatial summation of neural impulses resulting from noxious stimulation does not occur as regards pain sensation, Sherrington's (401) experiments with the flexor reflex indicate the existence of summation with respect to motor responses. He showed that stimulation of the internal saphenous nerve and the musculocutaneous nerve, together caused a greater muscular contraction in the semitendinosus muscle of the cat than when the nerves were stimulated individually with the same intensity of stimulus. Also, stimuli in themselves incapable of evoking contraction when applied to either nerve individually, did cause the muscle to contract when applied to both nerves simultaneously. The importance of such spatial summation of impulses from noxious stimulation, perhaps in themselves evoking little pain, may be seen in the spastic contraction of abdominal muscles in response to tissue damage in the peritoneum. Furthermore, this secondary contraction of skeletal muscle so induced may itself become a cause of pain. Such effects are not limited to skeletal muscle, but may involve vasomotor, other smooth muscle, and glandular structures, all adding to, and sometimes becoming the prime source of, discomfort.

THE DEPENDENCE OF PRICKING PAIN THRESHOLD UPON SKIN TEMPERATURE

That reduced skin temperature can result in cutaneous analgesia is well known, and skin temperatures near zero degrees Centigrade cause local anesthesia (183). Further, Schumacher (387), and Graham, Goodell and Wolff (166) have reported that vasodilatation of the superficial vessels of the skin lowers the local pain threshold. So far, no systematic investigation into the effect of varying levels of skin temperature upon the pain threshold for pricking pain evoked by thermal radiation had been reported. To investigate this matter quantitatively the following experiments were performed (189).

OBSERVATION 1

The pain threshold on the blackened skin of the forehead and back of the hand of four subjects was measured by the thermal radiation method, in a room at 26°C. Skin temperatures were measured with a radiometer (184) prior to each test of pain threshold.

The subjects then moved into a room at 8°C. and skin temperature and pain threshold on the forehead and back of the hand were measured at 5 to 10 minute intervals over a period of one hour. The subjects returned to the room at 26°C. where the measurements were continued for two additional hours, as the skin temperature returned to the previous levels.

The results of these observations are shown in figure 33 by the solid line drawn through the averages of readings plotted for the forehead and the hand. The same relationship of pain threshold to the level of skin temperature was observed for both areas. Cool-

ing of the skin by 10°C. resulted in an elevation in pain threshold
of roughly 200 mc./sec./cm.²

OBSERVATION 2

The blackened skin of the forehead of two subjects was irradiated continuously with low intensities of thermal radiation.
During this heating there was no visible sweat on the forehead

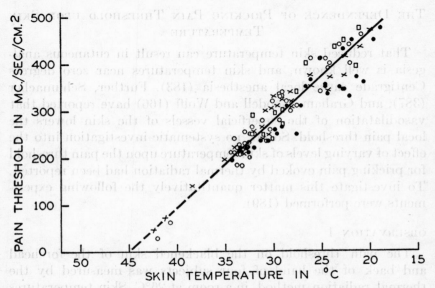

FIG. 33. RELATION OF PAIN THRESHOLD TO LEVEL OF SKIN TEMPERATURE

even though the skin temperature was maintained at levels between 38° and 43°C. When a constant skin temperature had been
attained the warm skin was exposed for three seconds to a second
source of radiation, the intensity of which was adjusted to give
a threshold pricking pain at the end of the three-second exposure.
The pain threshold was ascertained by measuring the intensity
of the radiation incident upon the skin from the second source.
Skin temperatures were measured with a bare wire thermocouple
laid on the forehead after the method described by Stoll and
Hardy (424). The dashed portion of the line in figure 33 is drawn
through the averages of the results of this series of measurements.

Heating the skin of the forehead by 10°C. caused a lowering of the pain threshold of approximately 200 mc./sec./cm.²

COMMENT

The fact that the relationship between levels of skin temperature and pain threshold is characterized by a straight line passing through zero stimulus at a skin temperature of 44.8° ± 0.5°C. suggests that the skin in the areas tested must be raised to this temperature before stimulation becomes noxious, regardless of the initial level of skin temperature. Thus, it is the actual skin temperature level which is critical as regards noxious stimulation, and neither the rate nor the degree of skin temperature elevation (189). Also, neither the amount of blood flowing to the skin nor the degree of vasoconstriction and dilatation of the skin blood vessels have any observable effect upon the pain threshold aside from their contribution to the establishment of the initial level of skin temperature. This somewhat surprising inference is made from the fact that the skin of the hands and of the forehead, under the conditions of this experiment areas of intense and mild vasomotor activity, respectively, behave in an identical fashion. In contrast is the sense of cold, the threshold of which is raised by roughly 300 per cent when vasoconstriction in the skin is replaced by vasodilatation (see fig. 34).

It follows from these observations that in order to obtain the most accurate measurements of pain threshold by the thermal radiation method it is necessary to make a correction for the temperature of the skin being tested. This can be done for the forehead and back of the hand from the curve in figure 33 or by the following formula:

Pricking pain threshold $= 220 + 20(34°C. - T_s)$ mc./sec./cm.²

where T_s = skin temperature in °C. at the time of observation.

Originally, the forehead was the only skin area used for pain threshold tests. It was selected because of the constancy of its skin temperature, 34° ± 0.5°C. under laboratory conditions. However, errors will be introduced into measurements of pain threshold even on the forehead if the room temperature is lower than 20°C.

In warm rooms (30° to 35°C.) the forehead temperature will not increase greatly but sweating will occur and thus interfere to some extent with the measurement. It is, therefore, desirable to keep the laboratory temperature betweed 20° and 30°C. When other parts of the body are being studied their skin temperature should be ascertained and corrections applied to the pain threshold measurement. The average skin temperature on parts of the body other

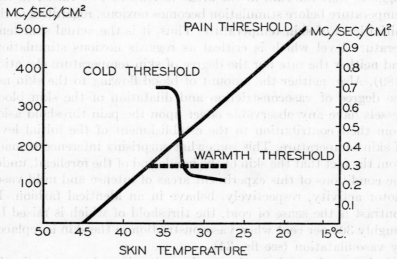

FIG. 34. A COMPARISON OF THE INFLUENCE OF LEVEL OF SKIN TEMPERATURE UPON THE THRESHOLDS OF PAIN, COLD AND WARMTH

than the forehead, in the comfort zone of environmental temperature, is roughly 33°C. (178).

Pain evoked by thermal radiation stands in marked contrast to the sensations of warmth and cold as regards the effects of altered skin temperature upon the threshold as seen in figure 34. Warmth shows no change in threshold between skin temperatures of 27° and 36°C., while there is ad *elevation* of the coln threshold as the skin temperature is increased from 32° to 34°C. (108). From these observations it can be concluded that the effects of the thermal stimulus on the skin in producing noxious stimulation are entirely different from those evoking thermal sensations, and that the cutaneous receptive mechanism subserving pain is distinct from that for warmth and cold.

Buettner (63), and Moritz and Henriques (316) have shown that reversible tissue damage in the skin of the forearm and upper leg of humans is produced at the critical temperature of 44° to 45°C. In the present experiments threshold pain was elicited by raising the skin temperature to roughly this same level, irrespective of the initial level of skin temperature. From these two independent observations the close relationship between tissue damage and noxious stimulation can be inferred, a conclusion which supports the concept that damaging tissue is the adequate stimulus for pain.

THE EFFECT OF DURATION OF STIMULUS UPON THE THRESHOLD OF PRICKING PAIN

The intensity-duration relationship for threshold pain was first investigated by Bigelow, Harrison, Goodell and Wolff (32). These authors reported a decrease in threshold stimulus intensity with increase in stimulus duration, a relationship characteristic of biological responses. This topic has been further explored in order to obtain the additional data on skin temperature.

OBSERVATION

Three thoroughly trained subjects participated in these experiments. It was necessary to exert special attention to the identification of the pricking pain threshold because with longer durations of stimuli the burning pain is evident some seconds before the pricking pain endpoint. All measurements were made using the forehead as test area.

The duration of the stimulus was controlled by an electronically operated shutter which could be set for exposures of 0.25 to 10.0 seconds. The exact time of exposure to radiation was measured to ±0.02 sec. by means of a photoelectric cell connected to a rapidly recording galvanometer. For longer exposures a stopwatch was used to measure the duration of the stimulus.

The skin temperature prior to irradiation was determined by means of a bare wire #28 gauge copper-constantan thermocouple held against the skin as described by Stoll and Hardy. This method gives estimates of skin temperature within ±0.4°C. Measurements of skin temperature during irradiation were not made as the thermocouple method is not dependable under such conditions.

Thresholds were measured for the short exposures, 0.25 to 10 sec. by the usual method of repeated tests with different intensities of stimulus until a stimulus just evoking threshold pain at the end of the exposure was found. For the longer exposures the intensity of radiation was set at a particular level. The exposure was begun by an observer who opened the shutter of the dolorimeter and at the same time started a stopwatch. The watch was stopped by the subject at the onset of pricking pain. Two to 5 determinations were made on each subject for each exposure or stimulus setting.

The results of these measurements are shown in figure 35. The intensity-duration relationship is similar to that previously reported. In these experiments no pricking pain was elicited after 60 to 85 sec. or with stimuli of lower intensity than 39.5 mc./sec./cm.² Thus, for this stimulus-response relationship 60 to 85 sec. and 39.5 mc./sec./cm.² represent the utilization time and rheobase, respectively.

In table 6 is shown a summary of the data of this experiment, together with the calculated value of the skin temperature at the time of experiencing threshold pain. This calculation was made on the basis of data obtained from experiments on the influence of skin temperature upon the pain threshold for a 3-sec. exposure. The formula used for the computation is:

$$T_s = T_i + KQ\sqrt{t}$$

in which T_s = temperature of the skin (°C.) at the time of pain
perception, i.e., at the end of an exposure
T_i = skin temperature prior to irradiation
K = constant
Q = stimulus strength in mc./sec./cm.²
t = exposure time in seconds.

The derivation of the formula is contained in papers by Buettner, and Moritz and Henriques.

From the last column of the table it is seen that regardless of the time of exposure, the threshold pricking pain is evoked when the skin is heated to 44.3 ± 0.5°C. In view of the limitations in the measurements of skin temperature this value compares well

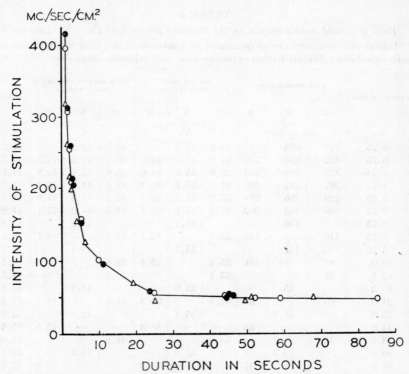

FIG. 35. THE RELATION OF THE DURATION OF STIMULATION TO THE INTENSITY OF THE STIMULUS FOR THE PRICKING PAIN THRESHOLD IN 3 NORMAL SUBJECTS
●, H. G.; ○, J. D. H.; △, H. G. W.

with that of 44.8°C. as previously found from the study of the influence of skin temperature upon the pain threshold (465a, 189a).

COMMENT

These experiments demonstrate that a report of threshold pricking pain is elicited when the skin temperature of the forehead is raised to 44.3 ± 0.5°C. regardless of whether the stimulus be delivered in 0.25 second or 60 seconds. The importance of thus relating the threshold pain, a subjective experience, to a predictable and objectively measureable event in the periphery lies in the establishment of the validity of such experience as an index

TABLE 6

Pain threshold measurements on the forehead for various times of exposure

Initial skin temperature as measured by thermocouples; skin temperature at pain threshold calculated from exposure time and stimulus intensity.

EXPOSURE TIME	PAIN THRESHOLDS			INITIAL SKIN TEMPERATURE			FINAL SKIN TEMPERATURE (CALCULATED)			AVE.
	G	W	H	G	W	H	G	W	H	
secs.	*mc./sec.cm.*^{2}			°C.			°C.			°C.
0.25	820	595	—	33.8	34.2	—	45.7	42.8	—	44.3
0.75	432	336	390	34.3	34.7	34.6	45.1	43.5	44.3	44.5
1.24	328	269	315	35.0	35.0	34.6	45.6	43.7	44.8	44.7
1.74	267	232	260	34.8	35.1	35.2	45.0	44.0	45.1	44.7
2.26	226	196	218	35.2	35.1	35.4	45.1	43.5	44.9	44.8
2.75	208	185	202	34.8	35.1	35.4	44.8	44.0	45.1	44.9
3.75	—	156	—	—	35.1	—	—	43.9	—	43.9
4.75	146	—	148	35.1	—	35.7	44.5	—	44.7	44.6
5.75	—	127	—	—	35.1	—	—	44.1	—	44.1
10.0	92	—	101	35.4	—	35.1	43.8	—	44.5	44.1
12.5	91	—	—	35.2	—	—	44.5	—	—	44.5
19.3	—	65	—	—	35.0	—	—	43.3	—	43.3
24.0	65	—	64	34.8	—	35.3	44.1	—	44.5	44.3
25.0	—	51.3	—	—	35.4	—	—	42.8	—	42.8
44.0	—	—	53	—	—	35.3	—	—	45.5	45.5
45.0	52	—	—	34.8	—	—	44.9	—	—	44.9
50.0	—	39.5	—	—	35.0	—	—	43.1	—	43.1
58.0	—	—	47	—	—	35.3	—	—	45.6	45.6
60.0+	40.5	—	41	34.7	—	35.4	—	—	—	—

of peripheral change. These data further support the concept that the adequate stimulus for pain is associated with tissue damage.

THE EFFECT OF BLACKENING OF THE SKIN

As the heating effect of radiation is dependent upon the absorbing power of the material it strikes, the pigmentation of the skin is an important factor with regard to the pain threshold level as measured by the thermal radiation method. The reflectance and transmittance of the skin for the spectral range from

0.4 to 3 μ are the determining factors in this respect and will vary with the degree of pigmentation of the subject's skin. Table 7 contains average measurements of pricking pain threshold for three white and six Negro subjects before and after blackening with India ink. The influence of skin pigment is demonstrated by comparison of the values of Column 1. After blackening with India ink the pain threshold values of both white and Negro

TABLE 7

Effect on the pain threshold of blackening the skin with India ink

WHITE SUBJECTS	PAIN THRESHOLD BEFORE BLACKENING	PAIN THRESHOLD AFTER BLACKENING	DIFFERENCE
	mc./sec./cm.^{2}	*mc./sec./cm.*^{2}	
1	470	248	222
2	430	230	200
3	385	215	170
Average.........	427	232	
NEGRO SUBJECTS			
1	336	188	148
2	370	210	160
3	343	203	140
4	349	212	137
5	411	199	112
6	339	184	155
Average.........	358	200	

subjects came within the normal range of 220 ± 20 mc./sec./cm.^{2} The relative effects of transmittance and reflectance of the skin as they affect the pain threshold have not been investigated as these quantities are difficult to measure (86). However, covering the skin with an opaque and highly absorbing material such as India ink avoids these problems completely.

Fortunately, it is possible to obtain with India ink a black coating which is reproducible from experiment to experiment, can be maintained for several hours, and is easily washed off. Other blacks and other skin stains can be used for absorption of the thermal radiation, but the average pain threshold may be altered from that reported above if the absorptive power of these pigments differs greatly from that of India ink.

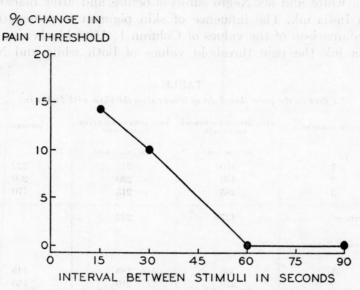

FIG. 36. THE PERCENTAGE EFFECT OF REPETITIVE STIMULATION IN LOWERING THE LEVEL OF PAIN THRESHOLD

A series of ten stimuli of three seconds each, intensity 220 mc./sec./cm.^{2}, was applied to an area of skin on the forehead. The interval between stimuli was 15, 30, 60, and 90 seconds, respectively, making four series of tests on four different skin areas. Immediately following each series the pain threshold was measured.

THE EFFECT OF SKIN WETNESS

The presence of moisture upon the skin causes a rise in the pain threshold. A rise of 17 per cent, 35 per cent, and 40 per cent, respectively, was observed in tests on three subjects who had warm water sprinkled on the forehead. The room temperature for these tests was 26°C. The effect of the moisture in preventing the usual rise in skin temperature during exposure to radiation was due to increased vaporization. It is thus desirable to use for pain threshold testing a dry skin. As a corollary to this, it can be said that any factor which markedly increases or diminishes the flow of heat into the stimulated skin will alter the level of the pain threshold.

THE EFFECT OF REPETITIVE STIMULATION

Repeated stimulation of the same area of skin if done in rapid succession will cause lowering of the pain threshold and local hyperalgesia (423). The change in pain threshold under repetitive stimulation is due both to a raised skin temperature and to the hyperalgesia. Tests were carried out upon two subjects who were submitted for 10 successive exposures to a threshold stimulus of 235 mc./sec./cm.² on the same skin area. In 4 series of tests the intervals between exposures were respectively 15, 30, 60, and 90 sec. Between exposures the subject moved his head away from the stimulator. At the end of each series the pain threshold was measured. The results of these tests are shown in figure 36.

After the 10 exposures 15 sec. apart, the pain threshold was found to be lowered by 14 per cent; after 10 exposures 60 seconds apart, no effect upon the pain threshold was found. Thus, at least 60 sec. should be allowed between successive stimulation at threshold level of the same skin area so as to avoid lowering of the pain threshold.

THE EFFECT OF SKIN INJURY AND DISEASE UPON THE PRICKING PAIN THRESHOLD

It is common experience that in the presence of certain dermatoses, or of skin injury, the sensitivity of the skin to pain is increased. Clinical estimations of these changes in sensation have been made through the use of various methods of thermal and tactile stimulation. For example, Ollendorf (329) made a systematic study of the sensitivity of the skin of patients with syphilitic dermatoses. In comparing the sensation in normal and affected areas of skin, this author used such methods as stroking with a hair, pinprick, pressure with a probe, and heat. She found that in patients with papules and inflammation of secondary syphilis the sensitivity of the skin was increased. The hyperalgesia demonstrable in the papules was so predictable and characteristic that she advocated it as a diagnostic sign. Mayr's (310) study of 311 patients with syphilis, in which he used a water manometer to exert pressure on the lesions, showed that the florid secondary eruptions were more sensitive than normal skin.

Schumacher showed in a series of 11 normal subjects that in inflammatory skin reaction induced by ultraviolet irradiation the pain threshold of the skin was lowered by 12 to 50 per cent. The variation in increased sensitivity was due to differences in severity of the burns (387).

Sixty-five patients in the dermatological clinic of The New York Hospital, who were suffering from pruritic and non-pruritic skin disorders, served as subjects for an additional study. The patients were of both sexes and ranged in age from 13 to 75 years.

It is to be appreciated that patients with pruritic lesions were not itching at all times, and not necessarily at the time of observation of their pain threshold. Indeed, most of the patients of this group were not itching at the time pain threshold measurements were made. Hence, when the phrase "pruritic state" is used in the following discussion it implies that the patients had skin lesions of which one of the usual prominent features was itching.

OBSERVATIONS

In each patient determinations were made on an area of affected skin and on a contralateral or an adjacent normal area. Subjects with diseases in which itching was a factor were asked to report on the effect of the radiation on itching. While some patients showed on the diseased skin both a lowered pain threshold and hyperalgesia, in others the pain threshold was unchanged. For this reason a second series of observations was carried out on 38 patients representing 18 types of skin disorders.

Measurements were made to determine the sensitivity of the skin to stimuli above the pain threshold. In these experiments a stimulus evoking a four-"dol" pain (i.e., pain of moderate intensity) was applied to an area of normal skin. A series of stimuli was then applied to the affected skin and the patient was asked to compare the intensity of these pains with the 4-"dol" pain evoked on normal skin. Measurements were completed when the patient reported the test pain from a pathological area to be the same in intensity as the 4-"dol" pain. The test pains were produced on different spots of the area at intervals of about 20 seconds and the standard pain was repeated only after the patient had reported the test pain as approximately equal to the standard 4-"dol" pain.

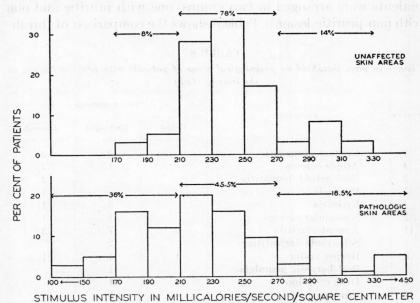

FIG. 37. DISTRIBUTION OF PAIN THRESHOLD MEASUREMENTS FOR 65 DERMATOLOGIC PATIENTS
Upper diagram: unaffected skin areas. Lower diagram: pathologic skin areas.

RESULTS

The upper part of figure 37 shows the results of measurements of the pain threshold on the unaffected skin of various body areas of 65 patients. This series of thresholds ranged from 170 to 330 mc./sec./cm.² In the lower part of the figure are shown the measurements of pain threshold on the skin lesions in contralateral areas of the body of the 65 patients. There is a considerably wider distribution of pain thresholds, the values ranging from 100 to 450 mc./sec./cm.² as compared with the control group. There were 28 per cent more reports at low pain threshold on pathologic areas, and 4.5 per cent with higher pain thresholds.

In comparing the pain threshold measurements on unaffected

with those on pathological skin areas, the principal differences are the wider spread in threshold values and the presence of hyperalgesia in the pathological areas.

To evaluate the effect of pruritis upon the pain threshold the patients were arranged in two groups, one with pruritic and one with non-pruritic lesions. Table 8 shows the comparison of thresh-

TABLE 8

Change in pain threshold on pathological areas of patients with pruritic lesions at the time of study

NUMBER	DIAGNOSIS	PAIN THRESHOLD		
		Raised	Unchanged	Lowered
7	Contact dermatitis		5	2
4	Atopic eczema		1	3
2	Eczematoid dermatitis			2
1	Psoriasis			1
4	Urticaria		3	1
2	Nummular eczema		1	1
11	Neurodermatitis	2	7	2
2	Seborrheic dermatitis		2	
3	Herpes zoster	1	1	1
1	Post-herpetic neuralgia		1	
1	Drug eruption		1	
1	Pruritus		1	
1	Static eczema		1	
1	Pityriasis rosea		1	
		3	25	13
		7%	61%	32%

old measurements on normal skin and pathologic skin in patients with pruritic lesions. Fourteen disease entities were studied in a total of 41 patients. Thirty-two per cent of these patients show a lowered pain threshold; 68 per cent an unchanged or raised pain threshold. Table 9 contains the comparative data obtained on 24 patients with non-pruritic lesions representing sixteen disease entities. Twenty-five per cent of these patients showed a lowered pain threshold and 21 per cent a raised pain threshold. The majority of patients in both groups, 61 per cent with pruritic and 54 per cent with non-pruritic lesions, had thresholds within the range of 210 to 270 mc./sec./cm.², regardless of body area tested.

COMMENT

In the group with pruritic lesions 61 per cent had unchanged pain thresholds in the pathologic areas; 32 per cent had lowered,

TABLE 9

Change in pain threshold on pathological areas of patients with nonpruritic lesions at the time of study

NUMBER	DIAGNOSIS	PAIN THRESHOLD		
		Raised	Unchanged	Lowered
3	Contact dermatitis	2		1
2	Atopic eczema		2	
1	Eczematoid dermatitis	1		
1	Necrobiosis	1		
3	Psoriasis		2	1
1	Urticaria			1
1	Epidermolysis bullosa		1	
1	Nummular eczema			1
2	Neurodermatitis		2	
3	Herpes zoster		3	
1	Ultraviolet exposure		1	
1	Pityriasis rosea		1	
1	Erythema nodosum			1
1	Sarcoid of Boeck		1	
1	Lepromatous leprosy	1		
1	Secondary syphilis			1
		5	13	6
		21%	54%	25%

and 7 per cent raised pain thresholds. Further, the test procedure either initiated or increased the itching in only 22 per cent of the patients, and it had no effect in 78 per cent. Thus, there is no predictable lowering of the pain threshold in sites of pruritic lesions. It will be shown in a subsequent chapter that when a pruritic state was experimentally induced by skin irritants, and itching ensued, there was always a lowering of the pain threshold. However, in the absence of itching in the same area the pain threshold may be normal. This may explain why many of the patients with "pruritic lesions" had either normal or even raised pain thresholds.

The group with non-pruritic lesions is characterized by a greater percentage of patients with raised pain thresholds. This may be due to edema, damage to the peripheral pain endings, keratinization of the skin, or a combination of these factors.

The possible existence of changes in skin sensibility not related to changes in pain threshold was investigated in 36 patients. Sensibility comparisons were made on unaffected and on pathologic skin areas. The results were as follows:

15 patients had lowered pain threshold and increased sensibility
3 patients had raised pain threshold and decreased sensibility
9 patients had unchanged pain threshold and unchanged sensibility
—
27 patients or 75 per cent of the group.

The above changes are those to be expected if the skin is the organ effecting the changes in pain sensation. However,

3 patients had unchanged pain threshold and increased sensibility
6 patients had unchanged pain threshold and decreased sensibility
—
9 patients or 25 per cent of the group showed changes in sensibility without any changes in threshold.

In this latter group, it is believed that factors affecting the conducting pathways subserving pain played an important role in modifying the sensation evoked by stimulation at the periphery. These results may be interpreted as follows:

a) Normal peripheral endings plus an augmented excitatory state in the path of the impulses from the skin to the sensory cortex may account for the three patients with unchanged pain threshold and increased pain sensibility. As a result of such a state, impulses passing from the periphery would be facilitated and thus the pain sensation perceived as more intense. This state has been termed "secondary" hyperalgesia. It will be discussed in detail in Chapter VIII.

b) A normal peripheral apparatus combined with a depressed

functional state in the nerve pathways can account for the six patients with unchanged pain thresholds and decreased sensibility above the threshold. This state may be similar to a transmission (217) across a partial nerve block or it may be a "secondary" hypalgesia in contrast to the "secondary" hyperalgesia.

The Effects upon the Pain Threshold of Factors Interfering with Concentration on the Test Situation

It is a common experience that a painful sensation can be made more bearable by inducing pain in some other part of the body. Examples of this effect are clenching the fist tightly or biting the lips during painful episodes. To investigate the effect of pain in one part of the body upon the pain threshold in another the following experiments were performed on three subjects:

In the first experiment pain thresholds were measured on the back of the left hand and on the forehead. A sphygmomanometer cuff around the left arm above the elbow was then inflated to 200 mm. Hg and kept inflated for 35 minutes. The pain thresholds on the left hand and forehead were measured at 5-minute intervals during the period of inflation and until control values were again obtained. Estimates of the pain resulting from the pressure of the cuff on the arm and from movement of the arm were made roughly in terms of "plus" values. Figure 38 demonstrates the course of the experiment. The solid line represents the change in threshold of the ischemic hand, and the dashed line the change in threshold of the forehead. Since the pain threshold of the ischemic hand was elevated to the same degree as that of the forehead, one may infer that the observed effect was due to causes other than the ischemia itself, probably to pain from the ischemic arm.

In a second series of experiments directed toward obtaining an answer to this question the pain threshold was measured on the back of the right hand of two subjects. The left hand was then immersed for 5 minutes in water at 46°C. and at 50°C., during which time the pain threshold on the right hand was measured. The pains induced by the immersion were of 3 "dols" and 5 "dols" intensity, respectively. During the first immersion the pain threshold was elevated from 230 to 250 mc./sec./cm.²; and during the second from 230 to 270 mc./sec./cm.²

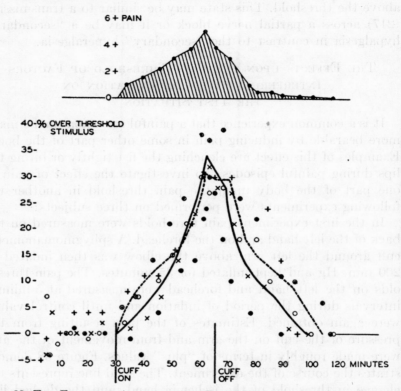

FIG. 38. THE EFFECT OF ARRESTING THE BLOOD FLOW OF THE LEFT ARM UPON THE PAIN THRESHOLD IN THE LEFT HAND (DASHED LINE) AND ON THE FOREHEAD (SOLID LINE)
Upper shaded area represents estimates of pain caused by ischemia in the arm.

COMMENT

The experiments demonstrate that the pain threshold is raised above the control level concurrently with pain in some other part of the body. The amount of elevation increases with the intensity of the co-existing pain. It has been observed when the forehead and hand are simultaneously exposed to noxious stimulation by thermal radiation, that a pain of approximately four dols intensity in one area will mask the sensation from thermal stimulation in the second area normally sufficient to induce threshold to one-dol pain (160). Also, Bender (27, 28) simultaneously stimulated a cheek and the contralateral hand with a pin and observed in a third of his normal adults and in half of his normal children under twelve years, that pricking pain on the cheek extinguished sensation from the pin prick on the hand. In some of his patients pin prick on a cheek and touch to the contralateral hand resulted in no perception of touch in the hand. This phenomenon, which is seen in patients, is termed "extinction". These observations are in keeping with the observations that intense pain in one part of the body influences the pain threshold in another anatomically remote area (332).

OBSERVATION

Other means of stimulating the subject during pain threshold measurements included clanging a bell loudly behind the subject's head, reading aloud to the subject an adventure story, or requiring the subject to repeat numbers in forward and reverse order. The effects of these procedures are shown in figure 39.

COMMENT

Elevations of pain threshold of from 19 to 45 per cent were caused by extraneous stimulation which tended to draw the subject's attention away from the test situation. Complete preoccupation of an individual's attention such as is encountered in athletic contests or battle makes possible the sustaining of extensive wounds without pain sensation. The experiments presented do not indicate the degree of effectiveness of distraction in elevating the pain threshold except under the particular circumstances of these experiments. The general usefulness of distraction as a method of managing pain is evidence, however, that "taking the mind off the pain" to the extent of becoming interested in an adventure story will have an analgesic effect comparable in degree to that of a medicinal agent such as acetylsalicylic acid. Indeed, during the day a moderately intense pain sensation can be supported for hours by occupation with interesting work, while it may become intolerable during the night when relaxation and sleep are desired.

The Effect of Suggestion

Under controlled laboratory conditions it is much easier to raise the pain threshold by suggestion than to lower it. The subjects were asked to report the pain threshold during the following experiences:

Autosuggestion was produced by having the subject repeat to himself over and over, "I don't feel the pain." The effect of this

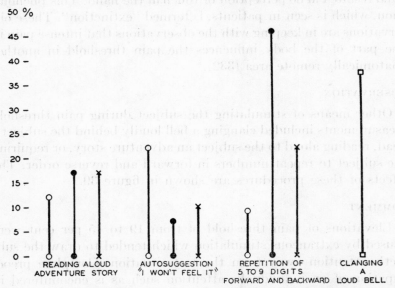

FIG. 39. THE PAIN THRESHOLD-RAISING EFFECTS OF DISTRACTION, SUGGESTION, AND "SHALLOW HYPNOSIS"

procedure was a small rise of 20 per cent in the pain threshold. The suggestion in this instance was rather weak and amounted to little more than distraction (see fig. 39). Strong autosuggestion was encountered in an hysterical patient who had local anesthesia with paralysis of the left hand. Under these conditions pain could not be elicited even with the highest stimulus intensities. A similar effect was demonstrated in the case of two medical students who, under the impression that they had received a strong analgesic, had elevations of the pain threshold of 90 per cent over the control levels. Blisters were produced in these subjects without reports of threshold pain. Subsequent testing of these students in the absence of such suggestion revealed normal pain thresholds.

It has not been possible under laboratory conditions in trained subjects, to bring about a lowering of the pain threshold by auto-suggestion. The inexperienced subject, however, can be so confused that he will give any report which he feels will satisfy the observer. For example, a student was being tested for pain threshold and was having difficulty in identifying the threshold sensation. After many trials, the operator turned the radiation source off and gave the subject only the click of the shutter which usually marks the beginning and end of an exposure. The subject immediately reported, "That is just the pain threshold." After a few minutes the testing was resumed and normal threshold values were obtained. This is not an instance of lowering of the pain threshold by suggestion but rather of irritation of the subject by prolonged testing. It is this type of report which is sometimes obtained from an overanxious patient. Reassurance and further instruction as regards identification of the threshold pain effectively eliminate this type of reporting.

The Influence of Age and Sex upon the Pricking Pain Threshold

As mentioned in the first part of the chapter, there was no correlation between pricking pain threshold, and age and sex, or the individual's personal concept of his or her "sensitiveness to pain" or ability to "stand pain". Chapman and Jones (79) came to somewhat different conclusions using the thermal radiation method on the skin and also testing for visceral sensitivity to pain by balloon distention of the lower esophagus. These authors used two endpoints, the first a "sharp jab sensation" for the "pain perception threshold", and the second, "wincing", for "pain reaction". They found that for "pain perception" the pain threshold increased with age; that the threshold of Negroes and Southern Europeans was lower than that of Northern Europeans; and that it was unaffected in certain psychoneurotic states such as neurocirculatory asthenia.

The most probable explanation of the differences between these and the findings reported herein, lies in the instructions given to the subjects tested. Chapman and Jones gave no instructions to their subjects and, thus, in all probability were not measuring the threshold for pricking pain alone, but were also observing effects related to the reaction as well as the perception of pain. In most instances the "perception" thresholds noted by these authors paralleled closely the "reaction" thresholds.

Sherman (399), in a study of 450 office patients, found that age

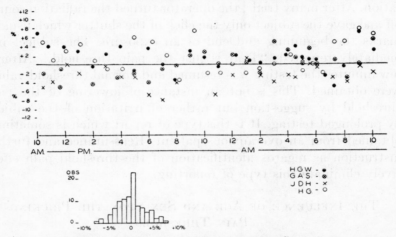

FIG. 40. PAIN THRESHOLD MEASUREMENTS ON FOUR SUBJECTS DURING A
TWENTY-FOUR-HOUR PERIOD OF WAKEFULNESS
At lower left is shown the distribution of results about the mean value.

was not a factor which would produce changes in pain threshold. Women, though, generally had a lower threshold than men. His method of study was to place a grating next to the skin under a blood pressure cuff and to note the pressure at which pain was reported. The differences in the skin of men and women may account for the differences reported from these tests. Wilder (472), using the same method, made similar observations.

THE EFFECTS OF FATIGUE AND EMOTIONAL STATE

To test whether or not the fatigue resulting from loss of a night's sleep would alter the pain threshold, observations were made on four subjects who remained awake over a 24-hour period.

During this time the subjects carried out their usual daily activities as far as possible. During the period of study the subjects variously reported apathy, dullness, restlessness, irritability, good humor, and even gaiety. The results of the tests are shown in figure 40. It was concluded from the data that the fatigue due to 24 hours' wakefulness and the feelings of lethargy and overirritability do not have any appreciable effect upon the pain threshold.

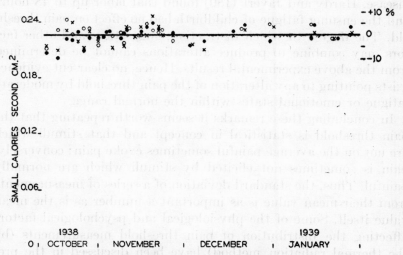

FIG. 41. AVERAGE PAIN THRESHOLDS IN THREE SUBJECTS AS DETERMINED OVER A FOUR-MONTH PERIOD

A second experiment was performed to determine the effects upon the pain threshold of day to day changes in mood. Observations were made on three subjects over a period of several weeks, always at the same time in the morning. Note was made of the subject's report of mood or of any unusual circumstance, after which the pain threshold was measured. Admitting the limitations of a subject's ability to report precisely his emotional state, there was no effect of such states upon the pain threshold, as may be seen from figure 41. Mood swings during this study were within the normal range.

Other investigators have reported findings indicating that conditions of considerable fatigue and emotional upsets do cause alterations in the pain threshold. Chapman and Jones showed that whereas epinephrine, acetylcholine, acidosis, and alkalosis had no effect on the pain "perception" threshold, severe mental and physical fatigue as well as nervous tension produced significant changes. Fatigue raised the threshold and tension lowered it. In "psychosomatic" patients, Wilder found the pain threshold to be lower than in a control group of patients with some "organic" disease. Hardy and Javert (180) found that labor up to 48 hours and the ensuing fatigue of childbirth had no effect on pain threshold. The degree to which distraction, suggestion, and other factors may combine to produce alterations cannot be determined from the above experimental results. Hence, no clear-cut evidence exists pointing to any alteration of the pain threshold by moderate fatigue or emotional states within the normal range.

In concluding these remarks it seems worth repeating that the pain threshold is statistical in concept and that stimuli which are not on the average painful sometimes evoke pain; conversely, pain is sometimes not elicited by stimuli which are normally painful. Thus, the standard deviation of a series of measurements from their mean value is as important a number as is the mean value itself. Some of the physiological and psychological factors affecting the distribution of pain threshold measurements (by the thermal radiation method) have been discussed in the preceding paragraphs. By giving attention to these factors, precision of measurement can be increased to the point at which the ability of the individual, under the most favorable conditions, to discriminate between stimuli of different intensities sets a final limit. Thus, location on the body of area of skin studied, skin temperature, blackness, wettness, and injury as well as repetition and duration of exposure of the skin to the thermal radiation are important physiological factors. On the other hand, age, sex, race, fatigue, and emotional state have little observable effect on the pain threshold level or distribution of measurements.

Chapter V
BURNING PAIN

In the course of several years of experimentation with measurements of the pricking pain threshold by use of the thermal radiation method, the reports of subjects, as regards sensation experienced during and immediately after the end of exposure to radiant heat, indicated the presence of two kinds of pain, one of burning, the other of pricking quality. Discussion as to whether burning pain resulted from a series of rapid pricking sensations or was a different sensory quality with its own threshold of excitation resulted in an attempt to compare these two pain thresholds under various experimental conditions.

The burning pain threshold is difficult to recognize when the time of stimulation is only a few seconds in length. But if it be longer the burning pain threshold is more easily identified. Largely for this reason, burning pain was not used originally as a threshold sensation for experimental purposes, although its presence was recognized as an after-sensation following a short exposure to noxious stimulation by thermal radiation. Thus, if a fingernail bed be briefly pressed against a hot electric light bulb (83) a sudden short-lived pricking pain is experienced, followed after a brief interval by a longer lasting sensation of intense heat and burning pain. Placing of this latter sensation into a quality category separate from those of pricking and aching pain was required for an understanding of observations in patients with certain types of hyperalgesia and itching.

MEASUREMENT OF THE BURNING PAIN THRESHOLD

Subjects were trained in the recognition of the burning pain sensation by repeated prolonged exposures to thermal radiation. The thresholds for burning and pricking pain for various times of exposure to thermal radiation were then ascertained on the skin of the forehead of 23 subjects. In this limited series, the maximum variation in level of threshold from subject to subject was ±16 per cent (32). The data for "burning" and "pricking" pain thresholds on the skin of the forehead of 11 subjects are averaged and represented in figure 42. Invariably, on normally

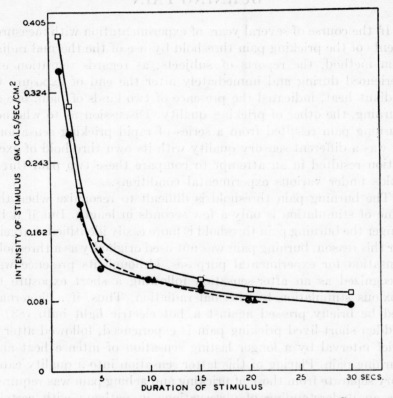

FIG. 42. RELATION OF INTENSITY OF STIMULUS TO DURATION OF STIMULATION FOR BURNING AND PRICKING PAIN ELICITED BY THERMAL RADIATION ON THE GLANS AND ON THE FOREHEAD

Forehead: "pricking" pain, □——□; "burning" pain, ●——●. Glans: "burning" pain, ▲- - - -▲.

innervated skin, the threshold for "burning" pain was found to be lower than that for "pricking" pain by 20 to 40 mc./sec./cm.²

The effects of two analgesic agents upon the thresholds of "pricking" and "burning" pain were also observed. In six observations made on three subjects, it was found that ingested ethyl alcohol (60 ml. 95 per cent) raised the threshold of both "burning" and "pricking" pain about the same percentage above their control levels. Acetylsalicylic acid also raised the threshold of both "burning" and "pricking" pain approximately the same percentage above control levels, although, to be sure, these two agents differed from each other in their effects (493, 492, 491).

To ascertain whether spatial summation occurs with "burning" pain, pain thresholds were measured on areas of skin 0.4 to 11.6 cm.^{2} in size. Thresholds for "burning" pain in four subjects tested varied not more than 25 per cent from the smallest to the largest areas of skin stimulated, which indicates that no spatial summation of any significance occurred. It has already been demonstrated that observable spatial summation does not occur for "pricking" pain (185) (see Chapter IV).

Comparative observations of pain thresholds were made on the skin of the forehead and on the surface of the glans penis in seven normal subjects. The data of the observations are presented in figure 42. With stimuli of over five seconds duration the "burning" pain threshold on the glans was found to be the same as that on the skin of the forehead. As the intensity of the stimulation on the surface of the glans was increased, the "burning" pain sensation became more intense. The subjects stated that they were unable to recognize a pricking quality of pain, but concluded that the sensation was a combination of burning and aching qualities.

Thresholds for "burning" and "pricking" pain were ascertained in four trials on each of three subjects who had "sunburn" or ultraviolet burn of various degrees of severity. The threshold for "pricking" pain was reduced by 43 to 52 per cent; that for "burning" pain by 63 to 97 per cent from the respective control levels, ascertained on the same areas of skin on the day prior to tissue damage (table 10). This greater reduction in the "burning" pain threshold explains why slight stimulation of a "sunburned" skin characteristically elicits a "burning" pain sensation.

In a patient with radiculitis, the thresholds for "pricking" and "burning" pain over an area of "hyperalgesic" skin on the left arm, were compared with those of normal skin areas on arms and forehead. The threshold for "burning" pain was about 20 per cent lower on the affected skin area, whereas the threshold for "pricking" pain was elevated by about 20 per cent (fig. 43).

Rubbing the skin of a patient who had "hypoalgesia" to pin

TABLE 10

Threshold for burning and pricking pain on an area of hyperalgesic skin compared with thresholds in control areas

SUBJECT	AREA OF SKIN INJURED	HOW INJURED	PAIN THRESHOLD CHANGE	
			"Pricking"	"Burning"
			%	%
N. B.	Over deltoid muscle	Sunlight	−43	−63
N. B.	Over forearm	Ultraviolet lamp	−52	−97
I. H.	Over deltoid muscle	Sunlight	−51	−86
O. B.	Over deltoid muscle	Sunlight	−47	−92

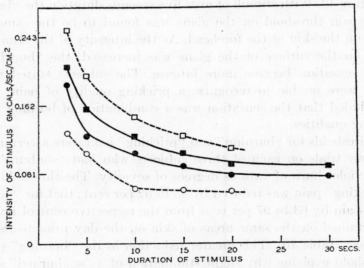

FIG. 43. A COMPARISON OF INTENSITY-DURATION CURVES OF PAIN THRESHOLDS OF BURNING AND PRICKING PAIN IN A PATIENT WITH HYPERALGESIA AS A RESULT OF RADICULITIS

Hyperalgesic skin: "pricking" pain, □- - - -□; "burning" pain, ○- - - -○. Normal skin: "pricking" pain, ■——■; "burning" pain, ●——●.

prick on parts of his left hand, induced a burning sensation. At surgical operation, a displaced nucleus of an intervertebral disc of the sixth cervical vertebra was found. In table 11 are shown the threshold measurements for "burning" and "pricking" pain ascertained on control areas of the intact hand and the forehead, compared with thresholds ascertained on the affected hand. It can be seen that the threshold for the "burning" pain on the affected side was less than on the opposite unaffected side, whereas the threshold for "pricking" pain was higher on the affected side.

Seventeen patients with "hyperalgesic" skin due to some pe-

TABLE 11

Thresholds for "burning" and "pricking" pain on an area of "hypoalgesic" skin compared with thresholds on control areas

DURATION OF STIMULUS	THRESHOLDS FOR "BURNING" PAIN			THRESHOLDS FOR "PRICKING" PAIN		
	Control	"Hypoalgesic"	Deviation	Control	"Hypoalgesic"	Deviation
sec.	*gm.cal./sec./cm.²*		%	*gm.cal./sec./cm.²*		%
5	0.134	0.089	−33	0.181	0.219	+21
10	0.112	0.068	−40	0.152	0.178	+17
15	0.096	0.064	−34	0.113	0.142	+26

ripheral nerve disorder were observed. Three patients with herpes zoster and 14 patients with peripheral neuritis from such varied causes as nutritional deficiency, dorsal root inflammation, or diabetes, exhibited a lowered threshold of "burning" pain, from 15 to 35 per cent below control thresholds of normal skin areas on the same subject. The "pricking" pain threshold in the affected areas was never observed to be lowered and was frequently elevated.

Ischemia was experimentally produced in six subjects by occlusion of the circulation of the upper arm with a blood pressure cuff inflated to 200 mm. Hg for 35 to 75 minutes. Care was taken that the arm was not moved and that pain did not occur spontaneously. Since the skin temperature of an ischemic arm falls gradually to room temperature, the latter was kept at 30° to 31°C. during experiments. Measurements of pain thresholds were made on the dorsum of the wrist at intervals of two to three minutes.

There was observed a slight fall in "pricking" pain threshold during the first ten minutes, followed by a rise (see fig. 44). The threshold for "burning" pain, however, fell for about 20 minutes and began to rise again after 25 minutes of ischemia. Thus, be-

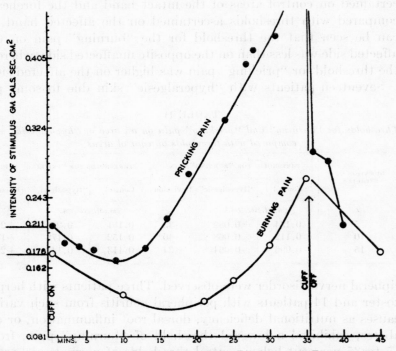

FIG. 44. THE EFFECT OF ISCHEMIA UPON THE PRICKING AND BURNING PAIN THRESHOLDS

After applying a blood pressure cuff (200 mg. Hg) to the upper arm measurements were made on the dorsum of the hand, using the thermal radiation method.

tween 10 and 25 minutes, the "burning" pain threshold was depressed by 28 to 32 per cent, while the "pricking" pain threshold was rapidly elevated. It was also noted that when the threshold of "burning" pain was most depressed during the ischemia, the pain elicited by noxious stimulation of the skin persisted often for five seconds or longer, after the stimulus had ended.

The persistence of pain after a noxious stimulus was most evident when the threshold of "burning" pain was most depressed.

However, the "after-pain" gradually diminished in duration as the threshold of "burning" pain became elevated during prolonged ischemia. Finally, even "burning" pain could not be elicited as the arm became almost insensitive to all types of stimulation.

THE DOUBLE RESPONSE

Many investigators have demonstrated, when pain is induced by pin prick or heat in the distal parts of an extremity, that the sensation of "pricking" pain is followed by a second painful sen-

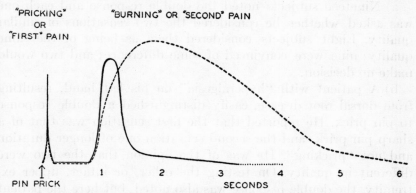

FIG. 45. SCHEMATIC REPRESENTATION OF TEMPORAL COMPONENTS OF "BURNING" AND "PRICKING" SKIN PAIN IN HEALTHY PERSONS AS CONTRASTED WITH PATIENTS HAVING "HYPERALGESIA" ASSOCIATED WITH PERIPHERAL NEUROPATHY
——, normal skin; - - - -, "hyperalgesic" skin

sation after a painless interval (234). This has been called the "double response" (145, 283, 279) (fig. 45). An attempt has been made in the following experiments to ascertain whether the quality of the first pain response, i.e., the rapidly perceived pain, which will be designated "fast" pain, was identical with that of the second response, i.e., the pain perceived later. The latter will be designated "slow" pain.

Method. For purposes of "burning" pain stimulation a sharp needle was thrust superficially and briefly into the skin surface; a brass cylinder heated to about 65°C. was momentarily touched against the skin; pain was also elicited by radiant heat. To clearly dissociate "burning" from "pricking" pain these noxious stimuli were applied to the distal portions of the upper and lower extremities. In a second series of observations, temporary hyperalgesia was achieved in normal subjects by wrapping a blood pressure cuff inflated to 200 mm. Hg about the upper arm. For another type of sensory dissociation a one per cent solution of procaine hydrochloride was infiltrated either around the ulnar nerve or intradermally.

Two Qualities of Pain of the Double Response

a) Nineteen subjects noted the double response and each one was asked whether he considered the two sensations of similar quality. Eight subjects considered them as being of the same quality; nine were convinced of some difference; and two would make no decision.

b) A patient with "hyperalgesia" on his left hand, resulting from dorsal root disease, easily distinguished a double response to pin prick. He reported that the first sensation was that of a sharp pin prick, and the second sensation one of longer duration and not "pricking". He was of the opinion that the two were different in quality. On testing the other, or intact, upper extremity, the double response was also noted, but here the patient was uncertain as to whether the two pains were different in quality.

c) A patient with "hyperalgesia", paresthesias, and wasting of the extremities resulting from peripheral neuropathy associated with nutritional deficiency, was certain that the second sensation was of a quality different from the first, describing the first as "pricking" and the second as a prolonged "burning" sensation (fig. 45).

d) A patient with "hyperalgesia" of the right arm associated with a herpetiform eruption, when pricked on the affected side, described a sharp, brief "prick", followed by a prolonged "burning" sensation; on his intact arm, the two sensations were considered to be the same (fig. 45).

Thus, the reports of 19 normal subjects demonstrated that the qualities of the two pain sensations of the double response on normal skin cannot always be recognized as different. The duration of each of the two sensations was short and contrasting their qualities was difficult. However, in three patients with "hyperalgesia" due to peripheral neuropathy the qualities of pricking and burning pain were predictably identified in the affected parts.

Comment. Boring (48), testing sensation on his arm following cutaneous nerve section, came to the conclusion that the qualities of the first and second responses differ. On the other hand, Lewis (274, 279), performing similar experiments with his co-workers, concluded that the two were the same. The observations cited in b, c, and d, above, are more significant than those on normal subjects because the prolonged duration of the second or "burning" quality on patients with peripheral neuritis and dorsal root disease afforded a better opportunity for discrimination. These observations suggested again that the sensations associated with the first and second response are not identical in quality.

Further Observations

In the following experiments, similar to those performed by Lewis and Pochin (283), an attempt has been made to ascertain which nerve fibers subserve "burning" and which ones "pricking" pain sensations:

a) In three subjects, ischemia of the forearm lasting from 35 to 75 minutes was produced. After pricking the skin with a pin, it was observed that "fast" pain was abolished before "slow" pain. After 35 minutes of ischemia, no sensation was felt when scratching the skin lightly with a pin, and none immediately upon impact of the pin. About a second after a forcible pin prick, however, a "burning" sensation was perceived. Pain of a "burning" quality was also produced by other means of noxious stimulation, including pinching, hair pulling, and heating. The delayed pain was always perceived as "burning".

b) In two experiments on one subject, a solution of procaine hydrochloride was infiltrated about the ulnar nerve. In 21 experiments on 11 subjects, procaine was infiltrated beneath an area of skin (5 x 7 cm.) on the dorsum of the hand. Observations were made during the period of incomplete anesthesia: 1) immediately after infiltration, and 2) as the effect of the procaine diminished.

During this period it was noted that "slow" pain was abolished, while "fast" pain was retained. The quality of pin prick was not the same as that obtained on normal skin. It seemed to be sharper and less "full" as though a very fine needle were penetrating the skin. When thermal radiation was used as a noxious stimulus, the sensation was that of many tiny sharp needles being applied, as in the familiar "pins and needles" sensation. There was no detectable sensation of "burning". The quality of the sensation perceived was distinctly different from that felt on stimulation during ischemia.

c) On three separate occasions in one subject, the tissues about the ulnar nerve were infiltrated with a one per cent solution of procaine hydrochloride. The pain threshold of the skin area on the medial aspect of the wrist innervated by the ulnar nerve was ascertained immediately after the injection and during the phase of diminishing action of the procaine. In all three observations the threshold for "pricking" pain was elevated; in one instance it was 189 per cent higher than the threshold on the control area. In this experiment, the first sensation perceived was a fine needle-like "pricking"; no "burning" pain was noted. The intensity of thermal radiation was great enough to produce a third degree burn. When the action of the procaine was ended, the subject experienced "burning" pain which persisted for 24 hours.

Comment. The observations of Lewis and his co-workers (283, 279), and those of Gasser and his co-workers (142, 143), have demonstrated the special significance of the double response. Lewis found that the "fast" pain was more readily altered by ischemia than the "slow" pain. Gasser found that during the ischemic state the function of myelinated fibers was more readily impaired than that of unmyelinated fibers, suggesting that "fast" pain is mediated by the former. Conversely, cocaine abolishes first the action of the slower-conducting, unmyelinated fibers. Lewis noted that when either the skin or the cutaneous nerve supplying it is cocainized, the "slow" pain response is abolished, while the "fast" pain response is retained. This also suggests that the "slow" pain is subserved by unmyelinated fibers. The interval between the first and second responses, which increases with the distance of the stimulus from the cord, approximates the calculated time interval based on the conduction rate of impulses traveling in either myelinated or unmyelinated fibers.

Two nerve fiber plexuses in the skin have been described (256): an intraepidermal, or superficial plexus supplied by myelinated fibers, and a subepithelial, or deeper, plexus supplied by unmyelinated fibers.

Lewis (274) is of the opinion that regardless of whether "fast" or "slow" there is only "one quality" of skin pain, and that brief noxious stimulation of the skin produces a sensation described as "pricking" whereas prolonged noxious stimulation produces a sensation described as "burning". However, in our opinion these two qualities of pain are subjectively distinguishable and quite independent of the duration of the stimulation. Thus, it is concluded that two qualities of pain, "burning" and "pricking", can be evoked by noxious stimulation of the skin and that the "pricking" quality of pain is predominantly "fast" pain, primarily conveyed by one set of fibers, myelinated fibers, whereas the "burning" pain quality is predominantly "slow" pain and conveyed primarily by another set of fibers, unmyelinated fibers.

As stated at the beginning of this chapter, the reports of subjects on a difference in the quality of pain sensations evoked by the thermal radiation stimulus, first led us to the conclusion that burning pain exists as distinct from pricking pain. Introspectional evidence is not always accepted, as just pointed out. However, dissociation between burning and pricking pain could be demonstrated by: 1) stimulating skin areas giving rise to burning pain only, 2) demonstrating quantitative difference in behavior of pricking and burning pain thresholds following ischemia, nerve block, and skin injury, and 3) noting the temporal differences in the pain responses from the fingers and toes. Thus, the differences in behavior, in innervation, and in feeling make necessary the adoption of "burning pain" as a separate pain sensation with its own peripheral neural apparatus. An even more clear cut distinction can be made between burning and pricking pain, and aching pain. Aching pain is not only distinctly different in quality but arises from noxious stimulation of deeper lying structures only. A study of this third quality of pain is presented in the next chapter.

Chapter VI

ACHING PAIN

Visceral and deep somatic structures, when noxiously stimulated, give rise to pain of aching and sometimes of burning quality. Because aching pain arises from noxious stimulation of vital organs, it is a quality of pain of great diagnostic importance to the physician. In spite of this importance, investigation of pain sensation has been more extensive for pricking and burning pain from the skin than for visceral pain, and methods for the study of skin pain have been more fully developed.

Aching pain can be induced by electrical, mechanical, thermal, and chemical means. The mechanical stimuli of compression and distention are most generally effective, while local electrical or thermal stimulation of the gut, even so strong as to destroy tissue, are sometimes ineffective in eliciting pain. This seems to be a contradiction of the thesis that production of tissue damage is the adequate stimulus for pain. However, it is likely that the sparse distribution of visceral afferent fibers and endings mediating pain accounts for this effect.

The relative inaccessibility of the visceral structures in the conscious subject for experimentation has retarded the development of methods of study of aching pain, but has not entirely excluded exploration. Electrical and mechanical stimulation has been applied to nearly all of the deep structures of the body and information has been obtained not only as to fiber pathways subserving pain, but also as to localization and spread of aching pain.

Mechanisms Involved in the Production of Aching Pain

The head (488) and abdomen (486) are the sites of a large share of human discomfort and afford examples of two entirely different mechanisms for the production of pain from the viscera. In the head, pain does not emanate from the parenchyma of the brain but from its coverings and supporting and vascular structures (353). The brain parenchyma and the linings of the ventricles are insensitive to stretching, cutting, burning, or electrical stimulation. Investigation of the sources of pain in the head has revealed that a large portion of such pain is caused by distention of or traction on cranial and extracranial blood vessels. As regards the source of pain from blood vessels in the region of the head, the cranium has three vascular strata: the most superficial, including the vessels on the surface of the head; the middle one, including the vessels of the dura; and the deepest layer, those of the pia and the parenchyma. For purposes of analysis we may start with the consideration of pain arising from the deepest layer of arteries.

The arteries of the brain are pain sensitive in certain regions, notably at the base. It was possible to demonstrate this on a number of conscious, cooperative individuals. Also, agents that dilate cerebral arteries such as histamine, the nitrites, and those that induce fever, sepsis and sudden great elevations of systemic blood pressure, induce headache. The latter is pulsatile and throbbing (82, 327, 341, 429, 488). Pain may also result from nerve or nerve root ischemia (235). Further, it is well known that muscle ischemia resulting from vessel occlusion or constriction may cause pain (274), although there is no evidence to show that the constriction itself is painful. Epinephrine, for example, when applied to the surface of the pain sensitive middle meningeal artery caused its walls to contract vigorously yet no pain was elicited by such temporary spasm (353).

Since blood vessels entering and leaving the brain act in part as supporting or anchoring structures, they may become the origin of pain through traction upon them. There are many pain fibers on the surface of these supporting structures. The method of studying pain due to traction was as follows (252): A hypodermic needle placed in the subarachnoid space was attached to a water manometer. It was possible to vary at will the pressure within the subarachnoid space, and to estimate the intracranial or vertex pressure. Under these circumstances traction could be exerted on anchoring venous structures. Often, pain could be evoked in a subject with increased intracranial pressure by lowering the pressure to normal. Inversely, a headache associated with low intracranial pressure could be reduced in intensity by raising the pressure to normal. Lastly, because there was no traction on sensitive structures, headache was not induced in normal subjects by raising the pressure eight to ten times above the normal level (253).

Further, after spinal drainage and tilting of the subject toward the upright position the cerebral veins dilated and pain was experienced when the disparity between the intracranial venous pressure and that in the subarachnoid space became sufficiently great. Raising the cerebral venous pressure by jugular compression increased the intensity of this pain. Hence, it may be inferred that changes in the cerebrospinal fluid pressure are not responsible for headache. The latter has its origin in traction on pain-sensitive vascular structures.

Attempts were made to differentiate in the same person the qualities of pain: a) in headache resulting from intravenous injection of histamine which caused noxious stimulation by distention of the cerebral arteries; b) in migraine headache emanating chiefly from distended branches of the external carotid artery; c) in headache due to venous traction arising after spinal fluid drainage; and d) in headache resulting from the injection of a hypertonic saline solution into the frontalis muscle. Although these headaches varied as regards site, pulsatile or non-pulsatile nature and other temporal aspects, and as to whether or not they could be modified in intensity by such factors as position, movement, or chemical agents, the quality of the pain was reported to be the same in all. The pain was of an aching quality, diffuse, quick to arouse a reaction in muscles and glands, such as lacrimation and injection of the sclera, and it was associated with feelings of nausea. It was indistinguishable in quality from that which results from painful stimulation of the teeth, the periosteum, or the muscles of the eye (296, 109, 370).

PAIN FROM NOXIOUS STIMULATION OF A VISCUS

The evidence for the existence of true visceral pain has been repeatedly challenged since it is difficult or impossible to stimulate one of the visceral organs without at the same time stimulating supporting structures. Mackenzie (302) emphasized that no conclusion conerning pain sensitivity of an organ should be drawn if stimulating pressure is exerted through it against structures which may in themselves be sensitive. Lewis (274) asks whether it is not possible that tenderness in patients with gastric ulcer sometimes emanates from the attachments of the stomach to the posterior abdominal wall. Resolution of this question is important to the problem of localization of pain from a viscus; for, if one admits that true visceral tenderness occurs, one implicitly agrees that pain can result from the stimulation of a viscus.

The stomach offers an excellent opportunity to resolve the question as to whether or not there is true visceral pain. Wolf and Wolff (486) studied a man who had a large gastric stoma, surgically produced because of esophageal occlusion. It was observed in this subject that when from 50 to 95 per cent alcohol was introduced into the cardiac end of the esophagus it produced a sensation of "heartburn", but when introduced into the stomach, it produced no pain. These observations confirm those made earlier by Jones and others (231, 334) in individuals with an intact gastrointestinal tract.

When the healthy mucosa of the fundus of the stomach was explored through the stoma and was pinched between the blades of a forecps, no pain resulted. Furthermore, faradic stimulation intense enough to cause pain on the tongue produced no pain when applied to the fundus mucosa. Neither 50 to 95 per cent alcohol, 1.0 N hydrochloric acid, 0.1 N sodium hydroxide, nor a 1:30 suspension of mustard produced pain when applied to the mucosa. However, when the mucosa was inflamed, congested, and edematous from whatever cause, these procedures evoked pain of considerable intensity. This change in pain sensitivity was not dependent on the mucus since when the latter was aspirated away from the normal mucosa and powdered mustard placed on this now dry and unprotected surface, pain did not immediately ensue. It was not until some time after the application of the mustard, when the mucosa had become red and edematous that painful sensations could be elicited by the mustard, pinching, or by faradic current. Under such conditions other agents such as 1.0 N hydrochloric acid and 50 to 95 per cent alcohol likewise became capable of evoking painful sensations.

Thus, although the number of pain fibers and endings in the

gastric mucosa may be relatively small as compared to their density in the skin, there can no longer be any doubt about pain originating from noxious stimulation of an inflamed gastric musoca.

The question whether pain stems directly from the muscularis or from the visceral peritoneum and mesentery is less readily answered. Lewis (274) inferred from a summary of the available evidence that contraction of the muscular layers of the gut does not give rise to painful sensations. It was his opinion that experiments aimed to resolve this question led to the conclusion that it is the mesenteric attachments which are the sources of pain.

Recent evidence (486) on this topic has come from two series of experiments on the above mentioned subject: 1) ordinarily when the stomach contracted with a force sufficient to support 35 mm. Hg pain was elicited. When the gastric mucosa was inflamed, a force only sufficient to support 20 mm. Hg would produce pain. It should not be inferred from such an experiment that the pain is elicited exclusively from the mucosa. It is doubtful, moreover, that it represents mesenteric traction since there is less traction as the result of a force supporting 20 mm. of mercury than one supporting 35 mm.; 2) when the stomach was stretched with glass rods it was found that when the stomach was moderately contracted the pressure necessary to produce pain was 100 gm./cm.^{2} However, when the stomach wall was strongly contracted pressure of 50 gm./cm.^{2} or half that originally applied, was found sufficient to produce pain. On the other hand, when the stomach was more relaxed, 150 gm./cm.^{2} of pressure was necessary to induce pain. These observations suggest that the muscularis and serosa may contribute to pain experienced from stimulation of the stomach.

To supplement these observations on the exposed gastric mucosa, indirect but significant evidence comes from the observations of Palmer (331) who has shown that pain from peptic ulcer occurs only when the gastric content is acid. The pain is reduced in intensity or eliminated entirely by emptying the stomach, as by emesis or aspiration, or by neutralizing the acid content with food or alkali. On the other hand, in the patient with peptic ulcer who is temporarily free of pain, the introduction into the stomach of dilute hydrochloric acid (0.25, 0.5 and 1.0 per cent) will induce pain while pain is not induced by the introduction of such concentrations into the healthy stomach or into the stomach with a healed peptic ulcer.

The evidence from x-ray examination, according to Palmer, indicates that the pain of ulcer is not dependent on either hyperperistalsis, or sustained contraction of the musculature, or pylorospasm, or distention of the antrum of the stomach. However, any one of these states in conjunction with hyperacidity and inflammation augments the pain of ulcer. Thus, peristaltic contractions may induce pain in a patient with ulcer when there is acid present but if the acid is neutralized peristalsis no longer induces pain. As in the skin, inflammation lowers the pain threshold of the gastric mucosa, the mucosa of the bladder (298), and that of the nose (296, 221).

From a study of exposed colons in four subjects, Grace, Wolf and Wolff (165) were able to draw further inferences concerning pain from the viscera. Sometimes, especially when the mucous membrane was inflamed, it was possible to elicit the sensation of pain by lacerating the colonic surface. It was observed in these subjects that usually a considerable incision was necessary before it evoked pain. This was of mixed quality with aching as the prevailing component. These observations further support the view that pain can be elicited from the visceral mucous membrane but that there is a relatively wide separation of pain endings in the mucosa.

To epitomize this analysis it may be said that there are three mechanisms involved in the production of aching pain:

1) True visceral and deep somatic pain. Such pain is felt at the site of primary noxious stimulation and may, or may not, be accompanied by referred pain. It can be eliminated by infiltration of procaine into the site of noxious stimulation or by blocking the afferent nerves, but it is not altered by infiltration of procaine into other structures supplied by the the same or by adjacent neural segments.

2) Referred pain. Such pain may occur in addition to or in the absence of the true visceral and deep somatic pain described above.

It is experienced at a site other than that of stimulation but in tissues supplied by the same or adjacent neural segments. It may occur either with or without associated hyperalgesia and hyperesthesia:

a) Without superficial and/or deep hyperalgesia. In this case pain depends only on the central effects of the spread of excitation of the primary afferent impulses from noxious stimulation to the same and adjacent segments of the cord, whence they are relayed to higher centers for perception and interpretation. Injection of procaine into superficial or deep regions of referred pain does not reduce the intensity of pain due to this mechanism.

b) With superficial and/or deep hyperalgesia. Referred pain may be accentuated in intensity by virtue of the effects of ordinarily non-noxious stimuli from zones of reference. Impulses from such sources, normally inadequate to produce pain, may do so upon reaching the cord in a segment involved in the central spread of excitation. Procaine injected into superficial or deep hyperalgesic structures will abolish this element of the referred pain phenomenon, resulting in greater or lesser reduction of the subject's discomfort, depending upon the amount of hyperalgesia.

3) Pain secondary to skeletal muscle contractions. Pain may result from secondary effects of the central spread of excitation on the effector structures, including painful contractions of skeletal muscles. Such disturbances may be widespread and the pains may be experienced in sites remote from the original source of noxious stimulation. Local infiltration of the contracted muscles with procaine abolishes this type of pain by disrupting its peripheral mechanism.

Measurement of Threshold of Aching Pain

Quantitative studies of pain threshold have been made by measurement of a) distending force exerted on a hollow viscus, b) pressure upon subcutaneous and periosteal tissues, c) voltage for faradic stimulation of teeth, and d) thermal changes in skin and superficial tissues. These procedures have been discussed and evaluated in Chapter III. Here it remains only to present observations from the most recent investigations and to correlate them with the information available for pricking and burning pain.

Distention of a Hollow Viscus

One of the commonly used methods of making such studies is that of placing in the viscus a balloon attached to a manometer. Measurements are made of the volume and pressure of water in the system when pain is evoked. It has been observed that whereas the pain threshold expressed in these terms is suitable for a particular subject at one time, it is highly variable from subject to subject, and in the same subject at different times. The characteristic observation is in agreement with those of Chapman and Jones (79) and Gaensler (140) and Wolf (486). From this it may be inferred that the measurable features of the stimulus, pressure upon and volume of the viscus, are not predictably related to the noxious stimulation of the viscus. As noxious stimulation from heat, at least, seems to depend on the *rate* of protein alteration (tissue injury), so is it possible that the *rate* of distention of a viscus may be more pertinent than the degree of distention and pressure.

Electrical Stimulation of Teeth

Electrical stimulation of the teeth elicits aching pain (152). However, the voltage required to elicit threshold pain in an individual varies greatly from tooth to tooth and in the same tooth from time to time, and in the corresponding tooth from individual to individual. Thus, it is not possible to establish a general level of voltage for the pain threshold in teeth. The relationship between voltage applied and noxious stimulation produced is obscure (370).

Thermal Stimulation

The threshold for aching pain by thermal radiation is, as noted in Chapter VII, higher than that for burning and pricking pain and lies at a level of 300 to 320 mc./sec./cm.^{2} Chapman and Jones used this threshold for experimental purposes and showed that it is uniform from subject to subject. The high level of the aching pain threshold as compared with those of pricking and burning pain is due to the fact that the structures mediating aching pain are located in the deeper dermal layers. Assuming that the aching pain threshold is reached when the subservient nerve endings and neighboring cells are raised to a temperature of 45°C., the location of these endings can be calculated to be about at a depth of 0.9 mm.

Cooling of tissue evokes aching pain and the threshold for this stimulus is 18°C. (483). Kunkle et al. (247–8) concluded that the noxious stimulation for such "cold pain" is the direct action of the low temperature on the subcutaneous tissues. The nature of the noxious stimulation is not understood, although it has been shown that isolated smooth and skeletal muscle of mammals undergo spontaneous contraction when cooled to between 18 and 20°C. and a possible connection between these phenomena has been suggested (176). The threshold for cold pain is a stable one.

As has been pointed out "spreading" is characteristic of aching pain. Thus, if one holds a finger in cold water, aching pain spreads into other fingers and also up the arm into the axilla. This tendency of excitation from noxious stimulation of one area to "spill over" and excite pain pathways from other areas points strongly to the possibility of spatial summation for aching pain. There are, however, two important pieces of evidence, obtained from experiments with thermal stimulation, that militate against the idea of spatial summation for aching pain. Wolf and Hardy showed that the threshold for aching pain due to immersion in cold water (18°C.) was not affected by the size of the area stimulated. That is, 18°C. was the pain threshold whether one finger, two fingers, the entire hand, or both hands were immersed. Secondly, the estimated intensity of the pain was the same for a given immersion temperature, irrespective of the size of the area stimulated. On this basis, it is inferred that spatial summation does not occur to an appreciable degree for aching pain and that in this respect it is similar to pricking and to burning pain.

Pressure

By far the most common method of inducing aching pain for experimental purposes is that of exerting pressure on subcutaneous tissues (284, 399). Measurements of pain threshold have been made using any of the various means described in Chapter III. The one chosen for investigation of aching pain in relation to pricking pain is a modification of Gluzek's (150) method.

The apparatus consists of a plunger surrounded by a metal sleeve within which is mounted a steel spring. The force in grams exerted on the tissue by the rounded plastic tip of the plunger, 1 cm. in diameter, is read from a scale which indicates the degree of compression of the steel spring. A diagram of this simple device is shown in figure 46. Measurements of pain threshold were made on the forehead on thirteen spots distributed symmetrically on both sides of a line from the bregma to the hairline. The spots were located in each experiment by use of a stencil fitted to the forehead, and were marked with India ink. The pain threshold measurements were obtained by placing the plunger tip upon a spot and increasing the pressure until the subject reported pain. Tests were made successively from alternate sides of the midline, every effort being made to direct the plunger perpendicular to the calvarium, thus to avoid dragging or pulling the skin. During the tests the subject lay supine on a table, with the head supported by a book.

The sensory experience elicited by this mode of stimulation was one of pressure increasing until minimal aching pain was perceived. Cutaneous sensations of burning and pricking pain were not experienced by this method of stimulation. From this it was inferred that the subcutaneous and periosteal tissues were the primary sites of noxious stimulation

The results of 800 pain threshold measurements in three adult subjects are shown in figure 47. The mean pressure required to evoke pain was 550 gm., with the highest values 695 and the lowest 390 gm. The standard deviation from the mean is ±130, a value smaller than that reported by Gluzek.

Expressed in terms of per cent of the average threshold stimulus, the variation (statistically, the "coefficient of variation") in the aching pain threshold measured in this way was large, ±24 per cent for the standard deviation, as compared to the threshold measurements for pricking and burning pains with standard deviation of ± four per cent. However, such a comparison is misleading. The ratio of the intensities of thermal radiation stimuli evoking ceiling pain to that eliciting threshold pain is roughly two to one, whereas the ratio of such stimuli for aching pain is greater than twelve to one. Thus, it is necessary to compare stimuli of different types in terms other than percentage of their respective threshold intensities. The most effective way of making such comparisons required the determination of the magnitude

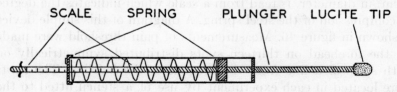

SCALE   SPRING   PLUNGER   LUCITE TIP

FIG. 46. COILED SPRING ESTHESIOMETER FOR MEASURING DEEP PAIN THRESHOLD

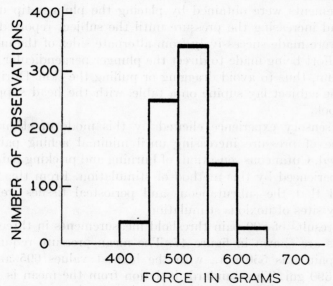

FIG. 47. FREQUENCY DISTRIBUTION OF 800 MEASUREMENTS OF ACHING PAIN THRESHOLD ON THE FOREHEAD OF THREE SUBJECTS, WITH THE COILED SPRING ESTHESIOMETER

of the two stimuli evoking a "just noticeable difference" (jnd) in pain sensation at all levels of pain intensity from threshold to "ceiling pain". It is then possible to determine the stimulus strength and variation in terms of the number of just noticeable differences. As seen by reference to the next chapter, the standard deviation for the pressure method of measuring aching pain threshold is ±1 jnd and this is also the range of precision for the thermal radiation pricking pain method.

It often becomes of great practical importance to compare data on pain thresholds obtained by different methods of stimulation, especially when studying analgesic action. For example, how can the data on pain threshold-raising effect of an analgesic obtained with the thermal radiation method be compared to that obtained with the electrical stimulation of the tooth pulp? This comparison cannot be made in terms of measureable units of the noxious stimulus evoking pain, but can be made in terms of the just noticeable difference. For example, a procedure such as hypnosis, or a chemical agent such as morphine sulfate, may raise the aching pain threshold stimulus several volts above the control level as measured by electrical stimulation of the teeth, or several hundred grams as measured by the pressure method just described. An elevation of the pricking pain threshold of several hundred mc./sec./cm^2, may also result. The question then arises as to whether there has been the same or different degrees of elevation of the pain threshold in the tooth, in the subcutaneous tissues of the forehead, and in the skin. If the changes of threshold are expressed in terms of numbers of jnd's above threshold, rather than, as is the usual practice, in percentages of the physical stimulus, the degree of sensory suppression can be estimated. Batterman and Miller (19, 312) have called attention to the artificiality of expressing threshold changes in terms of stimulus measurements, but at that time there was no apparent alternative. As will be seen in Chapter XIII, expressed in terms of jnd's, the elevation of pain threshold following administration of certain analgesics is the same for aching as for pricking pain.

In summary, aching pain is considered to be a separate pain sensation on the basis of its different quality, of its different ennervation (localized to deep structures), and of its different behavior, particularly with respect to spread and localization. This third sensation of pain completes the spectrum of painful qualities to the extent to which we have been able to identify separate esthetic components of complex pain sensations. Thus, any complex sensation of pain consists of varying proportions of pricking, burning, and aching qualities, and it remains to be demonstrated how the proportions of such qualities can be determined. This matter is the topic of the next chapter.

Chapter VII

PAIN INTENSITY AND THE "DOL" SCALE

The possibility of measuring pain intensity has been viewed with skepticism, although the concept of measuring the sensory dimension of intensity was introduced by Fechner (120) about the middle of the nineteenth century. Fechner was interested principally in the measurement of intensity of visual and auditory sensations and proposed the application of the "Weber Law" as the basis for such measurements. His modification of the relationship between stimulus intensity and intensity of sensation is often termed the "Weber-Fechner Law", i.e.,

$$S = K \log I/I_0$$

in which S = intensity of sensation, K = constant, I = intensity of the stimulus, and I_0 = the intensity of the threshold stimulus.

In spite of the doubts expressed on all sides as to the validity of measurements of sensory intensities, such measurements were being employed in the study of the sense of vision. Thus, from Young's publications (502) in 1801 to the present, the measurement of brightness, hue, and saturation has developed into a highly technical specialty. The practical benefits derived from this effort (color matching, measurement of illumination, measurement of color blindness, etc.) have been so important that no one any longer objects, even on theoretical grounds, to the scaling of the dimensions of visual sensation.

Measurement has been broadly defined by Stevens (419) as the process of relating or assigning, according to specific rules, distinctive terms or numerals to objects or events. The fact that relations can be assigned under different specifications provides the possibility of different kinds of scales of measurement. Thus, the question of measuring the dimensions of sensation becomes one of methodology. That is, are methods available for relating sensory quality, intensity, duration, and extension to names or numbers, and what are the formal rules these symbols must follow to make a useful model of the observable data?

146

As regards sensation, the first process of measurement involves the linking of a number or nominal system to the discriminable aspects of sensation, i.e., the dimensions of quality, intensity, duration, and extent. Thus, the qualities of pain have been termed pricking, burning, and aching. These terms of quality have great usefulness in permitting the description of the pain which is being experienced. The assignment of such terms constitutes a scale descriptive of pain quality. Such scales are known as nominal scales.

The nominal scale represents simply the assignment of numerals or descriptive terms to the components of a group in order to differentiate them in respect to some recognizable characteristic. Systematic biology is chiefly concerned with such scaling when dealing with the classification of living forms into classes, phyla, genera, species, etc. This type of scaling is generally recognized as one of the fundamental procedures for obtaining order out of the complexity of our empirical world. The nominal scale depends upon a single basic empirical operation, that is, the determination of equality. It is a general rule of this type of scaling to assign the same numeral or term to only one particular class.

Nominal scales of pain are in general use but as no clear analysis in terms of quality, intensity, duration, and extension is implied in the terms used, the description of the pain is confused. For example, "sharp" in reference to pain may mean either narrowly circumscribed, or of high intensity, or of short duration; also, "acute" may mean either narrowly circumscribed, of high intensity, of short duration, sudden in onset, or prostrating. On the other hand, terms such as "dull" or "lancinating" are somewhat more specific, "dull" always meaning of aching quality and of three-dimensional extension, but of no specific intensity or duration; while "lancinating" refers to a swift change in location with no specifications as to intensity or quality.

After classification into qualities comes the second step of measurement, i.e., ordering by rank within a quality series according to the concept "more or less than". This is the basic operation for the setting up of scales of degree or intensity.

Ordinal scales of pain were used at first with descriptive terms such as "mild", "moderate", "severe", and "intense". Wolff and his collaborators, in the 1930's, employed an ordinal scale of "plus" values in order to provide a closer description than that allowed by just the four categories mentioned. Revici, as recently as 1949, was using the descriptive classification to designate pain intensity. Descriptive terms, as well as numerical labels serve equally well to denote the order of increasing intensity. Wolff's scale of pain intensity in terms of "plus" values alone, although employing numerals, represented only the *order* of increasing intensity (358, 488).

When properties have been classified and the classes ordered as to rank, the third step in measurement can be made. This is to establish the magnitude of the orders of rank and to separate the ranks by intervals of equal size. The fundamental empirical operation that must be performed for this type of scaling is that of determining the equality of intervals or differences. The scale of equal intervals thus evolved is known as an "interval scale".

Physical equal-interval scales are familiar, as, for example, the temperature scales, Fahrenheit and Centigrade. For these particular scales the "zero" point is arbitrarily fixed. Thus, a temperature of 100°F. cannot be said to be twice as "high" as 50°F. This limitation applies to all interval scales with an arbitrary zero point.

Psychological measurement aspires to create equal-interval scales, and, depending upon the availability of experimental techniques, it succeeds. As an example of this may be cited the fact that the interval scale of loudness devised by Stevens, Morgan and Volkmann (422) was dependent upon the introduction of certain electronic techniques in the study of hearing. Following the development of adequate photometric techniques the determination of "equal sense differences" was possible for vision (51).

The fourth and final step in the hierarchy of measurement is that of determining values which bear a constant ratio to one another. To satisfy this requirement the scale must have a beginning, a true "zero point". For example, the absolute scale of temperature has its beginning at a zero temperature which is thermodynamically the lowest possible temperature. For this temperature scale it is proper to say that 10° absolute is twice as high a temperature as 5°A. and one-half as high as 20°A. Such a scale is termed a "ratio scale", and includes, as well, interval, ordinal, and nominal scaling. Some psychological scales fulfill all four requirements for a ratio scale, and as will be seen, the scale for pricking, and possibly that for aching pain are among those that do.

To summarize the operations which are necessary to produce a scale of equal sensory intervals, Stevens (419) lists the five necessary procedures as follows:

1. *Stimulus rating.* A controllable stimulus is desirable, which can be measured with precision and reproduced accurately. The precision and reproducibility of the measured quantity should be of a higher degree than the ability of the subject to recognize differences in stimulus intensity evoking just noticeable differences in sensation.

2. *Measurement of equality.* Which stimuli evoke responses that appear equal in intensity, or in quality, or in some other sensory dimension?

3. *Determination of order.* Arrangement of stimuli according to the sensory responses which can be serially ordered within a quality, as, for example, intensity of pain in "plus" values.

4. *Differential thresholds.* This requires the measurement of the smallest change in the stimulus that can be recognized at least half the time as a change in a sensory dimension. The determination of the just noticeable difference (jnd) reveals the limit of discrimination of the sensory equipment in respect to a particular sensory dimension. For example, there are about 570 jnd's (103) for visual brightness between threshold and dazzle point, and for the warmth sensation there are 90 jnd's between the warmth and the pain threshold (212).

5. *Establishment of equality of intervals.* This requires a determination of stimulus intensities producing responses which are successively equidistant in magnitude. If the dimension be that of sensory intensity, one may measure the jnd at all levels of stimulus intensity from the threshold to the ceiling sensation. Assuming with Fechner that one just noticeable difference in sensation is the same as another regardless of the level of sensation, then these

differences could be summed to obtain a measure of sensory intensity. Stevens found this to be correct for pitch, but it is not correct for loudness. Nevertheless, the concept is important because it has afforded a quantitative approach to the study of intensity of sensation above the threshold sensation.

The equal interval scale of pain intensity was devised in the above manner. The painful sensation which was studied in the experiments to be described, was induced in the skin by thermal radiation.

MEASUREMENT OF THE JUST NOTICEABLE DIFFERENCE FOR PRICKING PAIN

The method of measuring the just noticeable differences in stimulus intensity evoking pain was as follows: An intensity of radiation (at or greater than the pain threshold) was selected on each experimental day as the "standard" for that experiment. The method of choosing the standard was to increase systematically the intensity of the stimulus by approximately the amount of one jnd as determined from the previous experiment. A series of thirteen standard stimuli was used, including 220 mc./sec./cm.^{2} which is approximately the pain threshold. Each of the three authors, serving in turn as subject and observer, was stimulated with two exposures to the standard radiation. In most of the experiments the forehead was used as the test surface because of its uniform temperature and also because previously this area had served satisfactorily for pain threshold studies. However, in the series of experiments with stimuli greater than 500 mc./sec./cm.^{2} considerable tissue damage was produced, and for these experiments a second test area, the volar surface of the forearm, was used. This area had approximately the same pain threshold as the forehead and could be more easily cared for when blistered. Following exposure to the "standard stimulus" the subjects were presented with three test stimuli. The sensation induced by the standard stimulus was compared from memory with the sensations evoked by the test stimuli and a report was made as to whether the test stimuli elicited pain of equal, lesser, or greater intensity than the "standard". It required about ten minutes to present the test stimuli and record the reports. Following the first series of three test stimuli, the "standard" was again presented, the subject being so informed, and a second series of tests was then begun. This procedure was followed with increasing and decreasing intensities of stimuli until the jnd had been ascertained. The jnd was defined as the intensity difference which the subject recognized in two out of three trials.

A high degree of attention on the part of the subject was required to obtain uniform results. In some instances the experiment had to be delayed because of the temporary inability of the subject to concentrate sufficiently. Some improvement in discrimination was observed in the subjects as they became accustomed to the experimental procedure. This was apparent from more uniform results with fewer wide variations. The subjects were agreed that this experiment required much more in the way of concentration and attention than did measurements of pain threshold, and, for this reason, conversation and interruptions during an experiment were avoided.

The results of the experiments are contained in table 12. Each value of the jnd, ΔI, reported in column 2 of table 12 represents an average of three or more observations on each of the three individuals.

In the range of stimuli from threshold to 420 mc./sec./cm.², individual determination of ΔI usually deviated from the average value by approximately ± 20 per cent. At the higher intensities, because of the damage done to the skin, repeated measurements could not be made and just noticeable differences could not be so carefully ascertained. A variation in readings of as much as ± 50 per cent resulted.

The relationship between the intensity of the stimulus and ΔI is shown in figure 48. At threshold, ΔI is approximately 7 mc./sec./cm.², or three per cent of the threshold stimulus. This value of ΔI corresponds quite well with the observations previously reported on the precision with which the threshold can be measured by this method, i.e., with a spread of not more than $\pm$ four per cent for a single measurement. There is no significant increase in the value of ΔI between the threshold stimulus and 290 mc./sec./cm.², but between the latter intensity and 340 mc./sec./cm.²

ΔI more than doubles, attaining the value of 15 mc./sec./cm.² Between 340 and 400 mc./sec./cm.² there is again little change in ΔI, but beginning at about the latter intensity, there is a final sharp rise in the ΔI values.

Thus, although 420 and 480 mc./sec./cm.² can be distinguished, 480 and 580 mc./sec./cm.² cannot, and it is not until the stimulus has been increased to 680 mc./sec./cm.² that a barely perceptible difference can be noted. In tests on five subjects three reported

TABLE 12

Average values of ΔI and the Weber ratio for pricking pain sensation

STANDARD STIMULUS INTENSITIES	AVERAGE ΔI	AVERAGE $\dfrac{\Delta I}{I}$
mc./sec./cm.²	*mc./sec./cm.²*	
222	7	.03
240	7	.03
258	8	.03
270	6	.02
291	6	.02
300	11	.04
312	9	.03
330	15	.05
354	19	.06
366	16	.04
390	17	.04
420	29	.07
480	60	.13
680	200	.29
(1100)	(620)	(.56)

680 as more intense than 480 mc./sec./cm.², and two reported the sensations as indistinguishable. In two experiments, two subjects reported pain intensity evoked by 1100 mc./sec./cm.² as definitely more intense than that induced by 480 mc./sec./cm.². One subject reported 680 and 1100 mc./sec./cm.² as indistinguishable. Thus discrimination for stimuli greater than 680 mc./sec./cm.² is such that, although it is possible to recognize differences in stimuli lower than 680 mc./sec./cm.², it is not possible to distinguish between higher stimuli. The sensation evoked by a stimulus of roughly 680 mc./sec./cm.² is, therefore, a "ceiling" pain since stimuli of still greater intensity cause no perceptibly greater pain.

COMMENT

The stimulus. It is probable that the magnitude of the ΔI and its ratio to the intensity, I, will depend to a large extent upon the type of noxious stimulation used, and it is to be expected that

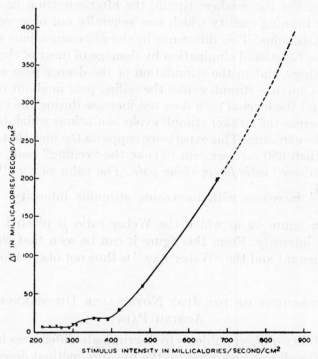

Fig. 48. ΔI, the Difference in Intensity of Two Stimuli Evoking a Just Noticeable Difference in Pain Sensation Plotted Against Stimulus Intensity

measurements of the jnd made with electrical and other types of stimuli will not correspond with the values given for thermal radiation. For example (see below), the relation of ΔI to I for noxious stimulation by pressure is in the ratio of 1:4 at threshold, but it is 1:30 for thermal radiation.

The painful sensation caused by the highest stimulus intensities is distinctly different in quality from the pain experienced in the

stimulus range below 480 mc./sec./cm.². After stimulation with
the highest stimulus intensities, the subjects reported an aching
quality as well as the bright burning quality during the three-
second exposure. At the termination of the exposure, the aching
pain persisted at a high intensity for some seconds as an after-
sensation. For the weaker stimuli, the after-sensation had a low
intensity burning quality which was generally not observed after
a strong stimulus. This difference in the after-sensations may be
due to the functional elimination by damage of most of the superficial endings, and to the stimulation of the deeper pain endings.
The most intense stimuli evoke the ceiling pain in about one-half
second and the level of pain does not increase during the exposure
time, whereas the weaker stimuli evoke sensations which build up
during the exposure. This experience supports the idea that stimuli
greater than 680 mc./sec./cm.² evoke the "ceiling" pain.

The "Weber" ratio for pricking pain. The value of the "Weber"
ratio, $\frac{\Delta I}{I}$, increases with increasing stimulus intensity. This is
shown in figure 49 in which the Weber ratio is plotted against
stimulus intensity. From this figure it can be seen that this ratio
is not constant and the "Weber Law" is thus not obeyed for pricking pain.

MEASUREMENT OF THE JUST NOTICEABLE DIFFERENCE FOR ACHING PAIN

The ability of three subjects to discriminate differences in intensity of stimuli was measured by the pressure method described in
the preceding chapter, over a range of from 400 to 6400 gm. These
measurements were made by presenting first a "standard" stimulus on a site on the right side of the forehead, followed by a
second stimulus on the left side, the intensity of which was increased until the subject reported that the pain evoked was greater
than that evoked by the standard stimulus. The procedure was
repeated by presenting the standard stimulus on the left side of
the forehead and the stimulus of unknown intensity on the right
side. When stimuli were of low intensity, and after a rest period
of ten minutes, the tests were repeated. The results of these series

of tests are shown in figure 50. It can be seen that in the range between 400 and 1000 gm. the subjects were able to discriminate, on the average, a change in pressure of 130 gm. For stimuli evoking more intense pain the ability to discriminate decreased progressively until at 6400 gm. an increment of approximately 1500 gm.

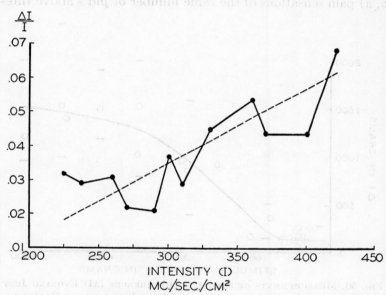

FIG. 49. PLOT OF THE "WEBER RATIO" (ΔI/I) FOR PRICKING PAIN AS A FUNCTION OF STIMULUS INTENSITY (I) (THERMAL RADIATION METHOD)

was necessary to produce a just noticeable difference in the sensation.

Only a limited number of readings could be made on any one experimental day on account of minor tissue damage following the application of the plunger. After the application of high intensity stimuli the tissue injury was too great to permit more than one series of observations per week.

COMMENT

The curve in figure 50 relating ΔI to I for aching pain is similar in form to that obtained for the same relationship for pricking pain. The number of jnd's for aching pain has been extended only to fourteen because of the rigors of the experimental regimen. It is inferred that further jnd's do exist between this level and the ceiling pain of aching quality. There are reasons to believe that aching pain has about the same number of jnd's as pricking pain, viz., a) pain sensations of the same number of jnd's above thresh-

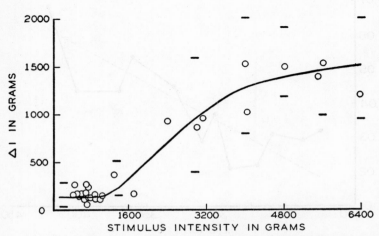

FIG. 50. MEASUREMENTS OF STIMULUS DIFFERENCES (ΔI) EVOKING JUST NOTICEABLE DIFFERENCES IN ACHING PAIN INTENSITY AT VARIOUS LEVELS OF INTENSITY

Circles represent averages of measurements, horizontal lines, maximum spread of data.

old, whether of pricking or aching quality, are of approximately the same intensity; b) the most intense aching pains, occurring during childbirth, could be matched in intensity by the most intense cutaneous pricking pain. Therefore it is postulated that there are approximately the same number of jnd's, i.e., 21, for aching and pricking pain between threshold and ceiling pain.

A SCALE OF PAIN INTENSITY

The stimulus intensity which gives rise to the threshold sensation marks the lower limit of the range of effective stimuli. The threshold sensation is arbitrarily assigned the value 0, meaning the lower end of the sensory scale. A stimulus which induces the ceiling pain determines the upper limit of the scale.

From table 13, it can be seen that there are 21 jnd's between the threshold sensation and ceiling pain. However, for convenience

TABLE 13
Scale of pain intensity

STIMULUS INTENSITY	SIZE OF STEP	NUMBER OF STEPS (jnd's)	NUMBER OF DOLS	AMOUNT OF STIMULUS ABOVE THRESHOLD
mc./sec./cm.²	*mc./sec./cm.²*			*mc./sec./cm.²*
220			0	0
227	7	1		
234	7	2	1	14
241	7	3		
248	7	4	2	28
255	7	5		
262	7	6	3	42
269	7	7		
276	7	8	4	56
283	7	9		
290	7	10	5	70
300	10	11		
310	10	12	6	90
320	10	13		
335	15	14	7	115
350	15	15		
365	15	16	8	145
380	15	17		
395	15	18	9	175
425	30	19		
480	55	20	10	260
680	200	21		

the unit for pain sensation was adopted as equivalent to the sum of two jnd's. The term "dol" is suggested to signify this unit. The ceiling pain intensity will, therefore, have the value of ten and one-half "dols".

A sensory scale of pain, such as that presented in table 13, is dependent upon the assumption made by Fechner that the intensity of sensation evoked by a given stimulus is equivalent to the number of the discriminable steps from the threshold sensation.

Figure 51 is a graphic representation of the relationship between stimulus intensity, number of discriminable steps and "dol" scale of pain intensity. The scale as represented in figure 51 refers only to skin areas which have a pain threshold of roughly 220 mc./sec./cm.².

There are two advantages in setting up a scale of pain sensation on the basis of the present data, namely: 1) the sensory range is clearly defined by the threshold sensation and the maximal pos-

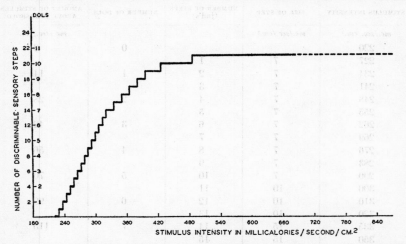

FIG. 51. A GRAPHIC REPRESENTATION OF THE RELATIONSHIP OF THE "DOL" SCALE OF PAIN INTENSITY TO INTENSITY OF STIMULUS AND NUMBER OF JUST NOTICEABLE DIFFERENCES ABOVE THRESHOLD

sible, or ceiling, pain sensation; and 2) the intensity of the pain can be related to an easily controlled and reproducible stimulus. In other words, intensity of pain sensation can be expressed in terms of the intensity of stimulus which evokes it.

Although the "dol" scale of pain intensity set up by the method described is a scale of equal intervals (the intervals being defined by the jnd), it cannot be assumed from this that the "dol" scale is a "ratio" scale. That is, it cannot be inferred from the procedure just outlined for the development of the "dol" scale that a four-"dol" pain is twice as intense as a two-"dol" pain or four times as intense as a one-"dol" pain.

As the term implies, the "ratio" scale is one permitting multiplication and division as well as addition and subtraction. An important consideration for a "ratio" scale is that it must have an absolute zero point. Two fundamental operations are required in addition to the five already listed for the interval scale. They are:

1. *Measurement of absolute thresholds.* This may be defined as the ascertaining of the stimulus values that mark the transition between response and no response. This intensity of stimulus marks the beginning or zero point of the "ratio" scale. In the case of pain it is the pain threshold.

2. *Determination of equal ratios.* The most satisfactory method of ascertaining the stimulus values which evoke responses bearing constant ratios to one another was established for loudness by Stevens (421) and others. This method, termed "fractionation", consists of presenting the subject with a stimulus of given intensity and requesting him to adjust a second stimulus so that it appears as one-half, or one-third, etc. of the test intensity. As Stevens points out (420), it must be assumed that the observer knows what the fractional part means and that he can adjust the stimulus so as to place the responses in the desired ratio. It is clear, however, that observers can visually divide a length into two equal parts with considerable accuracy. They also are in agreement, at least among themselves, when called upon to halve an interval of pitch or loudness. Furthermore, for pitch, the judgment ratios agree well with divisions of the intervals into ratios of the numbers of jnd's. Also, Hardy and his associates (211) showed for warmth sense on the forehead where stimulus intensity and size of skin area stimulated bear the same relationship to absolute threshold, that judgment of ratios of intensity of warmth sensation have the identical ratios for both stimuli and area values. Thus, on the basis of experience with other sensations, it would seem safe to use sensory estimates of ratios as the basis of a ratio scale of pain intensity.

Ratio scales have been established for a variety of sensory dimensions, e.g., loudness and pitch for hearing; visual flash rate and visual numerousness; sweetness, sourness, bitterness, saltiness; heaviness; and warmth sensation.

To establish the "dol" scale as a "ratio" scale it was necessary only to determine the stimulus values evoking known ratios of pain intensity, because the zero point of the scale, the pain threshold, has been thoroughly investigated. This study of sensory ratios was carried out by means of "fractionation" in the following way.

In one series of experiments the authors served both as experimental subjects and as observers; and in a second series, 70 medical students conducted carefully supervised experiments on each other, each one acting in turn as subject and observer. Each subject was exposed at the beginning of an experiment to a standard stimulus evoking a pain which, on the scale of just noticeable difference, corresponded to eight "dols". Subjects were then exposed to eight intensities of stimulus chosen to evoke pain intensities of one, two, three, · · · eight "dols". Three stimuli at each of the eight intensity levels were given in random order. The subjects were asked to report the intensity of the pains in terms of the initial, standard pain. As a rule, the standard stimulus was repeated once during the course of the experiment to refresh the subject's memory. Care was taken not to overstimulate any single area of the skin.

The pain intensities reported in Series 1 are shown in figure 52. This represents 72 tests on three subjects. The scatter of the reports was roughly one "dol" on either side of the mean report for a particular stimulus intensity, although reports which deviated as much as one and one-half or two "dols" from the mean were not uncommon. As the experiments proceeded, it became apparent that the experience of the subjects, as indicated by variations in the reports, did not appreciably increase the accuracy of reporting. Lack of concentration upon the procedure was the most important single factor causing variability. Memory was not a significant factor because the accuracy of reporting showed no change when in the course of the experiment the standard was presented repeatedly. The heavy line in the figure represents the "dol" scale based on measurements of the just noticeable differences, and this line coincides with the average of the reports of pain intensity obtained by the method of fractionation.

The second group of experiments, done by medical students

under supervision, indicates the scatter of reports from untrained but intelligent subjects and observers. The students followed the procedure outlined above and the results are shown in figure 53 as a series of scattergrams. In general, the average of the reports of the intensity of pain evoked by each unknown stimulus was within one "dol" of the value determined by the method of "just

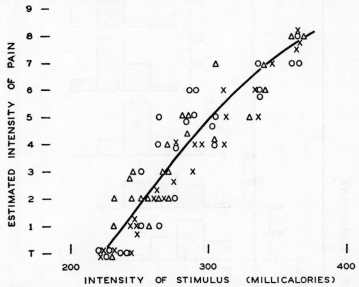

FIG. 52. ESTIMATES OF PAIN INTENSITY EVOKED BY VARIOUS INTENSITIES OF STIMULUS AT AND ABOVE THE PAIN THRESHOLD
Estimates were made as fractions of an eight-"dol" pain

noticeable differences" and the scatter of the reports was approximately the same as that obtained with experienced observers.

These results may be compared with those of experiments done in this laboratory prior to the evolution of a scale of painfulness. In the course of several years' experimentation with the thermal stimulus for producing pain, reports were made from time to time on the intensity of pain elicited by various intensities of thermal radiation. In these reports as well as in those for estimating intensity of headache (488), of intestinal pain (486), or of pain from immersion of an extremity in cold water (483, 251), the practice was for subjects to make reports of pain intensity in numbers of "pluses", using an ordinal scale of one to ten "plus" signs to represent the intensities from threshold to the most intense pain imaginable. The results of 45 such estimates of pain intensity

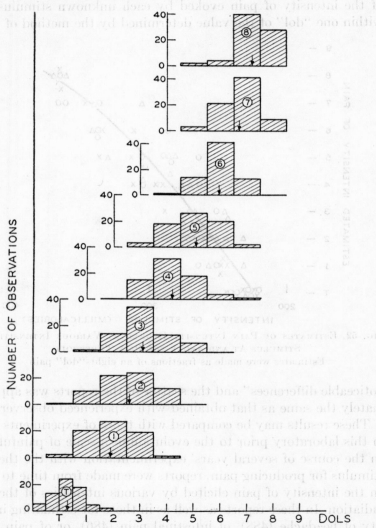

FIG. 53. DISTRIBUTION DIAGRAMS OF REPORTS OF 70 MEDICAL STUDENTS REPORTING PAIN INTENSITIES AS FRACTIONS OF AN EIGHT-"DOL" PAIN

made over a period of several months by three subjects are shown in figure 54.

It will be noticed that although "ten pluses" was considered

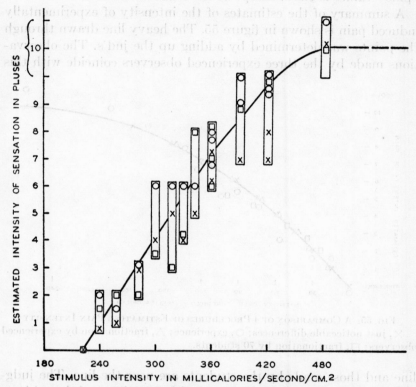

FIG. 54. ESTIMATES OF INTENSITY OF PAIN EVOKED BY STIMULI ABOVE THE PAIN
THRESHOLD IN TERMS OF "PLUS VALUES"
Ten "pluses" equals most intense pain imaginable

to be the most intense pain ever experienced, reports of eleven and twelve "pluses" were made for the most intense stimuli. This was due to the lack, at that time, of any standard pain with which to compare the painfulness of these intense stimuli. The subjects were consciously "stretching" the imaginary scale as it was evident to them that they could differentiate more increments of painfulness than they had imagined. The solid line drawn in figure

54 again refers to the scale of pain previously suggested from studies of the "just noticeable differences", equating one "dol" to one "plus" value. The agreement between the "dol" scale and the "plus" values is close, except at the highest intensities.

A summary of the estimates of the intensity of experimentally induced pain is shown in figure 55. The heavy line drawn through the points was determined by adding up the jnd's. The observations made by the three experienced observers coincide with this

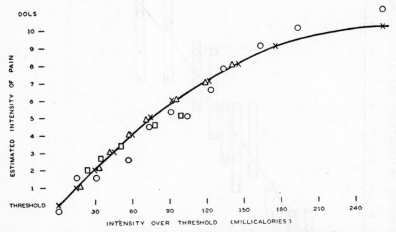

FIG. 55. A COMPARISON OF 4 PROCEDURES OF ESTIMATING PAIN INTENSITY
×, just noticeable differences; ○, experience; △, fractionation by experienced observers; □, fractionation by 70 students.

line and those made by the students are near the line. The judgments of pain intensity based on the life experience of the subjects are included to illustrate the fact that such estimates are in rough agreement with the "dol" scale.

A third series of experiments was designed to ascertain the effect of fatigue, minor mood changes and feelings of general effectiveness upon the perception of pain. It has been previously demonstrated that these variables did not affect the pain threshold measurement (388). Three subjects were studied almost daily over a period of six weeks in the following manner. At noon each day the subjects reported to the laboratory for testing. A record was made of the mood, feeling of effectiveness, and of any unusual activity or experience in the subject's life during the past 24 hours. Following this record, pain thresholds were measured and three test stimuli were given. A standard stimulus for comparative purposes was not presented in these experiments. The subject made a report of the intensity of the pain evoked. The unknown stimuli were distributed at random between the threshold stimulus and that causing a nine-"dol" pain.

The results of this study are shown in figure 56 in terms of

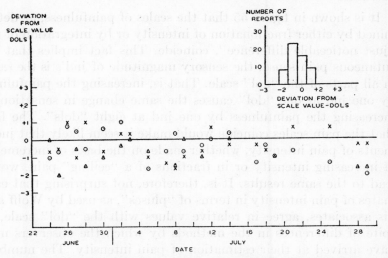

FIG. 56. DAY TO DAY VARIATIONS IN REPORTING PAIN INTENSITY BY 3 SUBJECTS

deviations from the report expected on the basis of the "dol" scale. The deviations are plotted as positive or negative according to whether the reports were more or less than the "dol" scale values. Each point is the average of the three reports of the subject for the day in question. The average deviation of the reports from the "dol" scale is minus one-half "dol", that is, the subjects underestimated rather than overestimated the intensity of the stimuli. The maximum deviation of the reports from the scale value was two "dols" and the standard deviation, plus-minus one-half "dol". Estimates of mood and of general effectiveness in the three subjects varied from day to day. Fatigue resulting from 30 hours of wakefulness was encountered in one subject, and acute disappointment in another. Tenseness, mild depression, exhilaration, contentment were reported on different days. These mood changes and the fatigue which did not interfere with attention and concentration were not associated with any predictable change in the ability of the subject to estimate pain intensity, a result which agrees with the observations previously made on the pain threshold.

COMMENT

It is shown in figure 55 that the scales of painfulness, as determined by either fractionation of intensity or by integration of the "just noticeable difference", coincide. This fact implies that for cutaneous pain sense, the sensory magnitude of jnd's is the same in all parts of the "dol" scale. That is, increasing the painfulness by one jnd at one "dol" causes the same change in sensation as increasing the painfulness by one jnd at eight "dols". The fact that the pain scales coincide would make it seem likely that judgments of pain intensity, whether made on the basis of increments of increasing intensity or in fractions of a "ceiling" pain, would lead to the same results. It is, therefore, not surprising that estimates of pain intensity in terms of "pluses", as used by Wolff and his associates, agree in relative values with the "dol" scale, in spite of differences in the methods by which the observers may have arrived at their estimation of pain intensity. The numbers of the pain scale which represent the intensity aspect of pain are capable of being manipulated according to the ordinary rules of arithmetic, and it is possible to define one "dol" both as the sum of two jnd's and as approximately one-tenth of the intensity of "ceiling" pain. It is proper, also, to speak of one pain as being either "twice as strong" as another, or as "being equivalent in intensity" to the sum of two smaller pains.

Although the "dol" scale was evolved from observations on cutaneous pain of pricking quality, it has also been found to apply to deep pain of aching quality. Thus, for cutaneous pain elicited by thermal radiation there are 21 jnd's between threshold pain and the "ceiling" pain. For aching pain elicited by pressure on the subcutaneous tissue, galea, and periosteum of the forehead there is also approximately the same number of jnd's. The general applicability of the "dol" scale to aching as well as to pricking pain is further supported by the fact that comparisons of intensity of aching pain with that of pricking pain are as precise as comparisons of intensity of one pricking pain with that of another.

The agreement of the estimations of pain intensity from general experience with the arbitrary though carefully determined "dol" scale is of significance as it suggests that there is only one scale of pain intensity and that the estimates by normal subjects on the basis of a standard pain will result in reports which can always be evaluated in terms of the "dol" scale. It is as if a normal adult had in his mind at all times a keen sense of the intensity aspect of pain, so that a person even without training in making judgments and discriminations of this sort can give a surprisingly accurate estimate of the intensity of a pain.

Overreaction to pain, due to anxiety and fixed attitudes toward pain sensation was encountered in four of the 70 medical students. These four at first exhibited an almost complete lack of discriminatory ability during the student experiments, often reporting a one-"dol" pain as six "dols" and vice versa. Their pain thresholds also were difficult to measure. It was apparent that the attitude of these subjects toward the experiment and toward their fellow student observers prevented them from making proper estimations. Following the class experiment, the four subjects were studied individually by the authors. After reassurance, reproducible reports were obtained from them. Two of the four had suffered major physical injuries and had experienced pain over long periods of time. Similar difficulties in estimating pain intensities and recognizing pain threshold are sometimes encountered in patients. However, with reassurance and repeated trials, reproducible results can usually be obtained.

As compared with other sensory scales, the scale of painfulness is a "coarse" scale; that is, it has only 21 discretely discriminable steps throughout its entire range. Two reports of intensity which differ by one "dol" usually are considered as being in satisfactory agreement rather than as indicating a real difference of painfulness. However, test values that show marked variations in reports of intensity of a given stimulus, such as two or three "dols" or more, are to be viewed with suspicion as this indicates failure on the part of the subject to concentrate. Reproducibility of the measurements is the most important single factor in the recognition of good data. Discrimination within the limits of plus-minus one "dol", or two jnd's, can be expected under nearly all circumstances with a cooperative subject. If after repeated tests the subject's reports are not consistent, it is good practice to delay further measurement to a more suitable time.

MEASUREMENT OF INTENSITY OF SPONTANEOUS PAIN

An illustration of the practical value of the "dol" scale and of a method of producing pain of standard intensity in a subject, is that of obtaining estimates of pain intensity in terms which are comparable from patient to patient. This permits a more accurate estimate of the patient's complaint and provides as well a basis for evaluating the effectiveness of procedures directed to the relief of pain. However, a patient's pain usually differs in duration, quality, and site from those features of the test pain, and the usefulness of measuring pain intensity depends upon the individual's ability to make reproducible comparisons of pain intensity in spite of these differences. It would be impractical to reproduce the patient's pain in every respect in order that comparisons can be made of intensity. Fortunately, experience has indicated that pain intensities can be compared even though the duration, quality, and origin of the pain be different from those of the test pain. It is not entirely surprising that two pains of different qualities can be compared as to their intensities, since satisfactory comparisons can be made of the brightness of two colors or the loudness of two tones.

The method of making measurements of pain intensity is that of requesting the subject to compare the intensity of the spontaneous pain with that of a test pain induced on the skin by the dolorimeter. It is a more accurate procedure to measure the intensity of a pain during its occurrence but good estimates can be made from memory. Thus, as demonstrated above, the intensity of a pain can be estimated within a "dol" even after several weeks, although usually the subject underestimates the intensity of a remembered pain as time goes on.

The intensity of a spontaneous pain can be related to the "dol" scale by comparison with a test pain only after the pain threshold has been determined. For example, a three-second exposure to 400 mc./sec./cm.^{2} will evoke a nine-"dol" pain on the forehead, whereas on the thickened skin of the heel of the foot this stimulus causes only a threshold pain (zero "dols").

Under a variety of laboratory and clinical conditions certain procedures have been found to facilitate the measurement of pain intensity. They are listed as follows:

1. The subject should be reassured regarding the procedure. For the normal subject this amounts to little more than an explanation of the test methods and assurance that he will not be injured. With patients a rather lengthy explanation with reassurance may need to be repeated with each series of tests. When reproducible reports of threshold and intensity are obtained, variables affecting pain intensity may be introduced and their effects assayed.

2. In order to minimize the number of stimuli employed in obtaining an estimate of pain intensity the routine of the measurement has been standardized as follows: First a pain threshold measurement is made. If it is found to be appreciably elevated (by 20 to 40 mc./sec./cm.^{2}) above the usual level it may be anticipated that the patient's spontaneous pain is of three-"dol" intensity or greater. (It is necessary then to obtain a measurement of pain threshold when the patient is free of pain in order to establish the zero point of the "dol" scale.) Next the patient is presented with a stimulus calculated to evoke a test pain of approximately the same intensity as his spontaneous pain. The subject's description of his pain serves as a guide for this calculation.

3. Stimulate once at this intensity and obtain a report of either "too much", "too little", or "can't tell". The subject's attention should be focussed on the pain which occurs at the very end of the three-second exposure and he is told to imagine this pain as continuing. This is found to be a very helpful expedient if the patient's spontaneous pain is one of long duration. Often patients remark on the difference in quality, duration, and site of the test pain from their spontaneous pain. This usually happens with a patient who is "trying too hard". His attention is continually directed to the fact that he has to report only "which one hurts more", the test pain or his spontaneous pain. Depending upon the

report obtained from the first stimulus, two or three additional
stimuli are given so as to get one report of "too much" and another
of "not enough". This "brackets" the pain and concludes the
measurement. The pain is estimated as the mean of the "too
much" and "too little" stimuli if they are as close together as 20
to 30 mc./sec./cm.[2]

ANALYSIS OF PAIN SENSATIONS

The description of a pain can be given with considerable precision by the use of the four sensory dimensions mentioned at the
beginning of this chapter:

Quality of pain means either ache, burn, prick, or a combination
of these.

Intensity of pain, expressed in "dols", runs roughly from threshold to ten and one-half "dols" for pricking and aching pain. The
intensity range for the third quality, i.e., burning pain, has not
been determined as yet.

Extension, in addition to localization in some region of the body,
has three dimensions in space; the pain may be confined at a point,
or may extend in a line, area, or in three dimensions.

Duration refers to all of the temporal aspects of the pain, such
as throbbing, pulsating, time of onset, short or long lasting.

The third and fourth dimensions, those of extension and duration, are usually well analyzed in clinical descriptions of pain. For
example, terms such as pulsatile, relating to the heart rate, or
periodic, relating to respiration or other repeated events, are useful
in characterizing duration. Extension is also carefully specified in
the examination of the patient. Words such as "highly localized"
or "sharp" refer to localization at a point, whereas "dull" or
"diffuse" refers to volume extension, and "widespread" and "radi-
ating" are terms denoting areal and linear extensions. Terms
which attempt to characterize two or more dimensions simultaneously may lead to confusion as to which dimension is prominent.
Thus, "lancinating" refers to changes in extension, duration, and
intensity, although the relative importance of one change to the
others is left uncertain.

The complete description of a pain thus requires an analysis of the sensation in terms of the four basic dimensions. For example, the pain of duodenal ulcer has both aching and burning *qualities*. Such pains vary in *intensity* from threshold to a maximum of about four "dols" and the aching quality is usually more prominent. Thus, one might have a four-"dol" aching pain combined with a two- or three-"dol" burning pain. The *duration* of the ulcer pain is variable, although some of its temporal aspects are predictable, such as its onset some hours after eating. The *extension* of the

TABLE 14

The "dimensions" of pain sensations

DIMENSION	QUALITY		
	Ache	Prick	Burn
Intensity range	Threshold–10½ dols	Threshold–10½ dols	Threshold–? dols
Extension	Regional localization Linear Area Volume	Regional localization Linear Area	Regional localization Linear Area Volume
Duration	Short Long Periodic Recurrent	Short Long Periodic Recurrent	Short Long Periodic Recurrent

ulcer pain is best described as localized to the right upper quadrant of the abdomen, with a volume rather than point distribution.

Complete specification of a pain is not only essential for clinical purposes, but it would greatly increase the understanding among investigators. Confusions which arise from identification of the dimensions of the sensation with anatomic structure (seen in the use of such terms as "symp-pain" and "sup-pain"), or with situations (seen in terms such as "pathologic" pain and "experimental" pain), could be largely eliminated by analyzing the pain sensation in terms of the basic dimensions shown in table 14.

On first perusal of such a scale of dimensions it apparently fails to describe the shades and varieties of painful sensations that accompany a host of bodily disorders. This is because there have been left out of this discussion the peculiar and often characteristic qualities given to a painful experience by having associated with it other sensations than pain. Thus, in the case of abdominal pain from excessive intestinal peristalsis with contraction and distention of the bowel, in addition to pain there are concurrent sensations of pressure. The resultant mixture of sensation is referred to as "tightness", "fullness", "distention", "piercing", "sticking", "cramping", and "drawing". Also the reflex skeletal muscle effects introduce postural changes that interfere with respiration, and perhaps nausea and sweating with sensations of chill. When the four dimensions of pain are combined with other sensations, like those just described, there results a spectrum of "pains" within which every such experience will find a place.

Equally important for bedside purposes and for the identification of the parts involved in noxious stimulation may be included a consideration of procedures that initiate or eliminate the pain, or modify any of its dimensions. Such procedures make it possible to reproduce and analyze a pain and, in some instances, to identify the source of noxious stimulation.

Finally, there remain for inclusion when analyzing the source and nature of noxious stimulation and pain, those phenomena associated with anatomical and functional disorders that indicate that a part or a function is seriously disturbed, adding further to the understanding of the noxious process. For example, when pain in the foot and leg is associated with absent or diminished pulsation of the dorsal pedal artery, the foot, in addition, being pale, cyanotic, and cold, the nature of the source of the pain as being due to anoxia is illuminated.

Chapter VIII

THE NATURE OF CUTANEOUS HYPERALGESIA

Hyperalgesia may be defined as a state of increased pain sensation induced by either noxious or ordinarily non-noxious stimulation of peripheral tissue. Hyperalgesia occurs in both superficial and deep tissues, in areas with pain thresholds that are normal, lowered, or raised (179). As seen at the bedside there are apparently several varieties of hyperalgesia, and few clinical phenomena are more difficult to understand and to evaluate. The literature on the subject includes work of a distinguished roster of investigators (202, 276, 277, 302, 373, 427). As a result of these studies two classes of hyperalgesia have been loosely formulated, namely, that occurring at the site of injury, and that associated with the injury but occurring in apparently undamaged tissue. Failure to outline clearly the characteristics of these two varieties of hyperalgesia has resulted in a controversy as regards the alteration responsible for the hyperalgesia occurring in undamaged tissue. One group holds that this hyperalgesia is attributable to changes in the periphery, whereas the other maintains that changes in the central nervous system are responsible. Due to the lack of quantitative methods of measuring pain perception, progress has been slow in clarifying an understanding of the underlying mechanisms.

This chapter is concerned primarily with that cutaneous hyperalgesia occurring in undamaged tissues adjacent to and at some distance from the site of an injury or a site of noxious stimulation.

SUBJECTS AND METHODS

The subjects for these experiments were for the most part the three authors, but also included from time to time were ten other trained observers, and ten women who were being investigated for patency of the Fallopian tubes.

A variety of experimental methods were used, depending upon the particular aspect of the problem under study, and including many of the technics employed by Lewis and others for producing and studying experimental hyperalgesia. Hyperalgesia was induced on the volar surface of the forearm by the following means:

a) Ultraviolet light from a lamp was applied for eleven minutes at a distance of 20 cm. over an area of skin of 4 by 6 cm.

b) High intensity thermal radiation (440 to 500 mc./sec./cm.^{2} for six to ten seconds) was applied on an area of skin 1.5 cm. in diameter which had been previously blackened with India ink.

c) A small area (approximately 3 cm.^{2}) of skin was infiltrated with a 1% solution of procaine in saline. When anesthesia had developed the skin was stimulated for ten minutes with a faradic stimulus at 24 volts.

d) An anterior branch of the external cutaneous nerve was located by light stimulation with a faradic current. The nerve was then stimulated at this point through the skin by a faradic stimulus at 24 volts for two minutes.

e) A small area of skin was crushed by means of forceps.

f) Three-tenths of a cc. of 6% saline was injected into the intraspinous ligament.

g) Ten women, patients of the "Sterility Clinic" of the New York Hospital, volunteered to be studied. Following insufflation of the Fallopian tubes with CO_2 there frequently developed a hyperalgesia and referred pain in the shoulder area, as a result of the escape of CO_2 into the peritoneal cavity and irritation of the peritoneum over the central portion of the diaphragm.

h) In two of the authors there was the opportunity of observing spontaneous hyperalgesias, one associated with an infection in the ear and the other with an injury of the back.

i) Histamine was introduced by iontophoresis into a 3 cm.^{2} area of skin at a current of 0.25 to 0.6 milliamperes for ten minutes.

The following methods were employed for the study of hyperalgesic skin areas:

a) The occurrence and area of hyperalgesia were ascertained by lightly tapping the skin with a pin attached to a light piece of wood 14 cm. in length.

b) The pain threshold was ascertained by the thermal radiation method and also by the use of calibrated von Frey hairs.

c) Altered sensibility to thermal radiation of hyperalgesic skin was ascertained by exposing the blackened areas of skin to thermal radiation above the pain threshold, and comparing the resultant pain with that induced by the same stimulus in control areas.

d) Altered sensibility to mechanical stimulation was ascertained by means of von Frey hairs. Pain induced by light mechanical stimulation in areas of hyperalgesia was compared to that in control areas.

Observations on the Characteristics of Hyperalgesia Developed at the Site of Injury (Primary Hyperalgesia)

Pain thresholds and pain sensibility were ascertained on both forearms after which areas 4 by 6 cm. on the right forearm (of

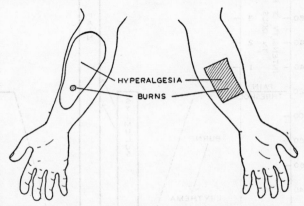

Fig. 57. Difference in Localization of Primary Hyperalgesia (Hatched Areas—Sites of Injury) and Secondary Hyperalgesia (Left) in Adjacent Undamaged Tissue

three subjects in seven series of observations) were irradiated with ultraviolet light. Four to five hours after the exposure, sharply defined areas of erythema and hyperalgesia became evident, increasing in intensity during the next 24 hours, and thereafter subsiding gradually.

Twenty-four hours after the irradiation (see arm on right, fig. 57) the pain thresholds measured in the erythematous areas were half of what they had been before exposure. Thus, whereas 220 mc./sec./cm.^{2} elicited threshold pain in control areas, pain threshold was lowered to 110 mc./sec./cm.^{2} in the erythematous areas. Also, ordinarily non-noxious stimuli such as resulted from stroking the skin with blunt objects, pressure of the sleeve, or contact with warm water caused the subjects to complain of burning pain. Furthermore, as seen in figure 58, pain sensibility in this area was altered. A stimulus intensity of 220 mc./sec./cm.[2] which before exposure to the ultraviolet light induced threshold pain now induced a pain of four-"dol" intensity. Since a four-"dol" pain is equivalent to eight jnds this may be said to be an eight-fold increase in "sensibility". Similar changes in pain threshold and sen-

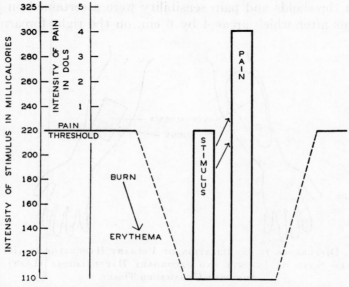

Fig. 58. Lowered Pain Threshold and Increased Pain Sensibility in an Area of Primary Hyperalgesia

sibility were observed in sites of tissue damage resulting from faradic current, crushing with forceps, and high intensity thermal radiation.

COMMENT

Here, as in the experiments of Schumacher (387), in areas of injury induced by ultraviolet rays the pain threshold was lowered to about half that of control areas. It has been postulated that in such injured areas the products of injury or a "pain substance" have been liberated from damaged cells, thus lowering the threshold by altering the chemical environment of the nerve endings in the skin.

Tissue injury and the "products of tissue damage" do not inevitably result in lowering of the pain threshold, and many instances of such "tissue damage" never result in secondary hyperalgesia. Thus, Hardy and his associates (345) have been able to demonstrate that many dermatological patients with a variety of skin lesions do not exhibit lowering of the pain threshold.

The above described experiments focus attention on the essential characteristics of primary hyperalgesia. These are:

1) Identical areas of tissue damage and hyperalgesia. In figure 57 on the right is shown the hyperalgesia following ultraviolet irradiation. The areas of the burn, the erythema, and the primary hyperalgesia are identical.

2) A lowered pain threshold occurs in the area of primary hyperalgesia, resulting in increased sensitivity to ordinarily non-noxious stimuli.

3) Primary hyperalgesia disappears only gradually as healing proceeds, and may indeed in some instances be detectable for several weeks following injury.

Observations on the Characteristics of Hyperalgesia in Undamaged Skin Areas at a Distance from a Site of Skin Injury (Secondary Hyperalgesia)
Production of Secondary Hyperalgesia

OBSERVATION

In 36 series of observations on three subjects and in three observations on a fourth subject, the forearms were injured by exposure to thermal radiation. In the ensuing ten to fifteen minutes a bleb became evident at the site of injury. Gradually there developed an area in which pin prick was experienced as sharper and longer lasting than in surrounding areas. This zone of secondary hyperalgesia spread over the volar surface of the forearm in a tongue-shaped area, much more proximally than distally. It reached its maximum extent of 8 to 20 cm. proximally, 2 to 5 cm. distally, and 5 to 10 cm. laterally (at its greatest width) in fifteen to 60 minutes, so to remain for varying periods of two to 48 hours.

The development of a typical area of secondary hyperalgesia following a burn is shown in figure 59 (A).

Characteristically the hyperalgesia which developed from the skin injury on the volar surface of the middle forearm was that of

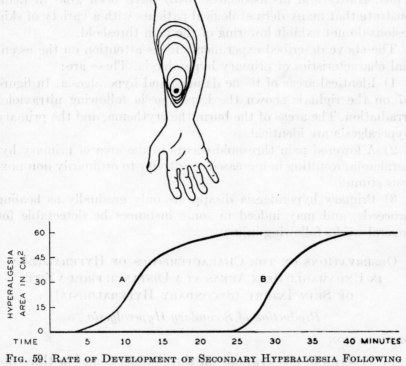

FIG. 59. RATE OF DEVELOPMENT OF SECONDARY HYPERALGESIA FOLLOWING
INJURY
A, injury; B, procaine + injury

a tongue-shaped island extending eccentrically around the site of injury. Distal development was slower, and was first to disappear as the hyperalgesia receded. Lateral spread was also slower than proximal. Grossly the shape of the hyperalgesic area was the shape of the forearm, its wider portion corresponding to the wider portion of the extremity. The hyperalgesic zones corresponded in general with the segmental dermatomes described by

Foerster (128, 129), by Head (201), by Richter (362), and recently by Keegan (237).

Following thermal irradiation of equal intensity and duration producing apparently equal injuries there was a marked variability in the rate of development and increased sensibility of the zones of secondary hyperalgesia. When injuries were made in close proximity, the rate of development of the hyperalgesia was faster, and the "increased sensibility" more marked, than occurred as the result of one injury. Thus in broad terms the area, speed of development, intensity, and duration of hyperalgesia were greater when tissue damage was greater.

The secondary hyperalgesia disappeared spontaneously at varying times following skin injury from burning but in no instance lasted more than 48 hours, whereas primary hyperalgesia (tenderness at the site of injury) persisted for several weeks until the healing process was completed.

In more than 400 series of observations on experimentally induced secondary hyperalgesia, whether the stimulus used to cause skin injury was thermal radiation, faradic current, or pinching by forceps, the hyperalgesia that developed was essentially similar to that described above. Facts concerning onset, speed of development and area of hyperalgesia were in complete accord with the observations made by Lewis (276, 277).

COMMENT

In 1936 Lewis put forward the hypothesis that the hyperalgesia we have termed primary and secondary have a common cause, i.e., the release of a stable "pain substance" in the tissues in close proximity to pain fiber terminations, resulting in lowering of the pain threshold.

Pain Threshold and Pain Sensibility in Areas of Secondary Hyperalgesia

OBSERVATION 1. PAIN THRESHOLD FOR THERMAL STIMULATION

Over 200 measurements of pain threshold were made by the radiant heat method in areas of secondary hyperalgesia. The hyperalgesic areas so studied were associated with experimentally

induced skin injuries and deep noxious stimulation, as well as with
infections and injuries in patients. Control observations of pain
threshold were made in adjacent and contralateral areas of skin.
These pain thresholds were observed to be the same in every instance although threshold pain in the areas of secondary hyperalgesia was experienced as more intense and longer lasting than
threshold pain in control areas.

COMMENT

These observations are in agreement with previous measurements of the pain threshold by the thermal radiation method, but
they are in apparent contradiction to the general observation that
light touch stimuli can evoke pain in zones of hyperalgesia.

This latter observation has led many observers in the past to
believe that the threshold for pain in zones of secondary hyperalgesia must be lowered.

Indeed, in our own experiments, drawing a wisp of cotton across
the hyperalgesic area gave rise to a vivid sensation of touch commingled with pain. Also, pin pricks were perceived as much sharper
and longer lasting than in control areas. Nevertheless, the pain
threshold to thermal stimuli was unaltered in zones of secondary
hyperalgesia. These observations indicated the necessity for quantitative comparisons of thermal and mechanical stimulation evoking minimal pain sensation.

OBSERVATION 2. PAIN THRESHOLD FOR MECHANICAL STIMULATION

In ten series of observations on three subjects calibrated von
Frey hairs were used to test the skin on the volar surface of the
forearms. An area of secondary hyperalgesia was induced in one
arm, and the other arm was used as control. The force required to
elicit minimal sensation in the control arm was found to be 0.9
to 1.3 gm. The sensation elicited was light touch with pricking
pain also occurring in at least 10% of the trials. In the zone of
hyperalgesia no sensation was elicited by a force less than 0.9 gm.
However, pricking pain was elicited in every trial in which any
sensation was evoked and this sensation was more intense and was
longer lasting than on the control arm.

COMMENT

It is concluded that in normal skin the thresholds for touch and for pain from mechanical stimulation closely approximate each other, this being in accord with the older observations of von Frey (449) and the more recent studies of Bishop (39). Furthermore, the pain threshold from mechanical stimulation is not lowered in areas of secondary hyperalgesia. However, in areas of secondary hyperalgesia threshold pain is more intense and thus more easily recognized than in control areas. As will be shown later, a threshold pain in any hyperalgesic area is more than twice as intense as in a control area. Thus, the evidence regarding the unaltered pain thresholds in zones of secondary hyperalgesia for both mechanical and thermal stimulation is in agreement. The inference of earlier observers that pain threshold in zones of secondary hyperalgesia must be lowered, resulted from a confusion of two independent entities, i.e., pain threshold and pain sensibility. As pointed out previously, in areas of primary hyperalgesia these two entities are predictably and inversely related, i.e., as pain threshold is lowered pain sensibility is increased and vice versa. However, this relationship cannot be assumed to apply to secondary hyperalgesia and indeed has been demonstrated to be absent, i.e., in areas of secondary hyperalgesia pain sensibility may be much increased with no change in pain threshold.

OBSERVATION 3. ALTERED SENSIBILITY TO PAIN FROM MECHANICAL STIMULATION IN AREAS OF SECONDARY HYPERALGESIA

Using calibrated von Frey hairs in the manner described, the sensations evoked in normal and hyperalgesic skin areas were compared. A given number of reports of sensation in a given number of stimulus trials, i.e., ten out of twenty, was used arbitrarily as a basis of comparison.

Typical experimental results are shown in figure 60. Pain sensation was evoked in hyperalgesic areas in ten out of twenty trials by a length of von Frey hair exerting approximately 1 gm. of force. It required 2 gm. of force on the control arm to evoke an equivalent intensity of sensation.

Fifty minutes after the first injury had been made to induce hyperalgesia, the skin was burned a second time, 5 cm. proximal to the first burn. When tested with von Frey hairs ten minutes later the skin in the analogous zones (of hyperalgesia) was found to require in the normal arm eight to ten times the force to elicit the same intensity of pain as was produced by 1 gm. of force in the hyperalgesic area.

In one subject a third burn was made in the already hyperalgesic zone approximately midway between the first two burns.

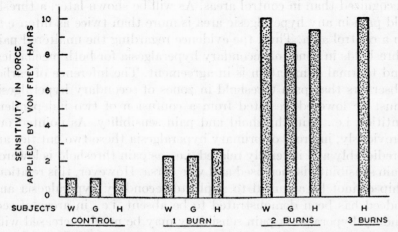

FIG. 60. SENSIBILITY TO MECHANICAL STIMULATION OF AREAS OF SECONDARY HYPERALGESIA FOLLOWING 1, 2, AND 3 THERMAL INJURIES ON THE VOLAR SURFACE OF THE FOREARM

Testing of the hyperalgesia twenty minutes later did not reveal any further increase in required force on the control arm beyond that which was needed following the two burns.

COMMENT

These observations demonstrate that a stimulus when applied to hyperalgesic skin causes a more intense pain than when applied to control areas of skin. Also, pain evoked by von Frey hairs in hyperalgesic zones has a characteristic persistent burning quality. Two to ten fold increase in a mechanical stimulus intensity is required on the control skin to evoke a comparable intensity of sensation to that elicited on the hyperalgesic skin. This evidence demonstrates an increased pain sensibility in the hyperalgesic areas as compared to control areas.

When the hyperalgesia was striking, the above described features were evident with stimuli at or only slightly above threshold. On the other hand, when hyperalgesia was slight, contrasts with control areas were evident only with painful stimuli of moderately high intensity.

OBSERVATION 4. INCREASED "SENSIBILITY" TO PAIN IN DEEP STRUCTURES ASSOCIATED WITH SKIN INJURY

It was noted while the second and third injuries were being produced that not only was a burning sensation in the zone of skin injury experienced but a deep ache as well extending to the elbow and shoulder. The skin pain subsided rapidly after the burns were produced but four minutes later the subjects complained of aching sensations in the wrist, and in the ulnar side of the hand as well as in the shoulder.

Twelve minutes after the injuries the subjects noted that the entire arm felt "sore" from the wrist to the elbow. Fifteen minutes later they observed that when the arm was held immobile no sensation was experienced. When, however, the wrist was flexed they experienced pain of a deep aching quality and of one-"dol" intensity in the entire forearm from wrist to elbow. Furthermore, there was experienced a brief pain of two to four-"dol" intensity as the wrist was extended and before relaxation was complete. With immobilization spontaneous pain was again absent.

It was repeatedly observed that when hyperalgesic areas were stimulated by pin prick as far away as 15 to 20 cm. from the site of skin injury pain when present in the injured skin was intensified, or if absent, could be revived.

OBSERVATION 5. ALTERED SENSIBILITY FROM THERMAL STIMULATION OF HYPERALGESIC SKIN

The exploration of the phenomenon of increased sensibility in zones of hyperalgesia is more satisfactory and accurate quantitatively with thermal stimulation than with touch, particularly as the intensity of the sensations evoked by thermal radiation can be compared on the "dol" scale of pain. The following data are taken from a series of 29 observations in four subjects.

In areas of experimentally induced secondary hyperalgesia on the forearm it was found that although the pain threshold was unchanged a stimulus of 280 mc./sec./cm.^{2} which induced three-"dol" pain on the control arm, induced pain of more than five "dols" in the hyperalgesic zone (fig. 61). Also, applying thermal

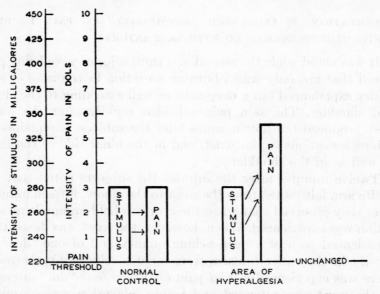

FIG. 61. SENSIBILITY TO THERMAL STIMULATION OF AREAS OF SECONDARY HYPERALGESIA FOLLOWING AN INJURY ON THE VOLAR SURFACE OF THE FOREARM

stimulation simultaneously to both hyperalgesic and control areas, it required a stimulus intensity of 360 mc./sec./cm.^{2} on the control side to elicit an intensity of pain equal to that evoked by a 280 mc./sec./cm.^{2} stimulus in the hyperalgesic zone, i.e., five and one-half "dols."

COMMENT

Although the "sensibility" as expressed in "dols" of pain is almost doubled in the hyperalgesic zone, the energy increase in the stimulus from 280 to 360 mc./sec./cm.^{2} is only as 1:1.25.

The ratio of stimulus intensities is a convenient means of expressing threshold changes (185) but it is not necessarily characteristic of sensory responses to supraliminal stimuli. The term "sensitivity" is generally understood to refer to the capability of the organism to respond to minimal stimulation and is measured in terms of the physical energy of the stimulus. Therefore, "sensitivity" is reserved for threshold changes and should not be confused with sensory responses to stimuli above the threshold. It is basic to an understanding of hyperalgesic phenomena to clearly differentiate changes of pain threshold from changes in the appreciation of pain intensity, because these factors are not necessarily interdependent although they may both lead to the same apparent end, for example, tenderness in superficial, deep somatic, and visceral tissues. It is suggested that the term "sensibility" connotes capability of appreciating change above threshold. With a given painful stimulus the skin of the hyperalgesic area gives rise to a more intense pain than does the skin of the control area whether the areas be tested with mechanical or thermal stimuli. This phenomenon represents an increased *sensibility* which for quantitative purposes can be defined as the ratio of the *intensity of sensation* evoked in the hyperalgesic area to that elicited by the same stimulus in control areas. Comparison of *sensitivities* can be expressed as the ratio of *threshold stimulus intensities* in a control area as compared to that in any other.

In the experiments using thermal radiation it was possible to compare the pain sensation in "dols" evoked by a given stimulus intensity in hyperalgesic and control areas (186). The "sensibility" thus observed in hyperalgesic areas was more than twice that of control areas.

The experiments with the von Frey hairs and with the pin prick stimulus agree with the estimations of sensibility made with the thermal radiation technique, i.e., an increase of several fold in intensity of sensation was appreciated when moving the hair or pin from control areas to hyperalgesic areas.

An important characteristic of secondary hyperalgesia is increased pain sensibility without lowering of the pain threshold.

Development of Secondary Hyperalgesia

It has been proposed by Lewis (277, 276) and others (405) that the liberation in the skin of a substance "P" resulted in erythema, lowering of the pain threshold, and secondary hyperalgesia.

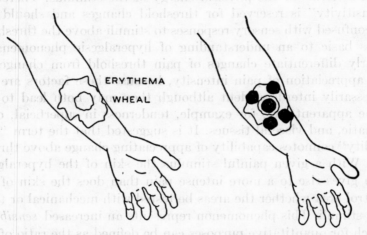

ERYTHEMA

WHEAL

FIG. 62. ZONES OF SECONDARY HYPERALGESIA AND ERYTHEMA SURROUNDING A WHEAL PRODUCED BY IONTOPHORESIS OF HISTAMINE PHOSPHATE

OBSERVATION 1. DEVELOPMENT FOLLOWING IONTOPHORESIS OF HISTAMINE

In three series of experiments on three subjects histamine phosphate was introduced by iontophoresis into the skin on the volar surface of the forearm. A wheal 3 cm. in diameter was produced, and a flare 9 by 8 cm. (see fig. 62). It was noted that an area of secondary hyperalgesia developed 10 cm. proximal and 5 cm. distal to the wheal. Pain threshold measurements were made in the area of the wheal, and in four areas adjacent to it within the zone of erythema. The pain threshold in the area of the wheal was 155 to 180 mc./sec./cm.^{2} and in the areas of erythema 210 to 230 mc./sec./cm.^{2} The area of the wheal, having a lowered pain threshold, was an area of primary hyperalgesia, and the area of the flare, although hyperalgesic, had a normal or slightly raised pain threshold. A stimulus evoking four- to five-"dol" pain in normal control areas of skin, elicited six- to seven-"dol" pain throughout the area of secondary hyperalgesia, whether the skin was erythematous or not.

During faradic stimulation over a sensory nerve on the volar surface of the forearm a zone averaging 7 by 4 cm. of "goose flesh" and sweating developed. Immediately following stimulation this zone became erythematous and usually was contained within the area of secondary hyperalgesia which subsequently developed. In a series of three experiments on three subjects the pain threshold was measured in several areas in the zones of erythema following faradic stimulation. The thresholds in all instances were observed to be normal or slightly raised.

COMMENT

In these experiments, the zone of secondary hyperalgesia contained the flare area, and there was no lowering of the pain threshold either in the flare or in the more distant parts of the hyperalgesic zone. Thus, it must be concluded that there is no relation between the pain threshold and the axone reflex which is evidenced by the presence of a flare. Furthermore, since increased pain sensibility was present throughout the zone of secondary hyperalgesia which included the area of reflex flare it cannot be assumed that this reflex activity is alone responsible for the hyperalgesia.

It is to be noted that the pain threshold is lowered in the area of the wheal. Thus, the presence of an irritant substance, such as histamine, in the skin induces a local primary hyperalgesia, associated with a secondary hyperalgesia in adjacent skin areas.

In an effort to demonstrate the release of a pain substance Lewis stimulated a cutaneous nerve distal to a procaine block of this nerve, under which circumstance he expected the elaboration of pain substance in the distribution of the nerve. He reported that immediately upon disappearance of the analgesic action of the procaine, hyperalgesia appeared full-blown. Stimulation of the nerve proximal to the block was reported to evoke no hyperalgesia and this was attributed to the fact that no pain substance had been released by a postulated system of "nocifensor" fibers. As these experiments of Lewis (276, 277, 274) were among the most significant in supporting his concept of such a "nocifensor" system, it seemed important to repeat them, paying particular attention to sensations elicited in the distribution of the cutaneous nerve following its stimulation through the skin.

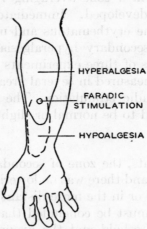

HYPERALGESIA

FARADIC
STIMULATION

HYPOALGESIA

FIG. 63. ZONES OF HYPOALGESIA (BROKEN LINES) AND SECONDARY
HYPERALGESIA (SOLID LINES) FOLLOWING FARADIC STIMULATION
OF A CUTANEOUS NERVE

OBSERVATION 2. HYPOALGESIA FOLLOWING FARADIC STIMULATION
OF CUTANEOUS NERVE

It was repeatedly observed immediately following faradic stimulation for two minutes directly over a cutaneous sensory nerve, that a zone of *hypo*algesia to pin prick extended for 10 to 15 cm. in the distribution of the nerve distal to the point stimulated. In six series of experiments in three subjects the pain threshold to thermal radiation was found to be raised as much as 35 per cent in this zone for as long as 30 to 60 minutes following stimulation. Also, mechanical and thermal stimuli above the pain threshold were appreciated as less intense than in control areas. However, an area of secondary hyperalgesia developed about the site of stimulation in the usual way, extending more proximally than distally and overlapping the distribution of the cutaneous nerve but slightly (see fig. 63 in which the broken lines outline region of hypoalgesia and the solid lines that of the later developing hyperalgesia).

OBSERVATION 3. DEVELOPMENT OF HYPERALGESIA FOLLOWING STIMULATION OF CUTANEOUS NERVE DISTAL TO NERVE BLOCK

Lewis' experiments with nerve block have been repeated. The results of these experiments are shown in figure 64. In the first instance, in six experiments in two subjects, the cutaneous nerve

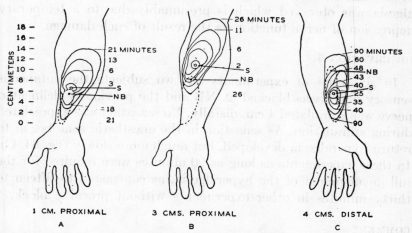

FIG. 64. DEVELOPMENT OF SECONDARY HYPERALGESIA (SOLID LINES) FOLLOWING FARADIC STIMULATION OF A CUTANEOUS NERVE PROXIMAL AND DISTAL TO NERVE BLOCK (ANESTHETIC AREA—BROKEN LINES)

was blocked at NB 1 cm. distal to the point of stimulation. The broken line indicates the zone of anesthesia resulting from the procaine infiltration about the nerve. The nerve was stimulated by faradic current for two minutes at S. The development of hyperalgesia progressed as shown, and when the effects of the procaine were dissipated, extended for 5 cm. distal to the point of stimulation.

In B, in six experiments in two subjects, the nerve was similarly infiltrated with procaine at NB and stimulated 3 cm. proximally. The hyperalgesia developed as shown, again with a distal extension of approximately 5 cm. but this time overlapping the previously anesthetic zone by only about 2 cm.

COMMENT

These observations demonstrate that the hyperalgesia occurring after faradic stimulation of a cutaneous nerve develops in the same manner about the point of stimulation, as it does about any other skin injury. The only difference is that longer faradic stimulation is required if the point of stimulation is not over a nerve, indicating that the tissues about the nerve are more easily damaged. Indeed, in the distribution of the cutaneous nerve hypoalgesia was observed which is presumably due to a temporary depression of nerve function as the result of such damage.

OBSERVATION 4.

In six series of experiments on two subjects the cutaneous sensory nerve was blocked at NB and the previously delineated nerve was stimulated 4 cm. distally. No sensation was appreciated during stimulation. As sensation in the anesthetic zone began to return hyperalgesia developed, but much more slowly (fig. 64, C). In these experiments as long as 90 minutes were required for the full development of the hyperalgesia, as contrasted to fifteen to thirty minutes in other experiments without procaine block.

COMMENT

These results are in keeping with the findings of Lewis regarding the rate of development of hyperalgesia in anesthetized areas. The time required for full development depends upon the duration of the anesthesia and the hyperalgesia does not begin to develop until after the effects of the procaine have been dissipated. Lewis, on the other hand, reports two experiments in which a full blown hyperalgesia occurred sixteen minutes after faradic stimulation of a nerve distal to a block which had been made with procaine 25 minutes before. It is suggested that Lewis' results are indicative of the fact that he stimulated nerve fibers which were not completely blocked, especially as he reported sensation of "local tingling" during stimulation.

In short, these experiments involving stimulation of nerve fibers demonstrate that the ensuing hyperalgesia does not depend in most instances upon the effects of stimulation of the fibers of passage in the nerve trunks. Indeed, to the extent to which these nerve trunks are injured by the noxious stimulation, hypoalgesia rather than hyperalgesia is exhibited in the skin supplied by these fibers. Thus, the resultant changes in peripheral sensation are a combination of the effects of procaine and of nerve injury.

Lewis cites the experiments of Foerster (128) in stimulating the distal stump of a freshly sectioned sensory nerve and the production of pain in support of the hypothesis of "nocifensor" nerves. However, it has been observed by Pool (342) that stimulation of the remains of such a nerve eight months after section also causes burning pain in the general distribution of the nerve. Thus, it is clear that fibers of passage in the distal stump are not necessary to the production of the described pain. It is likely that the distal remnant of the sectioned nerve and the blood vessels within or surrounding it are supplied by twigs from adjacent intracutaneous sensory nerves and that the latter are responsible for the sensation experienced and referred to the denervated tissue.

OBSERVATION 5. SECONDARY HYPERALGESIA RESULTING FROM PRO-LONGED MINIMALLY PAINFUL OR NON-PAINFUL STIMULATION OF THE SKIN

The skin was exposed to thermal radiation in an area of 1.5 cm.² and with a stimulus intensity sufficient to induce not more than from threshold to one-"dol" pain (see fig. 65). In order to maintain the pain at one "dol" it was necessary to alter the stimulus intensity constantly. The adjacent area of skin was repeatedly tested with pin pricks, in order to detect the development and define the spread of hyperalgesia. This was first clearly evidenced at seven minutes (see A, fig. 65), and continued to increase in size and intensity during 21 minutes (see C, fig. 65). At this time the hyperalgesia had extended 10 cm. proximally and 5 cm. distally and was approximately of the same extent as occurs after a first or second degree burn. With termination of the stimulation the hyperalgesia receded at an exceedingly rapid rate and could no longer be detected after a few seconds (point D, fig. 65). There was no obvious change in the appearance of the skin, with the exception of a slight erythema at the site of the application of the stimulus.

OBSERVATION 6.

In three series of experiments on three subjects, it was possible to demonstrate that prolonged thermal irradiation of 50 to 60 mc./sec./cm.^{2} intensity although not sufficiently strong to induce continuous pain sensation, was none the less capable of evoking

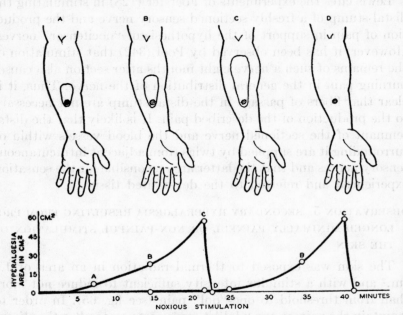

FIG. 65. DEVELOPMENT OF SECONDARY HYPERALGESIA DURING PROLONGED MINIMALLY PAINFUL (LEFT), AND NON-PAINFUL (RIGHT) STIMULATION

hyperalgesia. The sensation resulting from the stimulation was that of intense heat and occasional itching of short duration.

In one series of experiments the total duration of stimulation was 20 minutes; in the second series it was 40 minutes. At the end of 20 minutes, two of the three subjects were able to define a narrow zone of hyperalgesia adjacent to the site of noxious stimulation. The hyperalgesic area did not exceed 4 cm. in its longest axis and was dissipated at once when stimulation ended. The stimulated area of skin exhibited slight erythema which lasted for several minutes. At the end of 40 minutes of such stimulation the hyperalgesic area extended 10 cm. in its longest axis and was

4 to 6 cm. wide. This hyperalgesia also was dissipated within two minutes after stimulation ended. An area of erythema 3 cm. in diameter remained, indicating that despite the absence of painful sensation there had probably been slight tissue damage. Also, the pain threshold in the stimulated area was lowered by fifteen to twenty per cent.

COMMENT

Some years ago the following experiment was done: An area of secondary hyperalgesia was produced on the skin of the left cheek over the outer edge of the zygoma by placing under the left middle and inferior turbinates a tampon soaked with an epinephrin solution (1:1000). The pain threshold in the hyperalgesic area, as ascertained by the thermal radiation technique, was not lowered. Moreover, almost immediately after the pain on the face had been obliterated by placing procaine tampons over the irritated nasal mucosa, the hyperalgesia of the skin was eliminated. In other words, the hyperalgesia did not outlast the period of noxious stimulation. These observations concerning the prompt and complete elimination of hyperalgesia indicate the dependence of secondary hyperalgesia upon the flow of nerve impulses from the injured area (489).

Another important demonstration of the latent period in the development of hyperalgesia is seen in the experiment to follow, using procaine to interfere with afferent impulses from the periphery. Thus, when the skin which has been thoroughly anesthetized, either by local infiltration of procaine or by nerve block, is injured, the hyperalgesia does not begin to develop until "pin prick sensation" returns to the procainized area. Also, the hyperalgesia does not appear fully developed when first detected, but instead is noted only close to the injured area. It then gradually spreads after the return of sensation to the area of injury in the same manner as hyperalgesia develops following tissue damage without previous anesthetization. Further, the hyperalgesia thus fully developed may be promptly eliminated by again locally anesthetizing the injured area or by nerve block, only to recur after the sensation is again re-established (fig. 66). Further experimental evidence of this nature stems from the observation of Lewis, as well as from the following experiments, representing a total of 22 series of observations on four subjects.

OBSERVATION 7. THE EFFECTS OF PROCAINE BARRIERS UPON THE DEVELOPMENT AND PROPERTIES OF SECONDARY HYPERALGESIA

A small area of skin was infiltrated with one per cent procaine, producing an anesthetized area of about 3 to 4 cm.² after which an intense thermal stimulus was applied to the center of this area. No sensation was perceived, although the skin was obviously dam-

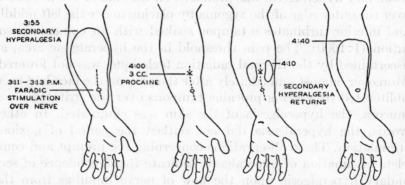

FIG. 66. EFFECT UPON SECONDARY HYPERALGESIA OF PROCAINE INFILTRATION AROUND A NERVE (NERVE BLOCK) PROXIMAL TO THE SITE OF FARADIC STIMULATION OF A CUTANEOUS NERVE

aged and a bleb subsequently formed at the site of injury. After about twelve minutes the effects of the procaine began to subside, as could be ascertained by repeated testing by tactile and thermal stimulation. Spontaneous pain occurred at no time, although after procaine effects subsided the pain threshold in the injured area was demonstrated to be markedly depressed. Under these circumstances, adjacent to the injured area, an area of hyperalgesia gradually developed. After the effects of the anesthetic had subsided, the usual time of approximately fifteen to 60 minutes was required for full development. When marked hyperalgesia had developed procaine was infiltrated intracutaneously. The hyperalgesia rapidly dwindled in area, but a narrow zone extending 2 to 3 cm. proximally persisted, even after superficial sensation in

the injured area was eliminated. Procaine was then infiltrated subcutaneously and immediately all of the hyperalgesia disappeared.
With dissipation of the procaine effects, hyperalgesia redeveloped.
Similar observations were made in a series of experiments in
which hyperalgesia followed injury by faradic stimulation (see
fig. 67) except that it was necessary to infiltrate intramuscularly

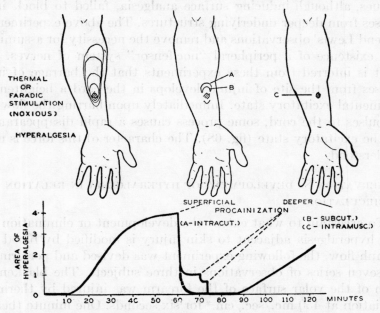

FIG. 67. EFFECTS ON SECONDARY HYPERALGESIA OF SUPERFICIAL AND DEEP
INFILTRATION OF THE SITE OF INJURY

to a depth of 14 mm. beneath the injury in order to eliminate the
hyperalgesia completely.

COMMENT

These experiments demonstrate that when noxious impulses
from the injured tissue are completely barred from entering the
central nervous system, hyperalgesia will be eliminated regardless
of whether it resulted from nerve stimulation or skin injury. However, partial blocking of neural pathways from the site of injury
reduces the size of the area of hyperalgesia but does not com-

pletely eliminate it. Thus, if the skin injury be superficial, intra-cutaneous infiltration of procaine will eliminate the secondary hyperalgesia, but if the injury is deep, deep procainization is required.

Lewis' conclusion to the contrary arose from experiments in which he used faradic stimulation, and in which his blocking tech-niques, although inducing surface analgesia, failed to block im-pulses from deeper underlying structures. The above experiments extend Lewis' observations and remove the necessity for assuming the existence of a peripheral "nocifensor" system of nerves.

It is inferred from these experiments that the barrage of im-pulses from the site of injury develops in the cord a heightened segmental excitatory state. Immediately upon barring the flow of impulses to the cord, some process causes a rapid disappearance of the excitatory state (fig. 68). The character of this force is not understood.

OBSERVATION 8. DEVELOPMENT OF HYPERALGESIA IN RELATION TO CIRCULATION

To ascertain to what extent the development or elimination of the hyperalgesia adjacent to skin injury is modified by blood or lymph flow, the following experiment was devised and performed in seven series of observations in three subjects. The blackened skin of the volar surface of the forearm was injured by thermal radiation at 450 mc./sec./cm.^{2} for six seconds. One minute there-after a manometer cuff just above the elbow was inflated to 220 mm. Hg, left in place for ten minutes, and then deflated. During the period of occlusion of the circulation, the skin was repeatedly examined for hyperalgesia. It was observed that the rate of de-velopment and the area of hyperalgesia differed in no remarkable way from that noted when blood and lymph flow were intact. Twenty-two minutes later when the hyperalgesia was fully de-veloped the cuff was again inflated to 220 mm. Hg, and left in place for five minutes. During this five minute period procainiza-tion of the lesion caused prompt elimination of the hyperalgesia in a manner identical with that observed in other experiments when the blood flow was intact (fig. 69).

In three additional experiments, tight elastic bands were put around the arm 1 cm. distal and 1 cm. proximal to the area of skin to be injured, and one minute before injuring the skin the manometer cuff was inflated to 200 mm. Hg. Under these conditions no movement of substances from the injured area by lymph

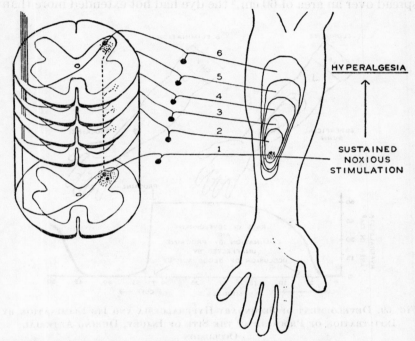

Fig. 68. Diagrammatic Representation of the Relationship of a Central Excitatory State to Cutaneous Secondary Hyperalgesia

or blood flow in deep or superficial vessels would be expected. Following injury to the skin the secondary hyperalgesia developed in the usual manner underneath and beyond the elastic bands so that in 20 minutes an area of 60 cm.² was established.

COMMENT

It is inferred from the observations that humoral factors operate in no significant way in the mechanism of development of secondary hyperalgesia or in its elimination by procaine block.

OBSERVATION 9.

In two series of observations in two subjects methylene blue was infiltrated into the area of injured skin immediately after termination of the thermal stimulation (460 mc./sec./cm.² for six seconds). An hour later when hyperalgesia was maximal, having spread over an area of 60 cm.² the dye had not extended more than

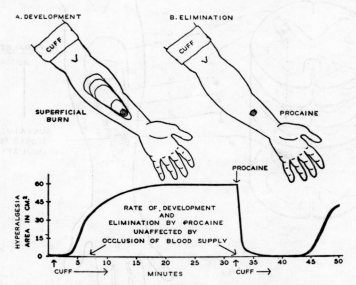

FIG. 69. DEVELOPMENT OF SECONDARY HYPERALGESIA AND ITS ELIMINATION BY INFILTRATION OF PROCAINE AT THE SITE OF INJURY, DURING ARTERIAL OCCLUSION

a few millimeters beyond the periphery of the injury. The rate and extent of diffusion of the dye into the skin adjacent to the injury and the development of the area of hyperalgesia were in no way related.

COMMENT

It must be inferred from these observations that the secondary hyperalgesia is essentially neural in origin rather than humoral. These observations further support the thesis that it is the persistence of impulses from peripheral tissue whether painful or non-painful which effects the development of secondary hyperalgesia. Furthermore, the maintenance of hyperalgesia is dependent upon this sustained barrage of afferent impulses.

Although the rate and area of development, and duration of hyperalgesia depend upon the amount of tissue damage, there are peculiar temporal aspects of the phenomenon which call for consideration. Thus, regardless of the amount of damage within the experimental range, the development of hyperalgesia is not immediate. It seems to require a lapse of minutes after injury for the first manifestations to occur. As described above, noxious stimulation of low intensity, producing minimal tissue damage, produced hyperalgesia only when the stimulation was sustained for some time, that is, for at least ten minutes. It requires a relatively long time, physiologically speaking, for whatever process is involved to become established, despite the fact that with cessation of afferent impulses the hyperalgesia is abolished within the space of time it takes to test for it.

OBSERVATION 10. HYPERALGESIA IN THE SKIN ASSOCIATED WITH DEEP SOMATIC NOXIOUS STIMULATION

Noxious stimulation of deep structures both somatic and visceral was associated with deep pain at the site of stimulation and deep as well as surface hyperalgesia. Thus, in six experiments in four subjects, the injection of 0.5 cc. of 6% saline into one side of the intraspinous ligament of the ninth dermatome was associated with the building up of an intense aching pain which spread into the chest and abdomen and gradually subsided in the subsequent three to five minutes. Each of the four subjects made essentially similar observations. In approximately ten minutes after the initial injury there developed a surface hyperalgesia in the corresponding dermatome, which became manifest by the fact that pin pricks were experienced as sharper and longer lasting than pricks of equal force in control areas on the opposite side. The pain threshold to thermal radiation remained unchanged. But, measured thermal stimuli which produced three- to four-"dol" pains, respectively, in control areas, produced five- to six-"dol" pains in the hyperalgesic areas (fig. 70). It was also reported by these subjects that the stimulus resulting from drawing a wisp of absorbent cotton across the hyperalgesic skin area produced a more vivid touch sensation in the hyperalgesic area than in control areas in corresponding dermatomes on the opposite side of the back. Hyperalgesia thus produced differed in no way from that which was secondary to the skin injury.

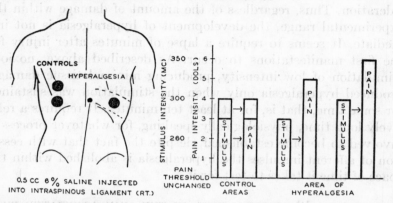

FIG. 70. UNCHANGED PAIN THRESHOLD, AND INCREASED PAIN SENSIBILITY IN AN AREA OF CUTANEOUS SECONDARY HYPERALGESIA ASSOCIATED WITH NOXIOUS STIMULATION OF DEEP STRUCTURES

OBSERVATION 11.

Hyperalgesia was produced by stimulating visceral afferent nerves with bubbles of CO_2 which accumulated on the peritoneal surface of the diaphragm, following a Rubin's test on ten subjects. Under these circumstances a deep pain was first experienced in the shoulder tip, to be followed soon by an area of hyperalgesia which could be demonstrated and roughly outlined as a circular area of approximately seven to eight cm. in diameter. The hyperalgesia was usually on one side, but occasionally on both. In the latter case, suitable control areas in adjacent segments were selected for comparison. It was found that the thermal pain threshold was not lowered, but that, as in secondary hyperalgesia induced by other means and described above, the sensation of pain at threshold was more intense and longer lasting. Moreover, a stimulus producing pain of four-"dol" intensity in control areas, produced pain of six-"dol" intensity in the hyperalgesic area (see fig. 71).

OBSERVATION 12. CUTANEOUS HYPERALGESIA ASSOCIATED WITH AN INJURY

Following a minor back injury in connection with a fall, a patient complained of deep aching pain of low intensity in the left flank at the costovertebral angle. On testing with pin pricks, an area of surface hyperalgesia approximately 8 cm. in diameter

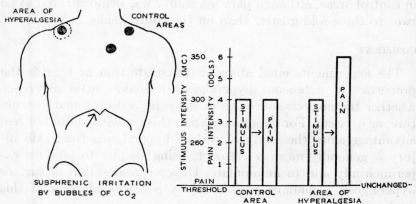

FIG. 71. UNCHANGED PAIN THRESHOLD, AND INCREASED PAIN SENSIBILITY IN AN AREA OF CUTANEOUS SECONDARY HYPERALGESIA ASSOCIATED WITH NOXIOUS STIMULATION OF THE DIAPHRAGM

on the left flank was defined. By means of thermal radiation testing procedures the pain threshold in the hyperalgesic and non-hyperalgesic zones was found to be the same and within normal limits. However, it was observed that the thermal stimuli which produced three-, four-, and six-"dol" pains on the control side, produced six-, eight-, and nine-"dol" pains, respectively, on the hyperalgesic side.

OBSERVATION 13. HYPERALGESIA ASSOCIATED WITH AN INFECTION

A patient with mild otitis media on the left complained of earache and tenderness to touch and pressure on the scalp and about the ear in an area supplied by sensory twigs from the fifth,

seventh, ninth, and tenth cranial nerves and the second cervical
nerve. When the area of tenderness was examined with pin pricks
the latter felt sharper and the pain lasted longer than in adjacent
non-tender areas. Moreover, when the hyperalgesic area was mechanically stimulated by tapping with the finger or by gentle
pressure, not only was local tenderness evoked, but the pain from
the inflammation in the ear was markedly increased from an
intensity of one "dol" to four "dols." The pain threshold for
thermal stimulation was the same in the hyperalgesic skin as that
in control areas, although pain sensibility was demonstrated to be
two- to three-fold greater than on the control side.

COMMENT

The experiments cited above demonstrate that as regards the
properties of cutaneous hyperalgesia it makes little difference
whether the noxious source be in the skin, a deep somatic structure, or a viscus. For experimentation this similarity affords a real
advantage since the study of surface hyperalgesia from skin injury is generally more convenient, being simpler to produce experimentally and to manipulate. Hence consideration of surface
hyperalgesia secondary to skin injury is the focal point of this
analysis.

Factors Influencing Secondary Hyperalgesia

OBSERVATION 1. DIMINUTION OF THE AREA OF HYPERALGESIA WITH
PIN PRICKS

Hyperalgesia was produced in eight subjects in a series of eleven
experiments by faradic current applied over the anterior branch
of the external cutaneous nerve. Subsequently the usual tongue
shaped area of hyperalgesia developed and the following procedure
was then undertaken. The extreme proximal border of the area
having been defined by pin pricks, the testing with pin was carried 3 cm. into the hyperalgesic area (A, fig. 72). Immediately
the testing was begun some distance proximal to the hyperalgesic
zone and proceeded distally until the margin of hyperalgesic area
was again well defined. This procedure took ten seconds from

the time the pricking began until the new border was defined
(A, fig. 72). It was noted that the border of the hyperalgesic zone
rapidly receded when the skin within the zone was stimulated by
pin pricks (B and C, fig. 72). However, it never completely disappeared as there always remained an area approximately three to
four cm. in diameter surrounding the injured area. The hyper-

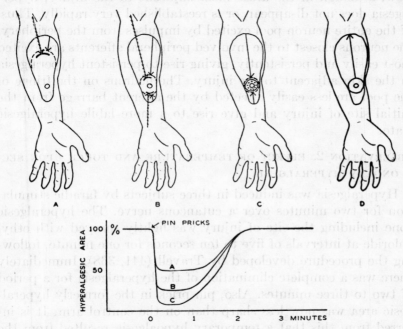

FIG. 72. DIMINUTION OF THE AREA OF SECONDARY HYPERALGESIA AFTER
REPEATED PIN PRICKS WITHIN ITS BORDERS

algesia in areas most distant from the site of injury was more
labile and more readily dispelled while the hyperalgesia nearest
the site of injury was far more stable and usually could not be
eliminated. It took from one to two minutes for the hyperalgesia
to reestablish itself after it had once dwindled. Also, and even
more striking, when the area within a diameter of 3 to 4 cm. from
the injured site was stimulated for ten seconds, the overall hyperalgesic zone greatly diminished, again requiring from one to two
minutes to become reestablished to its former borders (fig. 72).

COMMENT

The inference from this experiment is that noxious stimulation in the hyperalgesic area immediately causes a partial and temporary discharge of a central excitatory state. The reestablishment of the hyperalgesia in the skin to the previous extent is relatively slow, although in the areas most adjacent to the injury, hyperalgesia does not disappear, or is reestablished very rapidly. Thus, of the entire neuron pool excited by impulses from the periphery, the neurons closest to the involved peripheral afferents are excited most easily and persistently, giving rise to persistent hyperalgesia in the skin adjacent to the injury. The neurons on the fringe of the pool are less easily affected by the afferent barrage from the initial site of injury and give rise to a more labile hyperalgesic state.

OBSERVATION 2. EFFECT OF TEMPERATURE AND TOUCH UPON SECONDARY HYPERALGESIA

Hyperalgesia was induced in three subjects by faradic stimulation for two minutes over a cutaneous nerve. The hyperalgesic zone including the site of injury was lightly sprayed with ethyl chloride at intervals of five to ten seconds for one minute, following the procedure developed by Travell (441, 368). Immediately there was a complete elimination of the hyperalgesia for a period of two to three minutes. Also, pin prick in the formerly hyperalgesic area was now less sharp than on the control arm. It is inferred from this that a temporary hypoalgesia resulted from the local cooling action of the ethyl chloride, causing the disappearance of the hyperalgesia.

Cold water at 19°C. was poured over the hyperalgesic and injured areas for 30 seconds, and again the hyperalgesia was temporarily eliminated and hypoalgesia induced. The action of the cold water and the ethyl chloride spray were similar in all respects and therefore are assumed to result from the same effect, i.e., hypesthesia of the skin due to cooling of peripheral nerve end organs.

Water at 40°C. was poured over the hyperalgesic area for 30 seconds. This procedure not only did not eliminate the hyperalgesia, but temporarily increased its intensity. Since the warm water was slightly painful at the site of injury although not so in the area of secondary hyperalgesia, it is inferred that the changes in the hyperalgesia resulted from an increase in the barrage of impulses from the site of injury, thus increasing the intensity of the excitatory state.

Vigorous but not painful rubbing of the hyperalgesic arm for ten to twenty seconds also did not eliminate the hyperalgesia.

Gentle stroking of the hyperalgesic area with cotton wool for twenty seconds induced an intense tickle sensation but had no effect on the hyperalgesia.

COMMENT

These observations are in keeping with those of Travell et al. as to the effectiveness of ethyl chloride spray. Also, they point to the general conclusion that procedures which increase the noxious stimulation at the site of injury intensify hyperalgesia. Procedures decreasing the flow of impulses from the site of injury, or from the associated secondary hyperalgesia reduce or eliminate secondary hyperalgesia.

OBSERVATION 3

In three subjects two skin injuries 6 cm. apart were produced by thermal stimulation. Within five to ten minutes extensive and very marked hyperalgesia had developed as had been previously observed from two skin injuries. Sodium pentobarbital 0.2 gm. was then administered by mouth. The hyperalgesic zone persisted during the next hour and a half. At that time 30 cc. of 95% alcohol in 200 cc. of ice water was ingested. Although the pain threshold was raised by 35% within half an hour, painful stimuli were still perceived as more intense in the hyperalgesic zone.

COMMENT

In the amounts given in the above experiments sodium pentobarbital and ethyl alcohol had no observable effect on secondary hyperalgesia. However, the pain threshold was raised by 35% from which we infer that the centrally acting analgesic had no selective action on the neuron pool concerned with the persistence of the hyperalgesia.

Spatial Summation of Pain in Areas of Secondary Hyperalgesia

The increased pain "sensibility" in zones of secondary hyperalgesia points to a summative effect of disturbances here with those arising from the injured area. Thus, a critical experiment is that of ascertaining the presence or absence of spatial summation in areas of hyperalgesic skin.

Two types of spatial summative effects can be demonstrated for other sensation. They are: a) the threshold may be lowered by stimulating a larger area, as for example with temperature sensation (181) and vision (169); b) the threshold may not be lowered, but due to increased excitability in the neural pathway, facilitation may occur, giving rise to a more intense effect for impulses that do reach the final common path, as was demonstrated for vision by Hartline (198) and for motor function by Sherrington (400).

OBSERVATION 1. PAIN THRESHOLD VS. SIZE OF AREA OF SECONDARY HYPERALGESIC SKIN STIMULATED

An anterior branch of the cutaneous nerve was stimulated with faradic current for two minutes in three subjects in five series of experiments. One hour later when areas of intense secondary hyperalgesia would be identified by testing with pin prick, the pain threshold was measured by exposing such skin areas of different sizes to the thermal stimulation. Similar pain threshold measurements were made in control areas of non-hyperalgesic skin. The results of these tests are shown in table 15. There is no evidence of lowering of the pain threshold either in the control or hyperalgesic areas of skin as the size of area stimulated is increased.

OBSERVATION 2. PAIN SENSIBILITY VS. SIZE OF AREA OF SECONDARY HYPERALGESIC SKIN STIMULATED

In order to observe whether spatial summation above the pain threshold occurs, the following tests were carried out in fifteen experiments on three subjects. An area of hyperalgesic skin 1.2

cm.^{2} in size was exposed to a thermal stimulus which induced three- to four-"dol" pain. With the same intensity of stimulus, an area 10 cm.^{2} in size was exposed and the pain induced was reported to be of four- to five-"dols" intensity. These comparisons were repeated in control areas and pain intensity was reported to be the same as for similarly increased areas.

TABLE 15

Pain threshold measurements in various sized areas of hyperalgesic skin and control skin areas

	THRESHOLD STIMULUS INTENSITY IN MC./SEC./CM.^{2}					
AREA EXPOSED	Subject H		Subject G		Subject W	
	Hyperalgesic area	Control area	Hyperalgesic area	Control area	Hyperalgesic area	Control area
cm.^{2}						
0.19	215	200	208	170	265	
1.20	200	190	209	170	200	205
3.46	216	225	227	225	221	215
7.10	213	225	220	225	205	
10.0	218	221	214	221	216	
28.3	216	226	220	221	193	

COMMENT

This evidence demonstrates clearly that some type of spatial summation occurs in areas of secondary hyperalgesia, i.e., the intensity of pain sensation is increased with increase in area stimulated, whereas such effects have not been demonstrated in non-hyperalgesic skin.

DISCUSSION—A NEW FORMULATION

The observations which have been made on the various characteristics of primary and secondary hyperalgesia point to an excitatory state somewhere in the neural pathway from the skin to the sensorium. Although different opinions are held as to the site of the excitation, it is suggested by all investigators that such excitation is responsible for the phenomena observed. The following diagram is presented to show an arrangement of the neuron pool which may account for the known facts regarding "primary" and "secondary" hyperalgesia. Such a formulation is in a sense a restatement in modern physiological terms of views variously expressed by Sturge (427), Ross (373), Head (203), Mackenzie (302), Livingston (287), and Cohen (87). It is supported by the observations of Cajal (67, 68), Lorente de Nó (291), Hinsey and Phillips (216), and Ray and Wolff (354).

Figure 73 is a schematic diagram drawn in an attempt to

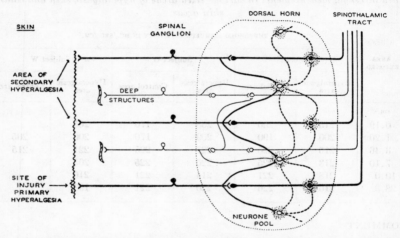

FIG. 73. SCHEMATIC DIAGRAM OF PAIN FIBER CONNECTIONS WITHIN THE NEURON POOL SHOWING FOCI OF EXCITATION (STIPPLED AREAS) WHICH RESULT FROM THE CONTINUOUS BARRAGE OF NOXIOUS IMPULSES FROM THE SITE OF INJURY

visualize the neuroanatomical relationships within the neuron pool which may account for the observed phenomena of primary and secondary hyperalgesia. The usefulness of such a diagram lies mainly in accounting for functional data and as an aid in thinking.

The skin is represented to the left in figure 73 with an injured area innervated by a typical neuron subserving superficial pain; an area of secondary hyperalgesia is innervated by a similar neuron. Neurons also are drawn in to represent pain fibers innervating structures below the skin surface.

All neurons are assumed to enter a neuron pool in the dorsal horn, and there to make synaptic connections, as shown in the figure. The neuron pool contains, in addition to the primary and secondary neurons, a network of internuncial neurons which make intimate connection between the neurons mediating both superficial and deep pain. These internuncial neurons serve the primary function of establishing and maintaining in the neuron pool an excitatory state as a result of impulses from the periphery. In general it is believed that these neurons are concerned principally with the control of the level of excitation at the synaptic junction between the secondary and tertiary neurons. Since superficial pain does not spread, even with the highest intensities, these internuncials probably cannot excite to threshold level the neurons between which they are intercalated.

This system of internuncial neurons is analogous to the nocifensor system of nerves which was proposed by Lewis, with the difference that the excitatory state was assumed by Lewis to be in the skin rather than in the spinal cord (276).

The production of secondary hyperalgesia is visualized as occurring in the following way. The skin is injured at the site of primary hyperalgesia and due to the state of hyperexcitability of the nerve endings a steady barrage of impulses enters the cord where they excite the network of internuncial neurons. If the barrage is great enough the impulses will pass over the intervening synapses of the primary pathways and give rise to sensation. However, as has been shown experimentally, continuous pain from the site of noxious stimulation is not essential to the production of secondary hyperalgesia. Thus, the network of internuncials must be assumed to be excited by subliminal stimuli. The excitation of the network induces in the pathway of other neurons states of excitation (shown by stippling in the figure) and as this excitation does *not* lower the pain threshold in the area of secondary hyperalgesia, it is assumed that it is the tertiary neuron that is excited rather than the primary or secondary fibers. If the skin is pricked in the area of secondary hyperalgesia, a burst of impulses passes into the cord and when reaching the tertiary neuron is facilitated, giving rise to a more intense sensation than usual. From such a network no lowering of pain threshold would be expected in the region of secondary hyperalgesia, but, rather, an intensification of pain sensation through facilitation of impulses above the pain threshold. This sensation will also be longer lasting as the impulses from the zone of secondary hyperalgesia will serve to give additional excitation to the network and therefore prolong the sensory response. The prick will not spread to adjacent neurons but due to the increased excitation in the internuncial neurons there may sometimes occur a slight increase in sensation from the injured area. Indeed, this has been found to be the case, and the increase in sensation was always slight.

Obviously, procaine blocking of impulses from the injured area or along the pathway of neurons subserving the area of primary hyperalgesia would allow the excitatory state in the internuncial network to subside and thereby eliminate the secondary hyperalgesia. The neurons in the more distant parts of the neuron pool may become less excited and therefore give rise to a more labile secondary hyperalgesia. Pricking the skin within this zone at its margins dissipates the hyperalgesia which is fully restored only after 60 to 90 seconds. Pricking has little effect in dissipating the secondary hyperalgesia very near the injured area. This indicates the discharge of the excited state in the more remote parts of the neuron pool which requires appreciable time for restoration. In the portion of the pool adjacent to the neurons from the injured skin the excited state is more difficult to discharge and more rapidly restored after being discharged.

An internuncial network of the type which has been assumed to exist also accounts satisfactorily for the observations as to no lowering of pain threshold, increased intensity of sensation and spatial summation in zones of secondary hyperalgesia. The interconnection of the neurons mediating superficial pain with those subserving deep pain through such a network provides for the observed interrelationships of these two types of pain. For example, the production of superficial hyperalgesia by noxious stimulation of deep structures is easily explained on the basis of the development of an excitatory state in the internuncial network as the result of impulses from the deeper structures. One would also expect the development of deep hyperalgesia as the result of skin injury, as indeed was demonstrated experimentally above. Thus, deep and superficial hyperalgesia should result from noxious stimulation of either superficial or deep structures. The type of network described not only explains the experiments of Lewis and his co-workers but also brings together much experimental and clinical data which heretofore have been considered in contradiction.

Clinical Implications

This discussion has been concerned with cutaneous hyperalgesia associated with more or less tissue damage and with that occurring in adjacent undamaged tissue in association with deep or superficial noxious stimulation. The analysis has been limited primarily to cutaneous hyperalgesia because of technical convenience and not because it is implied that a different process is involved in deep hyperalgesia. It has been experimentally demonstrated above that changes in sensitivity and sensibility of skin and deep tissues to pain sensation can be brought about by prolonged noxious stimulation of superficial or deep structures.

For purposes of analysis and experimentation the cutaneous hyperalgesia from visceral and deep somatic damage has often been considered apart from and as involving properties and mechanisms separate from the cutaneous hyperalgesia secondary to skin damage. Indeed, because of certain highly specific qualities of pain associated with superficial or deep injuries, respectively, and because the pathways taken by impulses from deeper structures to the central nervous system are different from those more superficial, the two types of pain have been sharply segregated. These differences being granted it would none the less seem more profitable from the point of view of understanding and manipulation if these various structures were considered as being linked with regard to the effects of noxious stimulation by the assumed internuncial network.

There are two general classifications of hyperalgesia, i.e.:

1. Hyperalgesia associated with tissue damage and occurring at the site of tissue damage (primary hyperalgesia).

2. Hyperalgesia associated with tissue damage but occurring in undamaged tissue adjacent to and extending some distance from the site of injury (secondary hyperalgesia).

In addition there may be listed the following loosely defined clinical categories of hyperalgesia:

1. Hyperalgesia associated with contractions of skeletal muscle which are secondary to injury or noxious stimulation and which provide a supplementary source of pain.

2. Hyperalgesia associated with disease or dysfunction of peripheral nerves (including deficiency syndromes and circulatory defects). (See p. 215.)

3. Hyperalgesia associated with lesions near or in the thalamus.

4. Hyperalgesia associated with abnormal stimulation of the distal end of a peripheral nerve (causalgia).

5. Hyperalgesia in the zone supplied by a regenerating sensory nerve.

6. Hyperalgesia on the margin of an area supplied by a degenerating sensory nerve.

7. Hyperalgesia associated with disturbed mental states involving judgment or unusual excitement.

8. Generalized deep and cutaneous hyperalgesia associated with acute infection and fever.

Analysis of these clinical syndromes depends upon the availability of data which determine whether or not the site of tenderness is also the site of injury. It is necessary therefore that some information be available on pain threshold and pain sensibility in areas of tenderness and it is equally important to have information regarding any dysfunction of neural pathways. For example, in category 2, herpes zoster is an important entity. It has been observed that in the area of skin lesion the pain threshold may be unchanged, raised, or lowered, and quite independently of pain thresholds, pains which are perceived may be facilitated or depressed in intensity. In this case, one is obviously dealing with both hyper- and hypo-excitability in the neural pathways, and depending upon the preponderance of one or the other of these factors, intensity of pain in the area of a lesion will be determined.

The interplay between deep and superficial hyperalgesia has long been recognized. For example, the association of superficial hyperalgesia with deep pain and the effects of anesthetization of the skin in modifying deep pain has caused confusion and controversy (495a).

Though described many years ago (427), the phenomenon was given fresh interest by Weiss and Davis (463) and more recently by Travell and Rinzler (441). These authors suggested that deep pain could be reduced or eliminated by anesthetization of the associated hyperalgesic areas of the skin. Anesthetization of the skin is reported to diminish pain from underlying painful joints and muscles. Morely (317) reported that hyperalgesia of the skin over the shoulders from diaphragmatic irritation could be eliminated or reduced by anesthetization of the hyperalgesic area. Cohen (89) described patients who had had amputations near the shoulder and subsequently developed pain from myocardial insufficiency. In one patient, walking 150 yards on the level would invariably precipitate pain in the phantom, then in the neck, then a feeling of constriction in the chest, and choking. In the scar on his amputation stump there was a small tender nodule which when pressed gave rise to sensations in the phantom similar to those experienced on exertion. If pressure was continued there was a complaint of constriction in the chest and pain in the neck as well. After procainization of the left brachial plexus the patient was able to walk 200 yards at the same rate before experiencing pain in the neck, chest, and phantom. Not until after 600 yards of walking did pain in the chest become intolerable and cause him to stop. Cohen also made the following observations:

Four patients with effort angina were each blistered over an area of 4 square inches on the inner side of the right elbow, or in the right mammary region, sites where they had previously never experienced pain. When their angina was precipitated by exertion, all complained of intensification of pain in the blistered areas. Furthermore, in three of these patients, hypertonic saline solution was injected into the back muscles two inches to the right of the fifth dorsal spine. Two hours later, when the pain so induced had passed, exertion caused its recurrence, though no pain in previous anginal attacks had been felt in this area.

These clinical experiments demonstrate clearly the facilitation of superficial sensation by deep noxious stimulation. Also, as the excitatory level in the internuncial network depends upon contributions both from the skin and the deeper structures, anesthetization of either will modify both the intensity and the extent of pain experienced.

On the other hand, Woollard, Roberts and Carmichael (498) demonstrated that the more intense pain resulting from direct phrenic nerve stimulation and experienced in the shoulder tip was in no way influenced by surface anesthetization of this area. Lewis was not able to modify the pain of angina pectoris by anesthetization of the precordial skin nor was it possible for McLellan and Goodell (298) to alter the pain experience associated with ureteral distention by anesthetization of the skin in the area of pain on the anterior abdominal wall. Neither could pain resulting from duodenal distention be modified by anesthetization of the skin of the anterior abdominal wall (485). Anesthetization of the skin over the calvarium (not hyperalgesic) in no way influenced the intensity of the headache resulting from intravenous histamine injection (402). Also, anesthetization of a digit adjacent to a finger immersed in ice water did not modify the spread of pain into the anesthetized digit (251). It is noteworthy that painful stimulation in most of these experiments was short-lived and hyperalgesia was minimal. In these experiments the spread of pain rather than secondary hyperalgesia was the important contribution of more distant structures to the pain experience. That is, the effects of impulses from the source of deep noxious stimulation spill over into the network of internuncial neurons, which serve the function of interrelating neurons from deeper structures (figure 73), thus giving rise to the development of an excitatory state in the internuncial networks which intercalate the deep and superficial structures. This latter state, as observed above, requires noxious stimulation for some minutes. Therefore, anesthetization of superficial structures would not be expected to modify in any way the extent or intensity of the pain experienced.

Thus, it was shown by Robertson, Goodell and Wolff (370) that when a tooth had been noxiously stimulated causing a local and short lived eight- to ten-"dol" toothache, followed in about ten minutes by headache and superficial and deep hyperalgesia of the temporal region of the head, infiltration of procaine into the hyperalgesic skin and underlying soft tissues reduced the amount of discomfort and produced analgesia in the region although it did not eliminate the headache. When the hyperalgesia was more marked the effect of procaine injection into the zone of hyperalgesia was more dramatic. Headache was eliminated, however, by infiltration of procaine into the tissue about the injured, but no longer aching tooth. It is therefore evident that when pain results from the persistence of primary visceral or other deep noxious stimulation and is associated with hyperalgesia, its intensity may be modified often dramatically by superficial and deep procaine infiltration in the zones of secondary hyperalgesia. However, it may not be eliminated until the impulses from the primary sources end spontaneously or are blocked.

Hutchins and Reynolds (224) made observations on fourteen patients with deep pain in the maxillary region associated with changes in barometric pressure experienced in airplane travel. These authors demonstrated that anesthetization of the peripheral sensory pathway from the dental pulp eliminated the pain in many individuals or, at least, depressed it in others. They showed also that the pain experienced could be correlated with a pathological condition in the teeth, which, although not painful in itself, was sufficient to facilitate the pain sensation in other structures. Rather than by the spatial summation proposed by other authors these observations can be more easily explained by the existence of a central excitatory state causing a secondary hyperalgesia.

The "Hyperalgesia" of Peripheral Neuropathy—"Paradoxic Pain"

The features of "paradoxic pain" are that many ordinarily innocuous stimuli are perceived as painful, whereas at the same time pin prick perception is impaired. These phenomena occur in many varieties of peripheral neuropathy (i.e., with asphyxia, nutritional deficiencies with or without alcoholism, infections, and trauma) (32, 495a). Wortis, Stein and Joliffe (500) suggested that "paradoxic pain" results because the loss of one type of pain enhances the perception of another. This view was not supported by Gordon and Whitteridge (162) who, using the time interval between onset of painful stimulation and disturbance of alpha rhythm of the cerebral cortex saw no evidence of destruction of fibers conducting fast pain. The data contained in Chapter 5 suggest a simple explanation of "paradoxic pain", i.e. the threshold for burning pain subserved by unmyelinated fibers is so depressed by the damage of these nerves that contact with bedclothes produces burning pain, whereas at the same time the threshold for pricking pain perception subserved by myelinated is elevated causing pin prick perception to be impaired.

Chapter IX
ITCH, "ITCHY SKIN", AND TICKLE SENSATIONS

Available evidence suggests that the sensation of itching is closely related to that of pain (374). Titchener (436) observed that when the skin was explored with a fine hair, well defined points were found which gave rise to itching when the intensity of stimulation was low, and to pain on stronger stimulation. Bishop (35) found that itching resulted from repetitive low intensity electrical stimulation of pain spots in the skin. Lewis, Grant and Marvin (278) pointed out that noxious stimuli, if their intensity is decreased, can be made to produce itching instead of pain. Foerster (129) and Bickford (31) reported that itch was abolished in patients who had undergone sectioning of the lateral spinothalamic tract, thereby abolishing perception of cutaneous pain but not of touch. Bickford also observed this combination of sensory changes in two patients with syringomyelia. Ehrenwald and Konigstein (115), however, stated that they had found two cases of syringomyelia with loss of pain but preservation of touch and itch, and one in which pain was intact but touch and itch absent. McMurray (299), and Kunkle and Chapman (249) found that individuals who were constitutionally insensitive to pain likewise were insensitive to itching, but experienced touch sensation. Bickford observed that both itching and pain disappeared when a cutaneous nerve was anesthetized. Hardy, Wolff and Goodell (186) observed that in addition to the feeling of warmth, occasional itching resulted from sustained thermal irradiation at an intensity not quite strong enough to induce continuous pain. Thöle (433) found that during spinal anesthesia, as the sensitivity of the skin to painful stimuli decreased, stimuli which initially induced pain later induced itching and finally there was no sensation at all.

Many of the experiments described by Goldscheider (156), Bickford, and Lewis (283) and his associates have been repeated and additional experiments were designed to illuminate further the neural mechanisms involved in itch, "itchy skin", and tickle sensation (166).

Itch

SUBJECTS AND METHODS

The subjects were three healthy adults with other individuals participating from time to time. Itching was elicited by the application of cowhage to an area of skin approximately 1 cm. in diameter. (Cowhage is the familiar "itch powder", consisting of the fine fibers or spicules of the plant, *Mucuna pruriens*.) It was found by trial that the itch produced was indistinguishable from that following the bites of mosquitoes, or the intracutaneous injection of histamine. When areas of skin on the arm, hand, leg, or back were used for experimental procedures the corresponding areas on the opposite side of the body served as controls.

Description of Sensation Induced Following Application
of Cowhage to the Skin

Cowhage applied to an area of skin approximately 1 cm. in diameter induced, usually within ten to twenty seconds, an intense itching sensation which had both burning and pricking qualities. It was localized but seemed to spread for a few millimeters beyond the borders of the stimulated area. These itch sensations sometimes merged into pain of burning and pricking qualities. The skin under the cowhage rapidly became red, and a flare sometimes spread into adjacent areas of skin. When the area involved was the volar surface of the forearm, the flare spread as far as 2 cm. proximally and distally and approximately $\frac{1}{2}$ to 1 cm. laterally. The itching from cowhage spontaneously diminished after a few minutes and did not return until the cowhage was mechanically disturbed; or until the itching was revived by stroking the surrounding skin with the finger tip or a blunt object.

Sometimes, when the cowhage applied to the skin produced intense itching, the sensation eventually became indistinguishable from pain. Furthermore, occasionally cowhage on normal skin and in areas of primary or secondary hyperalgesia induced only pain. Also, as mentioned above, a prolonged heat stimulus at an intensity just below that sufficient to elicit pain, caused itching.

Peripheral Fiber Pathways Involved in Itch Sensation

It has been demonstrated that stimulation of the human skin with a pin gives rise to two kinds of painful sensation (143, 32). Although Lewis did not feel that such experiences constituted different qualities of cutaneous pain, others have recognized the qualitative difference.

OBSERVATION 1. DEMONSTRATION OF AN ITCHING SENSATION WITH PRICKING QUALITY ONLY

In three subjects procaine hydrochloride 1% was infiltrated about a cutaneous nerve on the ventral aspect of the forearm. Within a few minutes there developed distal to the site of infiltration an area in which pin prick elicited only a sharp, superficial, well-localized pain after short latency—the "first" pain. The slower, diffuse and burning "second" pain was not felt.

Within this area of altered sensibility cowhage elicited itching which was sharp, pricking, superficial, and localized. There was no component of burning pain. In areas where there was complete absence of pain sensitivity, but where light touch was still present, itching was not felt.

OBSERVATION 2. DEMONSTRATION OF ITCHING SENSATION WITH A BURNING QUALITY ONLY

A) In a series of six experiments on four subjects ischemia of the forearm was obtained by a pressure of 200 mm. Hg around the upper arm. After about 20 minutes of ischemia a pin prick applied to the fingers and hand elicited pain after a long latency, which was poorly localized and burning in character. The "first" pain was absent, as was light touch.

Within these areas of altered sensibility the application of cowhage on a site approximately 1 cm. in diameter on the back of the hand resulted in itching which was different from that obtained in Experiment 1, in that it was diffuse, poorly localized, seemed to originate beneath the surface of the skin and was "burning" in quality.

However, in more proximal areas of the ischemic forearm, closer to the occluding cuff, where normal pain and touch sensations were retained, cowhage produced itching not different from that in the skin of the opposite arm with blood and nerve supply intact.

B) In two subjects the course of a branch of a superficial cutaneous nerve in the forearm was mapped through a distance of 4 to 6 cm. by means of faradic stimulation. A soft lead tubing was applied over the nerve and held in place by tapes. Brine at a temperature of −2 to −4°C. was circulated through the tube for 30 minutes, resulting in the progressive anesthetization of the area supplied by the nerve (30).

After 30 minutes, within this area of altered sensation "second" pain could be elicited by a pin point but "first" pain and light touch were absent. In these areas "burning" itch could be elicited by cowhage but not "pricking" itch.

COMMENT

It was thus possible to separate the usual itch sensation, as it occurs after insect bites or the application of cowhage, into two components. These corresponded in quality to the two types of cutaneous pain, and the results of differential blocking of cutaneous nerves indicate that they are mediated by different fibers. It is suggested that "pricking" itch is carried by the myelinated fibers responsible for "first" pain, and that "burning" itch is carried by unmyelinated fibers responsible for the "second" pain. Since either kind of itch could occur in skin in which touch perception was absent, it seems probable that touch receptors and nerves are not involved in the perception of itching.

It might be objected that the sensory changes following obstruction of the circulation are due to interference of fluid movement which might modify the function of the sensory end organs, rather than to any functional change in the nerves themselves. Against this assumption stands the evidence that normal sensation was retained in skin close to the occluding cuff, but still distal to the obstruction. Here the fluid movement was as much interfered with as in the more distal areas where sensory changes did occur.

It is not difficult, once the two sensory components of itching have been separately perceived, to identify them in spontaneously occurring itches or in itch induced by a heat stimulus, by intra-cutaneous puncture with histamine or by exposing the arm to multiple mosquito bites.

Since the sensations of itching and pain are apparently me-diated by the same fiber pathways an attempt was made to ascer-tain in what way a stimulus which produces itching differs from

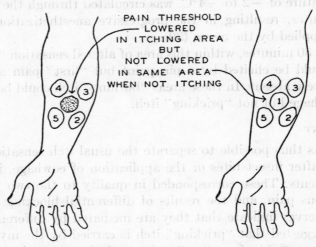

FIG. 74. LOWERING OF THE PAIN THRESHOLD IN AN AREA OF ITCHING SKIN
Cowhage was applied only to area 1. When itching occurred pain threshold was lowered in area 1, but not in adjacent areas 2, 3, 4, and 5.

one which produces pain. Experiments to test the thesis that the stimuli are of the same kind but of lower intensity were designed.

OBSERVATION 3. DEMONSTRATION OF LOWERED PAIN THRESHOLD IN ITCHING AREAS

Several areas of skin on the volar surface of the forearm were blackened with India ink, as shown in figure 74. Pain thresholds in all areas were measured by the thermal radiation method. Cow-hage was applied to the central area in the usual way. Pain thresh-olds were then measured repeatedly both when itching was present and in the intervals when it had spontaneously but temporarily ceased.

It was found that the pain threshold in all five areas was the same before cowhage was applied (190 ± 5 mc./sec./cm.^{2}). After itching started in the central area, however, the threshold in this zone was lowered (30 to 70 mc./sec./cm.^{2}), the lowest thresholds being found at the times of highest itch intensity. When itching temporarily ceased, the threshold returned to its initial level, and was lowered again on the resumption of itching. In the other areas the threshold remained constant or was slightly elevated to 210 ± 10 mc./sec./cm.^{2} when the central area was itching. These observations were made in three series of experiments on each of two subjects. The application of the heat stimulus to the central area in itch free intervals was usually followed by recrudescence of the itching.

COMMENT

These observations are consistent with the view that stimuli which give rise to itching activate pain endings in the skin at a stimulation intensity below the pain threshold. Less additional thermal energy is therefore required to produce definite pain sensation if itching is already occurring. Hence, the pain threshold as measured is lowered.

Alterations in Central Excitatory Processes Relevant to Itching

OBSERVATION 4. DEMONSTRATION THAT ITCH CAN BE ABOLISHED BY PAINFUL PIN PRICKS IN ADJACENT SKIN

It was found in 20 subjects that when itching occurred spontaneously or when it was induced by cowhage, a series of five or six light pin pricks repeated several times in the zone of itching on the surrounding skin, abolished the itching, sometimes for long intervals. It usually returned after periods up to several minutes in duration, although the slight pain from the prick had completely faded within ten to fifteen seconds. This has been observed not only with itching due to cowhage, but also in the itching resulting from insect bites, intracutaneous histamine puncture and intracutaneous foreign protein injection.

Pin prick applied not only locally but at considerable distance from the zone of itching abolished itching. With three subjects it was found that, if the cowhage was applied to the back, pin prick near the sternum in the same dermatome as the cowhage (fig. 75) was fully effective in eliminating itch.

In two subjects an attempt was made to delimit exactly the area within which pin prick abolished itching on the forearm. Cowhage was applied at approximately the mid-portion of the medial aspect of the forearm. After application of the cowhage the size of the area within which this effect could be demonstrated gradually increased and reached the eventual limit in about one hour following the beginning of itch. At this time the area meas-

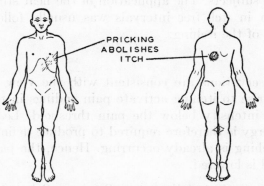

PRICKING
ABOLISHES
ITCH

FIG. 75. ITCHING INDUCED ON THE BACK BY COWHAGE WAS ABOLISHED BY PAINFUL PIN PRICKS IN THE SAME DERMATOME ON THE ANTERIOR CHEST WALL

ured approximately 5 x 15 cm. Figure 76 illustrates the area as mapped on the forearm of one subject on whom cowhage was applied as shown. It was essentially the same for the second subject.

After mapping had been completed, cowhage was applied at the distal end of the area. The effect of pin prick was again tested, and it was found that the area within which it abolished itching was approximately the same as in the first instance, extending only 1 to 2 cm. further distally. This zone was readily identified by the marked secondary hyperalgesia to pin prick at its outer margin.

A similar experiment was carried out on the legs of three subjects (fig. 77). The cowhage was applied just below the knee on the outer aspect of the left leg. Again there was an area within

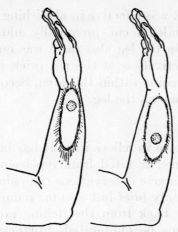

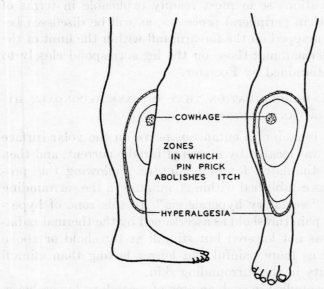

FIG. 76. ZONES IN WHICH PAINFUL PIN PRICKS ABOLISHED ITCHING INDUCED BY
COWHAGE ON THE MEDIAL ASPECT OF THE FOREARM
Sites of cowhage application are indicated by stippling

FIG. 77. ZONE OF THE LEG IN WHICH PAINFUL PIN PRICK ABOLISHED ITCHING
INDUCED BY COWHAGE

The inner line indicates the extent of the zone after 15 minutes of itching;
the outer border its extent at the end of an hour. Sites of cowhage application are
indicated by stippling. The zone was defined by the margin of secondary hyperalgesia.

which the pin prick was effective in abolishing itch. After 60 minutes the area extended 7 cm. proximally and 24 cm. distally to the itching spot. On the leg also there was only slight difference in the area of effectiveness of the pin prick if the cowhage was shifted to another point within this area. Secondary hyperalgesia also defined this zone on the leg.

COMMENT

Scratching is known to relieve itch. It has been held (374) that the relief so obtained resulted from replacement of the itch by frank pain. In the above observations the painful stimulus of the pin prick was not only brief but also far removed, as much as 24 cm., on the leg or back from the itching area, yet the itching sensation could thus be obliterated. Furthermore, the itch did not return until some time after the pain from the pin prick had subsided.

These observations seem most readily explicable in terms of central rather than peripheral processes, as will be discussed below. The areas mapped on the forearm fall within the limit of the first thoracic dermatome; those on the leg correspond closely to L4 or L5 as determined by Foerster.

OBSERVATION 5. DEMONSTRATION THAT INTENSE SECONDARY HYPERALGESIA IS "ANTI-PRURITIC"

A superficial branch of a cutaneous nerve on the volar surface of the forearm was located by means of faradic current, and then was painfully stimulated for two minutes. Following this procedure there was established within 20 minutes in the surrounding skin a zone of "secondary hyperalgesia". In this zone of hyperalgesic skin the pain threshold as ascertained by the thermal radiation method was not lowered but stimuli at threshold or above were perceived as more painful and longer lasting than stimuli of equal intensity in the surrounding skin.

Cowhage was applied in such an area of secondary hyperalgesia in four subjects in eleven observations. It evoked either occasional bursts of pain or no sensation at all, but not itching.

The secondary hyperalgesia was abolished in two subjects by

infiltrating procaine at the site of injury by faradization and by vigorous pin pricks in a zone within 1 to 2 cm. around the point of faradization. Cowhage was again applied and itching now occurred as it did in control areas on the other arm.

In twelve other experiments on two subjects, areas of secondary hyperalgesia were induced by painfully pinching with forceps a small fold of skin on the volar surface of the forearm. Approximately ten seconds after the pinch, when the secondary hyperalgesia was well developed, cowhage failed to elicit itching. When the cowhage was pressed into the skin, a maneuver which intensifies itching in control non-hyperalgesic skin, pricking pain was experienced, but itch did not ensue.

COMMENT

Lewis, Grant and Marvin observed that faradic stimulation of a cutaneous nerve was followed by a state in adjacent skin in which itching did not occur after intracutaneous histamine puncture. Bickford (31) called this state "anti-pruritic" and found that it also occurred after other forms of noxious stimulation, such as a sharp blow, a gnat bite, burn, or freeze.

The observations on the effect of pin prick in abolishing itch, and on the failure of itching to occur in areas of intense secondary hyperalgesia, seem to indicate the existence of events of a special sort in the central nervous system. Similarity of the size and shape of the affected areas to the dermatome suggests that the spinal cord is the site of such processes. Bickford also concluded that the "anti-pruritic" state must depend on some spinal cord mechanism.

Discussion

The use of cowhage as a stimulus has been criticized on the grounds that the itching which results is impure. Histamine has therefore often been employed, but it was found that the itching which resulted was not nearly so intense as that produced by cowhage, and seemed to be chiefly of the "second" type. The "impurity" of the cowhage-provoked itching may well be simply the result of the simultaneous presence of both types of itch.

The objection might be raised that one of the two kinds of itch described above was not really itch, but pain instead. The ultimate appeal in such a case must be to the introspection of the person experiencing the sensation, and the subjects in this investigation agreed that there were two kindred but distinguishable sensations which were both felt as "itch". Brack also referred to two qualitatively different itch experiences (54).

It seems likely, in view of all the available data, that stimuli which produce itching initiate impulses which, after traversing the peripheral pain nerves, pass up the spinothalamic tracts of the cord. Since many noxious stimuli of low intensity can be made to produce itching it is reasonable to suppose that the difference between a painful and an itch-producing stimulus is one of intensity. The reduction of the pain threshold at times when itching is being experienced is further evidence in support of this view. The probable reason for the lowered threshold is that the peripheral pain endings are already partially activated by the cowhage, so that the radiant energy required to give pain is less than that necessary if they have not been stimulated at all.

Potelunas, Meixner and Hardy (345) reported that there was no consistent difference in the cutaneous pain thresholds of patients with itching dermatoses as compared with healthy individuals. As they pointed out, however, structural changes such as thickening had often occurred in the diseased skin, with consequent alterations in pain sensitivity. All of the observations in the present investigations have been made on subjects without skin disorders, and without alteration of any sort except by the test procedures themselves. It must be emphasized that the threshold was found to be lowered only when the skin was itching.

One thesis which will explain all the findings is that itching depends on the presence in the cord of a circuit of internuncial neurons such as that described in Chapter VIII, around which impulses are constantly travelling. According to the hypothesis the establishment of such a circuit is the result of the low discharge frequency in a peripheral nerve which is excited by weak noxious stimulation. The effect of this circuit is to increase the level of excitation at the junction of the tertiary neuron (see stippling, fig. 78). As a result of a fleeting increase of excitation at the primary neuron, a low frequency volley of impulses is then able to set up an excitatory event which passes over the secondary neuron. At the tertiary neuron facilitation occurs and a brief discharge takes place resulting in a momentary sensation. Such intermittent dicharges of low frequency arouse the sensation of itch. On the other hand, if an intense secondary hyperalgesia exists in

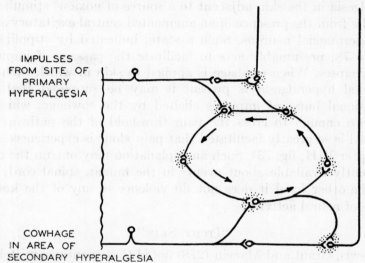

IMPULSES
FROM SITE OF
PRIMARY
HYPERALGESIA

COWHAGE
IN AREA OF
SECONDARY HYPERALGESIA

FIG. 78. INHIBITION OF ITCHING IN AREA OF SECONDARY HYPERALGESIA
The stippling represents the excitatory state of internuncial synapses which is responsible for the hyperalgesia and which prevents the formation of circuits necessary for itching.

the skin area in question, so great a facilitation takes place that pain sensation is evoked rather than itch. Thus, the presence of itch depends upon a low degree of primary hyperalgesia but itch is incompatible with marked secondary hyperalgesia.

Such a circuit of excitation in an internuncial system of neurons would, of course, require a delicate adjustment of impulse frequencies and refractory periods. A pin prick in the dermatome in which itch is arising would, it is assumed, bring about a diffuse discharge in the corresponding cord segment, ramifying along many of the internuncial neurons involved in the itch circuit. The states of excitation in the neural pathways from the itching area would thus be discharged and the mild hyperalgesia destroyed and the itching halted. It would presumably require an appreciable time for the excitatory state to be re-established, a time represented by the interval after pin pricking before itching is again perceived.

Hardy, Wolff and Goodell have concluded that secondary hyperalgesia in the skin adjacent to a source of noxious stimulation results from the presence of an augmented central excitatory state in internuncial neurons. Such a state, indicated by stippling in figure 78, presumably acts to facilitate the passage of impulses at synapses. When cowhage is applied to skin in which such additional hyperalgesia is present it may be supposed that the occasional burst of impulses elicited by the cowhage, which is intense enough to cross the pain threshold of the pathway involved is so greatly facilitated that pain alone is experienced (see Chapter VIII, fig. 73). Such an explanation may outrun the data currently available about events in the human spinal cord, but on the other hand it does not do violence to any of the known facts of neural activity.

"ITCHY SKIN"

Lewis, Grant and Marvin (278) noted that spontaneous itching is an accompaniment of nearly all forms of skin damage, provided the damage is relatively slight in amount. Also, Bickford observed that itchy skin extends beyond the actual skin damage. He described "itchy skin" as that which gives rise to an itching sensation when the skin is stroked with the finger or a blunt object. He investigated extensively the phenomenon of "itchy skin" associated with the itch induced by intracutaneous histamine puncture, and noted the close relationship of itch to tickle. Goldscheider described the occurrence of itching and "itchy skin" in the palm of the hand accompanying pinching of the web between two fingers. In the following investigations various modifications of both Goldscheider's and Bickford's experiments have been made in an attempt to illuminate further the mechanism of this phenomenon.

OBSERVATION 1. DEMONSTRATION OF "ITCHY SKIN" ADJACENT TO
A FOCUS OF ITCHING

Cowhage was applied to an area of skin 1 cm. in diameter on
the volar surface of the forearm in various locations. It was found
by trial that when the cowhage was placed on the wrist near the
hand, or somewhat toward the medial aspect of the arm, the
phenomenon of "itchy skin" could best be elicited. When the
itch had become intense, usually within 30 to 60 seconds after
application of the cowhage, stroking of the adjacent skin with
the tip of a finger frequently induced an itchy sensation and, more
frequently, intensified the primary itch. This zone extended
roughly 2 to 3 cm. proximally, 1 to 3 cm. distally, and 1 to 2 cm.
laterally. Indeed, when the primary itch had entirely subsided,
stroking the surrounding skin often revived it. Pin pricks in this
surrounding "itchy skin" zone were dulled. With the passage of
time (30 to 60 minutes) after a long-lasting and intense itch,
hyperalgesia was noted to extend 5 to 10 cm. proximally and 3 to
6 cm. distally. Such hyperalgesia after an intense itch sometimes
persisted for several hours.

OBSERVATION 2. DEMONSTRATION THAT THE SKIN ABOUT A SITE
OF NOXIOUS STIMULATION IS "ITCHY" UNTIL THE DEVELOPMENT
OF INTENSE SECONDARY HYPERALGESIA

In twelve experiments on three subjects a small fold of skin on
the volar surface of the forearm was painfully pinched by forceps for two to eight minutes. The following description of the
observations in an experiment on one subject is characteristic of
all this series (fig. 79). Pin pricks in a 1 cm. wide zone surrounding
the pinch during the first fifteen seconds intensified the pain of
the pinch and there was *hyper*algesia immediately surrounding
the pinch. Outside this zone stroking with the finger induced an
itchy sensation which was indistinguishable from intense tickle.
In the latter area itch was readily induced by cowhage. In the
fifth, sixth, and seventh minutes when pain was no longer experienced in the area of the pinch, rubbing the adjacent area
with a finger or a blunt tongue depressor evoked a sensation of
itching in the skin as well as at the point of the pinch.

The pinch was maintained for seven minutes, when the "itchy" area was found to extend 4 cm. distally and 10 cm. proximally from the injury. In five to ten minutes after removal of the forceps marked secondary *hyper*algesia completely filled the zone which had been "itchy". Cowhage applied to this hyperalgesic skin induced no itch, nor was the area "itchy" in response to stroking.

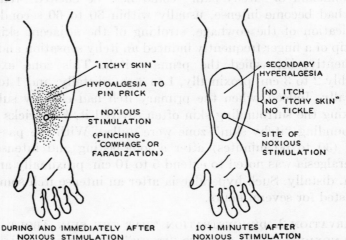

DURING AND IMMEDIATELY AFTER   10 + MINUTES AFTER
NOXIOUS STIMULATION   NOXIOUS STIMULATION

FIG. 79. SENSORY PHENOMENA IN THE SKIN, ASSOCIATED WITH NOXIOUS STIMULATION

COMMENT

The observations of the last two experiments correspond to those of Observation 5, in that skin in which intense secondary hyperalgesia existed was not "itchy" to stroking nor could itching be induced in it by cowhage. Neither was tickle elicited in the zone of secondary hyperalgesia. In short, although itchiness and secondary hyperalgesia are associated phenomena, they may not occur in the same area at the same time.

OBSERVATION 3. DEMONSTRATION OF THE OCCURRENCE OF BOTH "ITCHY SKIN" AND ITCHING ASSOCIATED WITH SKIN INJURY

Goldscheider's experiment was repeated in a series of 20 experiments on three subjects. The web between two fingers was tightly pinched with fine forceps. Within half a minute not only could "itchy skin" be demonstrated on stroking the palm and back of the hand, but itch also occurred in the palm of the hand spontaneously.

Similarly, pinching a web between the toes for less than two minutes gave rise to spontaneous itching and "itchy skin" in the sole of the foot, especially on the underside of the great toe and the ball of the foot. In one of the subjects, the itching induced by such slight injury between the toes continued for more than an hour.

In one subject itching in and around an insect bite on the medial aspect of the left thigh, about eight inches above the knee, persisted for three days. On the third day a zone of "itchy skin" was found to extend for 5 to 6 cm. around the reddened bite, which was itself spontaneously itching, and hyperalgesic to pin prick. In the zone of "itchy skin" a few pin pricks abolished the itching from the bite for 30 to 60 seconds.

Similar observations were made in a second subject who had "itchy skin" on the top of the left foot associated with a slight abrasion of the skin.

OBSERVATION 4. DEMONSTRATION OF THE SPREAD OF ITCHING FROM A PRIMARY FOCUS OF ITCHING

In a series of four experiments on two subjects cowhage was placed on an area of skin approximately 1 cm. in diameter on the volar surface of the wrist at the junction between the hand and the arm. Accompanying the intense itch elicited on this site not only was the itchiness in response to stroking of adjacent skin marked, but spontaneous itching which spread into the thenar and hypothenar eminences and into the palm of the hand occurred.

COMMENT

Goldscheider reported that painfully pinching the skin led to the development of hyperalgesia in the surrounding area and he inferred that "itchy skin" was related to hyperalgesia. The present findings are in agreement with his observations except that itch is not induced in a zone of intense secondary *hyper*algesia.

This is evidence of fundamental similarities between "spontaneous itching" which follows the application of cowhage or histamine, and that which can be elicited by stroking in skin adjacent to a source of noxious stimulation.

OBSERVATION 5. DEMONSTRATION OF THE RELATION OF "ITCHY SKIN" AND PAIN, AND OF THE OCCURRENCE OF "ITCHY SKIN" IN THE ABSENCE OF TOUCH SENSATION

In three subjects a blood pressure cuff was wrapped around the upper arm, inflated to 200 mm. Hg, and kept at this pressure for the duration of the experiment. At the end of eight to fifteen minutes drawing the end of a tongue depressor across the palmar skin elicited an intense burning itch, and stroking with a finger also elicited tickle or itch. At the end of 20 minutes in all three subjects the sensation of touch in response to laying the flat side of the tongue depressor on the wrist was gone. Itch powder was then applied and within two minutes elicited a burning itch. Stroking the skin both proximal and distal to the cowhage was felt as "itchy" and also intensified the itch from the cowhage. The zone in which "itchy skin" could be detected was well demarcated for a distance of 8 to 10 cm. proximal to the itch spot, and throughout the palm to the tips of the fingers. In the distal zone of "itchy skin" no touch sensation could be detected.

COMMENT

Bickford reported that the perception of "itchy skin" failed at a stage of asphyxia at which both touch and pain sensibility were still present. This forced him to postulate that special peripheral nerves transmitted the sensation. The observations described above, however, are evidence that "itchy skin" can occur in the absence of touch as long as pain is preserved. They indicate that both itch and "itchy skin" occur independently of touch sensation, as long as some fibers are still conducting pain impulses. Bickford perhaps failed to make this observation because he used intracutaneous histamine puncture to produce spontaneous itching and "itchy skin". In our experience the latter was less intense and more difficult to detect when histamine was used to evoke itch.

Discussion

The "itchy skin" phenomenon is indistinguishable subjectively from tickle. The sensation evoked by light stroking of otherwise unstimulated skin is called "tickle", that evoked by light stroking of skin in the neighborhood of a source of itching has been called "itchy". The two are otherwise alike, and both provoke a desire to scratch. "Itchy skin" is like itch and tickle in that it could not be elicited in skin manifesting intense secondary hyperalgesia. Bickford observed that if it was impossible to elicit "itchy skin" in the presence of some nervous system disease or of experimental procedures, it was also impossible to elicit tickle. He concluded that the development of "itchy skin" depended on axon-reflexes similar to those responsible for the development of the flare around sites of skin injury. Whether or not this is correct, the "itchy" sensation elicited in the area presumably results from a kind of activity in internuncial neurons similar to that which is responsible for primary itching.

TICKLE

When a stiff nylon thread is drawn across the skin a peculiar esthetic experience usually ensues, which long outlasts the period of stimulation. This is best demonstrated on the margin of the upper lip. The sensation has two distinct components. The first of these resembles itch and has in common with it an associated urge to rub or scratch the skin. The second consists of an awareness of movement of a light object touching the skin. In some parts of the body, e.g., the finger pads and the extensor surface of the elbow, only the second component is prominent, whereas at the lip margin the itching component is conspicuous. It is for the itching component of the sensation evolved by a moving stimulus that the term "tickle" has been reserved in this study.

In the following experiments the relation of tickle, itch, "itchy skin", and pain were further investigated.

OBSERVATION 1. DEMONSTRATION THAT TICKLE AND ITCH DIFFER
ONLY IN THAT TICKLE HAS THE ADDITIONAL ELEMENT OF MOVE-
MENT

A fine nylon thread was touched to the skin of the forehead in
one spot. Ten subjects so tested reported that the sensation elicited was itch, and was accompanied by the urge to rub or scratch.
When the thread was lightly *drawn across* the skin, some of the
subjects changed their report of the sensation to tickle, but stated
that the only change in the quality of the experience was the
additional perception of movement of the thread, although the
desire to rub or scratch was intensified.

In six subjects, the difference between touch and tickle or itch
was clearly demonstrated by touching first the pad of one finger
and then the forehead. A light touch by the finger of the experimenter on the finger pad of the subject elicited only touch, but
on the forehead itch or tickle was elicited, with an invariable
accompaniment of a desire to rub or scratch the stimulated skin.

COMMENT

These observations make it clear that the conception of tickle
in everyday experience conforms exactly to the definition given
above, i.e., tickle is the itching component of the sensation evoked
by a light moving stimulus on the skin.

OBSERVATION 2. DEMONSTRATION THAT TICKLE IS OBLITERATED BY
STIMULATION OF PAIN ENDINGS

The forehead was rubbed briskly so that a slight afterpain was
experienced, and again tested by lightly drawing the nylon thread
across the skin. Now the sensation elicited was purely that of
touch without the unpleasant component arousing the urge to
rub or scratch. Similarly, immediately after the forehead was
pricked vigorously with a pin, for at least as long as the faint
afterpain of the pricking persisted the sensation elicited by the
thread was again only touch.

COMMENT

Although drawing a wisp of cotton across the skin in most skin
areas is used as a bedside testing procedure to indicate perception

of light touch, it is also used on the upper lip, a very "ticklish" area, to test for the integrity of fiber systems subserving pain in the skin areas supplied by the fifth cranial nerve.

It is apparent that the drawing of a thread or wisp of cotton across the skin may under varying conditions give rise to qualitatively distinct sensations. As stated above, it has seemed profitable to reserve the word "tickle" for that part of the sensation thus elicited which resembles itch and arouses the desire to rub or scratch. The effect of painful stimuli in abolishing or preventing tickle is apparently analogous to the phenomenon of abolishing itch by pin prick.

OBSERVATION 3. DEMONSTRATION OF THE ABSENCE OF TICKLE IN A ZONE OF SECONDARY HYPERALGESIA

In two subjects zones of secondary hyperalgesia were defined on the volar surfaces of the forearms after faradic stimulation of a superficial cutaneous sensory nerve. When the intense hyperalgesia was fully developed a nylon thread drawn lightly across the area elicited a sensation of touch; when the thread was applied with slightly greater force, touch commingled with pain was elicited, but the sensation was definitely not tickle. The same thread elicited tickle in control areas on the opposite arm, and in areas of skin on the same arm outside the area of secondary hyperalgesia. In these two subjects the secondary hyperalgesia was abolished by pin prick within its borders. Immediately thereafter, tickle could again be elicited.

COMMENT

Tickle, like itch, is inhibited by the presence of marked secondary hyperalgesia of the skin; a stimulus clearly eliciting tickle in control skin, elicits in hyperalgesic skin either a sensation of touch without the special quality of tickle or itch, or of touch commingled with pain. Areas of intense secondary hyperalgesia have thus been demonstrated to be "anti-ticklish" as well as "anti-pruritic".

OBSERVATION 4. DEMONSTRATION OF THE OCCURRENCE OF TICKLE
IN THE ABSENCE OF TOUCH SENSATION

In three subjects a blood pressure cuff was inflated about the
upper arm at a pressure of 200 mm. Hg. About 20 minutes later
the light touch of a flat tongue depressor could not be perceived
on the back and side of the forefinger. At this time, however, a
stiff nylon thread drawn across this area elicited a distinct tickle
which merged into an itching sensation.

COMMENT

It has been previously noted that during asphyxia of an arm
touch sensation disappears at a time when pain can still be elicited.
This experiment demonstrates that tickle, like itch, is independent
of touch, and may indeed also be carried over the afferent fibers
which mediate pain.

Discussion

No general agreement on the relation of the sensation of tickle
to touch, pain, and itch has previously been reached. Discussion
has focused upon whether tickle was essentially different from
itch, and whether the mediation of tickle sensation was to be
assigned to touch or pain receptors.

With regard to the first question, Murray (324) reported that
her subjects found that itch differed from tickle only in being
"more persistent, painful and intolerable". Török (437), on the
other hand, asked patients with pruritus to compare their spontaneous itching with the sensation elicited by drawing a wisp of
cotton across the skin. From these comparisons he concluded that
itch and tickle were different sensations which could be distinguished by his subject. It should be noted, however, that motion
adds an element to the sensation which makes it different from
itching, and probably accounts for the patient's statements that
they could distinguish between the two. It is also important that
under certain circumstances, as discussed above, the same moving
stimulus provokes a sensation which induces no desire to scratch,
consists entirely of touch, and is not ordinarily called tickle by
the subject experiencing it. It is conceivable that difficulties of

communication with patients might lead to a report of "tickle" for this sensation also.

Thöle also separated itch and tickle as regards the structures involved, concluding that tickle was related to stimulation of touch receptors. He failed to make the observation that tickle can be elicited in areas of skin in which touch is no longer present, nor did he differentiate between true tickle and a sensation of moving touch in areas where pain could not be elicited.

Bishop (39, 37, 38) suggested that tickle sensation was a function of touch rather than pain receptors. He found that weak and rapid electrical stimulation of touch endings failed completely to elicit tickle but this he attributed to the lack of movement of the stimulus. He argued that tickle can be elicited by a contact with the skin so light that it is clear that the receptors concerned must have a very low threshold, and that, therefore, participation of pain receptors is out of the question. In his own observations on cutaneous sensation, however, he found that in most areas of skin, except notably on the balls of the finger, prick has a *lower* threshold than touch. Furthermore, in reviewing von Frey's observations, Bishop calls attention to the fact that in using mechanical stimulators of small diameter, thresholds for touch and pain closely approximate each other. Also, Hardy, Wolff and Goodell, testing for touch threshold with von Frey hairs in hyperalgesic and control areas of skin, found that the thresholds for touch and for pain were not grossly different. Bishop's second piece of evidence linking tickle with touch was that tickle, like touch, "adapts" to continued stimulation. However, continuous noxious stimulation also ceases to produce pain, as can be readily demonstrated by holding a pin point steadily against the skin for several seconds, or by pinching a fold of skin with forceps.

Bickford observed that tickle, "itchy skin", itch, and pain were all absent in patients with anterolateral tract lesions, even though touch sensation remained intact.

Pritchard (348) considered that tickle, itch and pain all lay on the same continuum of sensation, and that tickle, like itch, was a variety of pain. He nevertheless concluded that tickle and pain involved different peripheral pathways. He failed to present evidence that tickle could be elicited in the complete absence of pain. On the other hand, Sarnoff and Arrowood (378) reported that tickle sensation elicited "by scratching the soles of the feet" persisted in some of their patients in the absence of pain from pin prick during spinal block with procaine. However, the intensity of their scratch stimulus was not described, and it is not clear that it elicited true tickle, especially since there was no description of the qualities of the sensation experienced. It is also possible that their observations may be related to Thöle's findings.

Zotterman (504) on the basis of his studies of axon potentials in cat nerves concluded that tickle and itching sensations are mediated by the fibers which are responsible for the pain elicited by pin prick. He also observed that tickle could not be elicited in patients with analgesia of the face following trigeminal tractotomy, although touch sensation was intact.

On the basis of the observations reported here it is inferred that the sensation called "tickle" is mediated by the same neural fibers as are involved in itch and pain. This conclusion is based on the experiments involving differential anesthetization, for tickle could be elicited when touch sensitivity was absent and pain sensitivity retained, thus exactly paralleling cowhage-induced itching in like circumstances. Furthermore, tickle is inhibited in an area of secondary hyperalgesia, as is itch; and it is obliterated in skin to which a painful pricking or rubbing has been applied, just as itch is obliterated by pricking in adjacent areas of skin. It is concluded, therefore, that the pathways concerned in the perception of tickle are those for pain, and that touch mechanisms do not participate, except to add something which is essentially extraneous (166).

Chapter X
REACTIONS TO NOXIOUS STIMULATION

In the preceding chapters attention has been focussed upon the reports of pain sensation by individuals who were intent upon making discriminations in respect to intensity, quality, duration, and extension of the sensation. In such individuals the predictability of pain sensation as regards its threshold has been expressed quantitatively by measurements of intensity and duration of stimulus, of skin temperature, and of size of area stimulated. The close relationship between intensity of pain sensation and intensity of stimulus applied was demonstrated, and the relation of noxious stimulation to the rate of tissue damage was noted. Yet, despite the predictability of these features as regards the especially alerted individual, precise relationships between suffering and the intensity of noxious stimulation are not immediately apparent in the patient. Thus, many suffering individuals seem at first glance to have variable rather than uniform sensitivity to noxious stimulation, i.e., to have "pain" modifiable by factors which do not influence the pain threshold in normal subjects, such as fatigue or the emotional state. So striking is the apparent contradiction between the observations of "pain" in the subject trained in the analysis of sensation and in the patient enduring a pain associated with disease or injury, that some observers prefer to term the latter pain "pathologic" as distinguished from "experimental" pain (99, 236). However, this contradiction is resolved in the realization that for the trained subject the pain sensation can be isolated as an entity to be focussed upon for special analysis. On the other hand, the "pain experience" of the patient is a complex phenomenon involving such a variety of features that concentration on the actual pain sensation is more difficult. Pain sensation is but a part of the total pain experience, and, indeed, may not even be the major feature. To analyze such an experience and to evaluate the contribution of pain sensation thereto, it is desirable to define the pain experience broadly as those reactions involving consciousness which have been observed to be highly correlated with noxious stimulation and pain. Pain sensation is thus the particular response to noxious *stimuli* identified by the report of pain by the individual.

Some responses to noxious stimulation, although themselves of a reflex nature and not dependent upon consciousness, may give rise to pain and associated sensations, either by augmenting the initial noxious stimulation or by establishing additional sources of noxious stimulation. So important is the relation of these reactions to the phenomenology of pain that they are given special attention in the present chapter.

A second group of reactions, involving consciousness and observed in persons reporting pain, are less predictable and are more easily affected by suggestion, analgesic agents, fatigue and by individual and cultural attitudes. These reactions, which include such feeling states as anxiety and hostility and associated adaptive and protective behavior patterns, are discussed in the next chapter and are denoted as reactions to pain. Pain sensation, and the associated feeling states elicited by the reactions to noxious stimulation and pain, taken together, make up the pain experience. A division can be made of the levels of integration within the neural equipment mediating pain, which corresponds roughly to the observable reactions to noxious stimulation and pain. This is shown in diagram A.

Obviously, the above is a simplified scheme of the relationship of noxious stimulation to the various structures and functions involved. However, evidence from neuroanatomy and neurophysiology justifies such a concept of integration within the central nervous system for the impulses arising from the noxious stimulation. Thus, responses of the type indicated in the scheme can be elicited in animals suitably prepared by eliminating successively the cephalad portions of the fore-brain, the mid-brain, the hind-brain, and by spinal cord section. Observations indicate similar reaction patterns for man despite the increased encephalization of function as compared to that in laboratory animals. It should not be inferred that in the intact human, levels of integration can be neatly separated one from the other. Besides, only under grossly pathological circumstances, such as cord section, does one find striking justification for such a functional separation. Nevertheless, the scheme serves as a framework within which the responses to noxious stimulation can be analyzed.

It is from such a point of view that the topic of these reactions is presented in this and the following chapter. In the present chapter are considered the data available as to the influence of the interactions of the local effects with those at the segmental levels of integration upon pain sensation; and in the chapter following,

Diagram A

Noxious stimulation		
	1. Local reaction at the site of stimulation	Inflammatory reaction (axon reflex), local excitatory states
	2. Reactions at the segmental levels of integration, including neural structures up to the mesencephalon	Skeletal muscle, smooth muscle, and glandular reactions, i.e., patterns exhibiting automatic withdrawal, blushing, sweating, bladder and bowel emptying, etc.
	3. a) Reactions at the suprasegmental levels, including mesencephalon, basal ganglia, hypothalamus, thalamus, and parts of the cerebral cortex	More highly integrated but still automatic protective and adaptive patterns, including respiratory and cardiovascular reactions, and "quasi-purposive" movements
	b) Reactions at the highest integrative levels involving the cerebral cortex	The phenomenology of pain sensation and complex reactions at various levels of consciousness, including feeling and emotional states

the available information as regards the interactions at the highest integrative level is discussed.

LOCAL REACTIONS AT THE SITE OF NOXIOUS STIMULATION

Of the varied tissue reactions to injurious influences none has been specifically assigned to the production of pain. That is, all aspects of tissue injury and inflammation may be associated with pain, but the precise connection between any aspect of these conditions and pain has not been extensively explored. However, the identification of 45°C. as the critical temperature for the pain threshold in the skin, the temperature at which skin injury begins, now makes it possible to infer a causal link between the processes of tissue injury and those causing excitation of the nerve fibers mediating pain. Even though pain and tissue injury have the same threshold temperature, they behave differently as regards temperatures above 45°C. Thus, pain intensity from thermal stimulation increases with the temperature of the skin but does not increase with the time the skin is maintained at an elevated temperature. Tissue damage from heat, on the other hand, increases both with the degree of elevation of skin temperature and the duration of the state of increased skin temperature. As a consequence of this difference, a second or third degree burn can be produced, with pain intensity not exceeding threshold, by warming the skin to 44° to 45°C. and keeping it at that temperature for five or six hours (316). Conversely, six-"dol" pain may be maintained a few seconds without readily perceptible damage to epidermal tissues. Thus, the existence of processes of repair as well as of injury must be considered to exist, the latter becoming relatively greater as the temperature is increased. Henriques (209) has pointed out that the mechanism of this destructive process implicates alteration in cellular proteins. He based this conclusion on two striking similarities between the phenomena of thermal inactivation of proteins and those of skin injury by heat. Both of these have: 1) the same activation (i.e., threshold) energies near 150 kilogram calories per mol, (no other known cellular reactions have even a third as high an activation energy); and 2) the same free energy changes (ca. 20 kilogram calories per mol). The above evidence is sufficiently strong to warrant the inference that tissue damage from heat involves in large part protein inactivation.

Thus, pain may be considered as indicating the beginning of protein inactivation of some sort which, if continued, results in irreversible damage to and death of the cell. As thermal pain depends only upon the temperature attained by the cells of the skin and not upon how long the temperature is maintained, as does the amount of tissue injury produced, it is postulated that the stimulation of the pain fibers is related to the *rate* rather than the amount of protein inactivation. This thesis can be deduced from the equation of protein inactivation rates which shows this rate to depend upon temperature (149), and which is as follows:

$$r = Pe^{-\frac{\Delta E}{RT}}$$

in which r = rate of inactivation (mols per second)

$\quad$ P = constant

$\quad \Delta E$ = threshold energy = 150,000 calories per mol

$\quad$ T = absolute temperature

$\quad$ R = universal gas constant (roughly 2 calories per mol)

Putting into this equation the constants obtained experimentally by Hendriques, the degree of tissue damage to the skin can be related to its temperature and the time of exposure to the heat. Thus:

$$r = \frac{\Omega}{t} = 3.1 \times 10^{98} e^{-\frac{75,000}{T_0 + 273}}$$

in which Ω = amount of protein inactivation

$\quad T_0$ = temperature (°C.) of the basal skin layer, roughly 0.08 mm. below the skin surface, and

$\quad$ t = time in seconds.

Ω has the arbitrary value of 1 when cellular death occurs.

From the data contained in Chapters IV and VII concerning pain threshold and pain intensity as related to thermal radiation, it is possible to calculate the temperature of the basal layer of the skin of the forehead when pain of various intensities is induced by a three-second exposure to thermal radiation. The results of the calculation of the skin temperature are shown in figure 80 showing the temperature level at which pains from threshold to $10\frac{1}{2}$ "dols" intensity are evoked. A substitution of these data into the formula shows that at $10\frac{1}{2}$ "dols" the rate of protein inactivation is more than 3,000,000 times as great as that at threshold. Sustained pain of high intensity is not compatible with tissue integrity. These relationships are contained in table 16 which gives the calculated values for pain intensity, skin temperature at the end of a three-second exposure, the rate of protein inactivation, and the time required to produce tissue injury if the temperature of the skin and pain intensity were maintained at this level.

If the above relationships be inferred to exist for noxious stimulation in general one sees the biologic importance of pain as indicating progressive tissue damage, but not the amount of damage.

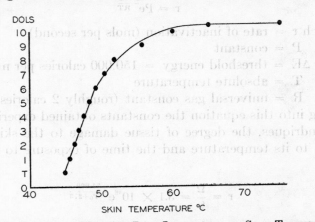

FIG. 80. RELATIONSHIP BETWEEN PAIN INTENSITY AND SKIN TEMPERATURE

TABLE 16

Relation of pain sensitivity to skin temperature and tissue alteration

PAIN INTENSITY *"Dols"*	SKIN TEMPERATURE °C.	PROTEIN INACTIVATION RATE × 10^{-4}
0	44.0	0.56
T	45.0	1.2
1	45.5	
2	46.0	2.4
3	46.7	4.2
4	47.5	8.2
5	48.2	12
6	49.2	24
7	50.5	64
8	52.0	176
9	56.0	2900
10	60.0	42000
10½	67	4.7×10^{6}

Pain is a warning that tissue injury is in progress rather than a warning of potential or existing tissue damage. Thus, extensive wounds may be painless, whereas slight wounds may be extremely painful due to a progressive increase in tissue damage. The latter condition is a familiar one to those who have experienced the intense pain that can arise from a tooth. As an example of the former, Beecher (25) gives data on 215 severely wounded men at a front-line hospital in the European theater during World War II. These men were asked to rate their pains to serve as a guide to the administration of proper amounts of analgesics. In spite of extensive peripheral soft tissue injury, penetrating wounds of the head, chest, or abdomen, one-half of these badly wounded men reported "no pain".

REACTIONS TO NOXIOUS STIMULATION AT THE SEGMENTAL LEVEL

Pain and Reaction Threshold

In concept, the relation of tissue injury to noxious stimulation is quite broad, and some response to the damaging of tissue might be expected of all species. In conscious man the response is characterized by the sensation of pain. In animals and unconscious man certain reflex responses have been used as indicating the presence of noxious stimulation. The flexor reflex in spinal man and dog, the tail flick of the rat, and the reflex contraction of the musculus cutaneous maximus of the guinea pig are examples. The inference that such responses denote noxious stimulation has been drawn from the reasonable assumption that withdrawal is the appropriate response to noxious stimulus (366). With better understanding available as regards the nature of the noxious thermal stimulus it becomes possible to test the hypothesis that noxious stimulation is the common factor evoking pain and withdrawal reactions. One test of this hypothesis is that of determining the thresholds of pain and reflex reaction to ascertain whether or not they are the same.

METHOD

Human pain thresholds were measured for various durations of stimulus in the manner described in Chapter III. The threshold of the flexor reflex was measured in a paraplegic subject (section T9–T10) by observing the minimal intensities of radiation evoking a flexor response when the dorsum of the foot was exposed for varying lengths of time to thermal radiation. The minimal intensity of radiation evoking a tail flick (rats), and the contraction of the musculus cutaneous maximus (guinea pigs) were measured when the tail or back of the animal was stimulated for varying durations. All test areas were blackened with India ink and skin temperatures were measured prior to making each threshold measurement.

RESULTS

Thresholds for pain and reaction are plotted in the form of intensity-duration curves and are shown in figure 81. It is seen that there is no significant difference between the pain threshold and reaction threshold stimulus intensities at any exposure duration. The closeness of the agreement in the various sets of data is even more convincing when the calculation is made of the average temperature to which the skin was raised for all exposure times. These data are contained in table 17.

The thresholds of pain perception and reaction to noxious stimulation, though often identical, are not necessarily so. Reaction thresholds may vary with changes in the state of central excitation without a concurrent change in pain threshold (29a, 172a).

Sherrington's (400) studies of the flexor reflex afford conclusive evidence that the effects of noxious stimulation from adjacent body areas are summated at the segmental level both spatially and temporally. In brief, subthreshold stimuli will evoke the scratch reflex when two areas within the same segment are stimulated simultaneously or when the same area is repeatedly stimulated. Also, the magnitude of the reflex contraction is affected by these properties. Facilitation and occlusion are characteristic of these responses. Thus, the responses to noxious stimulation may be both summative and non-summative, i.e., there is spatial summation as regards some motor responses, but there is no spatial summation for pain sensation; temporal summation is characteristic for both. While applying specifically to certain skeletal muscle responses, glandular and smooth muscle responses may also be summated (235). The biological significance of such an arrangement may be that the mobilization for adaptive-protective reac-

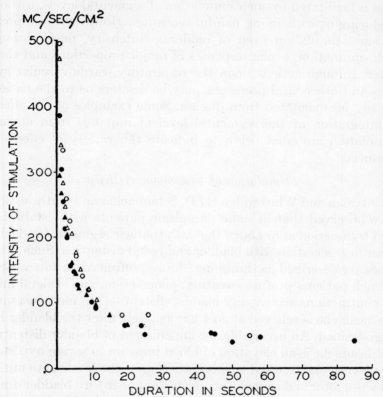

FIG. 81. THE STRENGTH-DURATION CURVE FOR PAIN THRESHOLD IN MAN AND
REACTION THRESHOLDS IN SEVERAL SPECIES

●, pain threshold (human); ○, reaction threshold (human); △, reaction
threshold (rat); ▲, reaction threshold (guinea pig).

TABLE 17
Comparison of pricking pain and reaction thresholds

	Ave. skin temperature
Human pain threshold	44.3 ±0.80°C.
Human flexion threshold	44.7 ±0.65°C.
Guinea pig flexion threshold	44.7 ±0.51°C.
Rat tail-flick threshold	44.6 ±0.75°C.

tions is facilitated by such summation at segmental levels, without producing overwhelming painful sensation. However, widespread noxious stimulation even of moderate intensity, may, through such summation, evoke responses of major proportions and these latter, through actions upon the respiratory, cardiovascular systems and other vital processes, may be deleterious to the patient already incapacitated from disease. Some examples of the effects of integration at the segmental level of impulses from noxious stimulation are cited below to indicate the variety of effects so produced.

Stimulation of Vasomotor Activity

Guttman and Whitteridge (172), Schumacher and Guthrie (389) have observed that in some paraplegic patients with established cord transection at or above the sixth thoracic segment, headaches occur in association with bladder and rectal distention. Such headaches are described as throbbing, diffuse, bifrontal, or bitemporal. In such patients profuse sweating, piloerection, and skeletal muscle contractions accompany bladder distention. In most instances the headache is relieved almost immediately after the bladder has been drained. An invariable accompaniment of bladder distention and headache is an elevation of blood pressure to severe hypertensive levels, and marked vasoconstriction of the lower extremities. All vasomotor and sudomotor effects disappear with bladder drainage. It is likely that such pain in the head results from dilatation of cranial vessels in response to the elevated blood pressure, secondary to reflex vasoconstriction. Evidence that the headache is so caused is that it is promptly terminated a) by direct pressure on the carotid artery; b) by increasing the intracranial pressure and thus preventing distention of intracranial vessels; and c) by lowering the blood pressure, while still maintaining bladder distention.

The point that is relevant to this discussion and is to be emphasized is that the noxious stimulation of the bladder of a paraplegic individual is not perceived as pain but gives rise to a variety of other reflex effects, especially elevation of blood pressure, sweating, and skeletal muscle contractions, and only incidentally to headache (151b, 389).

Secondary Hyperalgesia

A reaction to noxious stimulation at the segmental level was discussed in Chapter IX in which it was shown that it is extremely doubtful that there is liberated in the skin of the hyperalgesic area a chemical agent which lowers the pain threshold (274). Repeated observations of patients with surface hyperalgesia associated with deep injury and pain reveal no significant lowering of the threshold of either pricking or burning pain. On the other hand, minimal pricking and burning pain, when they are perceived, are experienced as more intense and seem to be of longer duration. In other words, there is apparently an intensification of the pain. It appears more likely that such intensification results from a change *within* the nervous system (417, 318). It was suggested in the last chapter that the central excitatory states initiated and sustained by the barrage of impulses from noxious stimulation of the same or adjacent segments increase the level of excitability so as to make pain stimulated at the usual pain threshold level seem more intense and persistent (186).

Muscle Contraction and Tenderness

It is a common observation that the effects of deep noxious stimulation and pain are accompanied by contraction of adjacent and sometimes even of distant skeletal muscles (274, 298, 403). The head is a suitable place for the demonstration of such muscle rigidity and tenderness in association with visceral pain (404). When pain-sensitive structures of the head are stimulated, muscles in that region of the head contract. If this stimulus is short-lived, muscle effects are also brief. If, on the other hand, the noxious stimulation from deep structures is intense or persists, local sustained contraction of adjacent muscles takes place and such effects may spread so as to involve more distant regions. Such sustained contraction may, in turn, induce pain and tenderness of the muscles involved.

Recent experimental evidence (370) permits a more precise statement as to the degree and nature of such pain of muscular origin. Pain arising from structures in the head caused contractions especially of the frontal, masseter, and temporal muscles, greatly accentuated winking, and ultimately involved the occipital

and cervical muscles. There was also vasoconstriction and ischemia in the area of muscle contraction. Lacrimation, nasal congestion, edema of the eyelids, reddening of the conjunctiva, photophobia, sweating, nausea, and vomiting were common. Similar
contraction effects followed pain due to the introduction of a
foreign body into the conjunctival sac or onto the cornea (109).
They also followed diplopia experimentally induced through the
use of lenses. In patients with long-standing paranasal disease, too,
sustained painful contraction of the head and neck muscles was
observed (403). Muscle pain and tenderness resulted from painful
distention and faradic stimulation of the ureter (298). Occasionally, after a sustained distention of the ureter, muscle contraction
effects increased to such a degree as to become the major factor
in the individual's discomfort for as long as 24 hours after cessation of the stimulation. Thus, it is apparent that pain, whether
emanating from somatic or visceral structures, gave rise to the
same type of muscle contraction effects, a conclusion originally
formulated by Lewis from his experience with pain arising in abdominal structures (274).

Lewis and Kellgren (280) demonstrated the non-specificity of
such muscle reactions and also that muscles themselves may become the source of pain. Furthermore, it has been shown that the
pain due to sustained contraction of skeletal muscle is ended by
disrupting the mechanism of noxious stimulation in the muscle by
infiltration of procaine into the latter (403).

Though muscle tenderness is often a sequel of prolonged muscle
contraction, coupled, perhaps, with ischemia (404, 281), not all
subcutaneous or muscle tenderness can be explained on this basis.
The experiments of Robertson, Goodell and Wolff (370) demonstrated another mechanism of deep tenderness. After inducing
headache, deep tenderness, surface hyperalgesia, and hyperesthesia in the temporal region of the head by prolonged stimulation of
a tooth, procaine was infiltrated intracutaneously at the site of
most intense temporal headache, tenderness, and surface hyperalgesia. Within a few seconds after the injection there was analgesia of the skin and the subject reported that the headache was
reduced in intensity. The temporal muscle beneath the analgesic
skin remained tender to palpation. When procaine was injected

into the temporal muscle as well as intracutaneously, pain still persisted although local tenderness was eliminated. Yet, when the tissue about the noxiously stimulated tooth was infiltrated with procaine, there was complete elimination of all pain. It was suggested, therefore, that such tenderness may sometimes result from the central spread of hyperexcitatory effects induced by sustained noxious stimulation.

Localization and spread of deep pain were also studied by stimulation of the nasal and paranasal structures (296). When the mucosa about the ostium of the maxillary sinus was stimulated either mechanically or by faradic current there resulted at first a localized painful sensation in the nose. When stimulation was continued, the subject experienced pain which spread on the same side over a portion of the nose and cheek, along the zygoma, into the temporal region, and into the upper teeth. In short, the pain spread from the site of stimulation to sites innervated by the same division of the trigeminal nerve. When stimulation of the turbinates by epinephrine packs was continued for ten minutes the area of pain spread over most of the area of distribution of the second division of the nerve and ultimately involved adjacent portions supplied by the third and first divisions. The pain in this more widespread area had an aching quality which became more intense than the pain from the nose.

The aching sensation was associated with blushing of the skin over the cheek, reddening of the conjunctiva, lacrimation, and photophobia. Hence, although pain may be localized initially, and correctly identified as to the site of stimulation, subsequently it may be experienced far from the site of stimulation. Noxious stimulation of widely separate structures of the nasal and paranasal region caused an identical distribution of pain in remote portions of the face or head. Depending upon the intensity and duration of stimulation the pain may remain localized within the same nerve division or cord segment, or it may spread so that it seems to emanate from peripheral structures innervated by adjacent divisions or from neighboring segments.

The localization and spread observed in pain resulting from stimulation of nasal and paranasal structures are similar to those of pain from visceral structures. For instance, pain elicited by noxious stimulation of the gastric mucosa is experienced initially as coming from the stomach, but subsequently it may seem to emanate from other structures innervated from the same and adjacent cord segments. The latter sensations may dominate so that the pain from the site of initial stimulation becomes less apparent.

McLellan and Goodell (298) have shown that briefly stimulating the mucosa of the ureter with a low intensity faradic current elicits prompt and severe pain along the medial border of the rectus abdominis muscle. Spreading of pain from a limited focus to other areas supplied from the same cord segment, and ultimately into its sites innervated from adjacent segments, was also experienced when the ureter was stimulated at various levels proximal to the bladder orifice. When such stimulation was intense or prolonged the pain spread so as to include other parts belonging to the same segment, starting on the ventral abdominal wall and ultimately spreading to the dorsal. However, the effects of muscle contraction soon masked the initial pain induced by stimulation of the ureter to such an extent that the entire flank became tender. Apparently the muscle contraction itself became the dominant source of noxious impulses resulting in pain.

Similar observations were made by Travell, Berry and Bigelow (439, 440) who mapped the distribution of this referred pain from noxious stimulation of various muscles. They observed that referred pain was experienced either within the reference area belonging to one segment, or within different zones of one segment, or in fragments of several segments without entirely including any one segmental area.

With angina of effort accompanying coronary artery occlusion, pain at first seems to emanate from one or more of the anterior portions of the first four or five thoracic segments and then to spread cephalad as if arising within the structures supplied by the lower, and then also by the upper, cervical segments. Ultimately, it may seem to emanate from the lower jaw and teeth. The spreading of pain until it includes the lower teeth involves the cervical dorsal horn and the spinal nucleus of the trigeminal nerve, these structures being contiguous in the upper cervical cord.

To further the study of mechanisms involved in the distribution of referred pain, the commonly experienced "ice cream" headache was analyzed in a subject in whom it was possible to examine separate parts of the esophagus, stomach, and mouth (250, 489). It was found that frontal headache developed when ice was applied to the roof of the mouth but not when a considerable amount of ice was put into the stomach through a stoma, nor when it was held for several minutes in the esophagus. Thus, noxious stimulation of structures supplied by the maxillary division of the fifth cranial nerve caused pain to be experienced in structures supplied by the first division of the nerve. Also, but less constantly, pain was experienced in and behind the ear when ice was applied to the region of the lateral pharyngeal recess, and to the posterior wall of the pharynx. These areas are supplied by the ninth and tenth cranial nerves, possibly with a few fibers from the fifth and seventh.

In certain persons the digits of the hand are particularly suitable for studying the spread of pain from a site of noxious stimulation since here the pain can be recognized in readily separable zones. The "cold pain" induced by immersing one digit for ten minutes in water at 0°C. spreads from the immersed finger to the adjacent sides of the neighboring fingers and even to a part of a finger beyond.

The pattern of spread having been well defined, the fifth finger was completely anesthetized by a digital block with two per cent procaine solution. The infiltration of the paired dorsal and volar digital nerves was extended to encircle the base of the digit and included skin and periosteum. The resultant sensory loss in the finger was complete, with absence of pain, touch, temperature, position, and vibration sense. When the fourth finger was immersed in cold water, the spread of pain to the fifth and third fingers was essentially of the same pattern and of the same intensity as in control experiments in which the sensation of the digit was intact. Repetition of this experiment with procaine block of the third finger and immersion of the second in cold water again revealed no interference with the apparent spread of pain into the anesthetized digit. It is inferred that the spread of pain is a central rather than a peripheral phenomenon; and that the spread is not a consequence of afferent impulses from the tissues into which the spread seems to occur (248, 251).

Such segmental spread of the effects of noxious stimulation associated with deep pain would be based solely on anatomical arrangements within the spinal cord or brain stem. Ray and Wolff (354) studied a patient who had a metastatic tumor involving the right hip joint. Slightest movement of the right hip joint caused severe pain in the right buttock and lower leg. This pain was eliminated by section, on the left side only, of the ventrolateral portion of the cord at the first thoracic segment. After operation gross movement of the right hip joint or compression of the right gastrocnemius muscle induced pain which, however, was referred only to the left side of the body. The pain was of low intensity, diffuse, poorly localized, deep, and widespread, and it outlasted the period of stimulation by about half a second. It seemed to arise from the tissues supplied by adjacent segments on the opposite side. On the other hand, noxious stimulation of low intensity or repeated pin pricking on the right side gave no sensation on the left. Also, severe deep pain induced by compressing muscles on the left (normal) lower limb or abdomen was felt on the left side only. It is postulated from these observations that excitation travels along two possible routes from the primary sensory neurons and their collaterals: 1) the primary pathway, by neurons in the cord segments of their entry and in adjacent segments that cross to the opposite side and ascend the cord in the spinothalamic tract; and 2) the pathway demonstrated by this patient, that of internuncial neurons that cross in the posterior commissure to connect with neurons on the opposite side of the cord. The latter cross back again to ascend the cord in the spinothalamic tract on the same side as the entering afferent impulses. Thus it is possible for pain to be experienced on the side opposite to the site of noxious stimulation in such special circumstances as existed for this patient after operation. Furthermore, this observation fits in well with the information already available on the spread of excitation in the spinal cord (144).

The observations of Gellhorn and Thompson (146, 434) may be cited as further evidence of the effects of spread from noxious stimulation on sensory and motor phenomena. They have shown that spinal reflex movements, as well as those resulting from stimulation of the motor areas of the cerebral cortex, are altered during periods of stimulation of either deep or cutaneous tissues. During such periods the effect of stimulation of the motor cortex is either intensified or qualitatively altered so that different movements may be substituted temporarily for those obtained under control conditions. These afferent impulses are not limited in their effects to the same side but may also involve the reactivity of the opposite side. Gellhorn suggested that these phenomena might result from the cortical spread of excitatory effects of the peripheral stimulation although the possibility of their occurring also at the spinal cord level exists.

DEVELOPMENT OF HYPEREXCITABILITY AT SUPRASEGMENTAL LEVELS

A summation effect analogous to the phenomenon of surface hyperalgesia is encountered in the eye. It is a common experience that persons with a cinder in the eye will, on looking into a light, experience the light as momentarily brighter and the cinder as more painful. It is as though a mutual reinforcement of visual sensation and pain had occurred.

The following experiment may make this more evident (489). There was injected into the muscles of the forehead a small amount of hypertonic saline solution. This procedure caused moderately intense pain. The rate of winking was measured repeatedly before and after the injection. It was noticed that during the painful episode this rate multiplied seven to eight times when the eye was exposed to a light, and dropped to zero when the subject was put in a dark room. Also, immediately after the onset of pain the light seemed brighter than during the control period (45), while at the same time the pain due to the salt injection was increased in intensity (109).

A possible explanation of this phenomenon is as follows: the visual impulses entering the colliculi from the retina exert an excitatory influence on the facial nerve nucleus, causing the increase in winking frequency. The spread of pain from the site of noxious stimulation in the muscles of the forehead to other parts of the head results from a spread of excitation to most of the sensory nuclei of the trigeminal nerve nucleus so that the peripheral origin of the pain is no longer precise. Impulses arising from noxious stimulation of the head, after entering and spreading throughout the trigeminal nucleus, exert an additional excitatory influence on the facial nerve motor nucleus so as further to increase the winking frequency (148). The spread of excitation both caudad and cephalad causes the facial, masseter, temporal, and cervical muscles to contract. Additional evidence that the motor effects of this experiment are segmental in origin (mid-brain or hind-brain) was afforded by patients with Argyll-Robertson miotic pupil (indicating mid-brain disease). Such persons had faulty or absent wink responses when a strong light was projected onto the retina. Yet, they also experienced mutual intensification of light and pain.

This mutual intensification of pain and visual sensations must involve association areas in the cerebral cortex. Nervous impulses from stimulation of the retina by light, entirely separate from those which go to the colliculus, enter the lateral geniculate body directly. There, over a synapse, secondary disturbances are conveyed to the cerebral cortex. In the light of the present knowledge of neuroanatomy it is apparent that neither at the brain stem nor at the thalamic level is it possible for neural activities involved in vision to be influenced or modified by those for pain. Such phenomena can take place only at the cortical level (2, 495a).

Intractable pain, especially as represented by phantom limb can be looked upon as an example of facilitation due to central excitatory states at the highest integrative levels. It is well known that most individuals, following amputation, retain for an indefinite period an awareness of the localization of the amputated part in space. The great majority of amputees is troubled but little by this effect and may even lose it after a time. However, a small proportion not only retain vivid kinesthetic impressions but, in addition to this, they have painful sensations such as might be experienced from cramps or when the limb is held for a long period in an awkward or unnatural position. The striking feature of such a state is the minimal amount of noxious stimulation necessary for maintenance or accentuation of the complaint. It may be relevant that these patients, when examined, exhibited evidence of emotional tension and excitement as part of a general maladjustment.

This emotional tension may represent a heightened central excitatory state which combines its effects with those maintained by the centripetal afferent volleys from both noxious and non-noxious stimulation of the stump and thus give rise to the painful phenomena. (See also page 307)

White and Sweet (468) made observations on the effectiveness of cordotomy in fourteen patients with phantom limb phenomena. In thirteen complete elimination of painful phantom limb followed radical ventrolateral cordotomy. Under these circumstances what amounted to section of a quadrant from the ventrolateral portion of the cord eliminated the painful components of the phantom limb phenomena. Although thorough studies were made no defect in sensation other than pain and temperature resulted from this procedure.

However, despite even such complete section and even though there was complete analgesia in the lower extremity involved, pain persisted in one of these fourteen. It may be inferred that an extraordinarily small number of afferent pathways involved in conveying minimal afferent inflow from the site of noxious stimulation is sufficient in certain individuals to maintain a heightened state of central excitation.

This view is further supported by the observations of Cronholm (90). After an extensive review and analysis of the phenomenon he also inferred that "the possibility of eliciting referred sensations assigned to a phantom limb perception via a centripetal volley of impulses in nerves other than those severed can to a large extent be satisfactorily explained in most cases by the hypothesis of a central state of hyperexcitability with a definite, topical arrangement." He further states, "the occurrence of abnormal sensations appears to be determined chiefly by the intensity of the centripetal stream of impulses, especially from the stump, and by the presence of a central state of hyperexcitability. Their localization to a phantom limb perception or to the stump perception appears, on the other hand, to be ultimately determined by the central state of functional organization." Moreover, he calls attention to the observation that abnormal sensations with high intensity are far more frequent when the patient suffered from a painful disease in the limb for some time before amputation.

SUMMARY

In summarizing this chapter the concept of noxious stimulation furnishes a convenient starting point. Stimulation which excites the nerve endings mediating pain sensation is termed noxious, and evidence has been offered to show that noxious stimulation depends upon the rate at which the noxious agent causes damage to tissue in the immediate neighborhood of pain fiber endings. Pain sensation is a sequel to noxious stimulation and the pain threshold is reached when the intensity of stimulation approaches the critical level. Characteristic of this level is that prolonged, constant stimulation at this intensity produces cellular death whereas stimulation at less intensity does not. For a thermal stimulus this critical level is reached when tissue is heated to roughly 44°–45°C. In addition to pain there are many other responses to noxious stimulation. These include local tissue reactions at the site of stimulation, neural, muscular, and glandular activity, and the establishment of states of hyperexcitability within the central nervous system at segmental and suprasegmental levels sometimes exhibited as hyperalgesia. Many of these reactions (viz. reflex muscular contractions and establishment of hyperexcitable states) to noxious stimulation have been shown to have the same threshold as does pain sensation. However, pain intensity is generally not increased by the summation of neural impulses from simultaneous stimulation of different sites. On the other hand, the magnitude of many reactions to noxious stimulation is thus increased. It was suggested that such summation in case of reactions was biologically useful in facilitating mobilization for adaptation and protection.

Prolonged noxious stimulation from the viscera, although not painful in itself, may induce skeletal muscle contraction which may provide a further source of noxious stimulation and pain. The pain so experienced may long outlast and may be anatomically remote from the site of original noxious stimulation (239). In such instances procaine infiltration onto muscle may relieve the contraction and by thus interrupting the pain mechanism it may abolish the pain.

Important among the reactions to prolonged noxious stimulation are those which result in the establishment of states of hyperexcitability within the central nervous system. Such states, maintained by the constant inflow of impulses from low intensity noxious stimulation, make possible the intensification of pain from stimulation of other body regions (secondary hyperalgesia) or

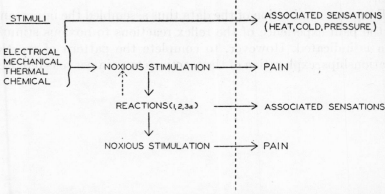

FIG. 82. SCHEME OF THE RELATIONSHIPS OF NOXIOUS STIMULATION AND REACTIONS THERETO, TO PAIN

To the left of the dotted line: reactions not dependent upon consciousness. To the right of the dotted line: responses involving consciousness.

from the same locality (phantom limb, intractable pain) (89, 88, 193). Due possibly to such summative effects the reactions to noxious stimulation may be the source of far more suffering than is the pain from the original sites of stimulation.

A diagram (fig. 82) indicating the patterns of interplay of the reactions to noxious stimulation may serve to clarify the complex. Thus, the chain of events is initiated by the original noxious stimulus, be it electrical, mechanical, thermal, or chemical. This stimulation evokes pain directly with associated sensations such as heat, cold, pressure, etc., and, in addition, gives rise to a host of *reactions* such as were indicated in diagram A at the beginning of the chapter as 1, 2, and 3a. These reactions can serve both to intensify the effects of the original noxious stimulus by producing states of central hyperexcitability exhibiting themselves in part as secondary hyperalgesia. The broken arrow indicates such a relationship. Also, these reactions may result in additional sources of noxious stimulation and pain through intense reflex activity, i.e., smooth and skeletal muscle contraction, vasomotor and glandular effects. The sequence of relationships is indicated in the chart by arrows. For convenience in charting, there is shown only one cycle of reaction to the initial noxious stimulus; many are known to exist.

From an examination of the data thus assembled the importance to the pain experience of the reflex reactions to noxious stimulation is indicated. However, to complete the pattern of reaction relationships, exploration of the reactions to pain per se is required.

Chapter XI

REACTIONS TO PAIN

As distinguished from the reactions to noxious stimulation, locally and at the segmental level, discussed in the foregoing chapter, there are also both conscious and partly conscious reactions associated with the sensation of pain. These latter presuppose the existence of pain, whereas the former can be elicited even in the anesthetized animal or in an unconscious human. The distinction between the two response patterns appears to be justified on the basis of the greater complexity and lesser predictability of the reactions to pain as compared to the reactions to noxious stimulation without pain. However, the patterns of reflexes elicited by noxious stimulation, and the acquired reaction patterns to pain, have many features in common and it is frequently difficult to distinguish one from the other. Thus, while by the end of the nineteenth century it was already considered useful by some to separate pain sensation from the "feelings" associated with it (426), recent experimental data have furnished the background for a fuller development of this concept.

Man reacts not only to actual noxious stimulation, as do all living forms, but, having the highest integrative equipment, he is particularly sensitive to threats and symbols of danger. These call forth reactions little different from those elicited by a painful episode itself. Depending upon the rapidity and magnitude of the adjustments, these reactions may be so intense as to induce pain sensation. Pricking sensations in the face and scalp associated with sudden fearful situations, and the painful abdominal cramps elicited in similar circumstances, are examples. Since the adaptive, protective reaction elicited by either noxious stimulation, or pain, or symbols of danger, may long outlive the precipitating episodes, such reactions may be far more injurious to the individual than the primary tissue damage.

Also, and most important, man is a tribal or group creature with a long period of development and dependence. He is dependent for his existence upon the aid, support, and encouragement of other men. He lives his life so much in contact with men, and with so much concern for their expectations of him that he is jeopardized as well as supported by his fellows. Moreover, he may feel threatened more by cultural and individual human pressures than by potentially painful environmental forces.

Hence, the culture in which a man finds himself becomes the conditioning influence in the formation of his individual reaction patterns to pain. Although until now these relationships have not been thoroughly explored, it is generally realized that a knowledge of group attitudes toward pain is extremely important to an understanding of the individual's reaction. A classical example is the attitude presented by the Spartans of ancient Greece.

In addition to culturally conditioned reactions to pain, the meaning of pain to the individual may be affected by a number of factors, such as hypnosis, suggestion, analgesic agents, or brain injury. As described below, in the hypnotic state the suggestion of analgesia significantly reduces the "alarm" reaction to pain. Further, since the cerebral cortex is the organ of integration involved in sensation, brain damage or chemical agents which depress cerebral function, may not only modify the effects of noxious stimulation, but also alter the attitude toward pain. In short, even a most intense noxious stimulation may arouse no visible reaction, whereas the mildest noxious stimulation, because of some symbolic significance, may evoke protective and adaptive reactions of major proportions. In this chapter factors that condition the individual to pain and threat of pain, and which modify the meaning of pain to him, will be the focus of interest.

PAIN AND THE PSYCHOGALVANIC RESPONSE

As mentioned in Chapter IV, the threshold of pain sensation was demonstrated to be remarkably constant in the same individual from day to day. Regardless of mood and in spite of attempts to increase fatigue and irritability by staying awake throughout 24 hours, the threshold did not vary more than ± twelve per cent from the usual mean. Further, the pain threshold as measured in several hundred individuals was of this same constancy regardless of age, sex, and experience, although statements regarding reactions to pain varied from "I can take any amount of it" to "I am exquisitely sensitive to pain."

These facts all pointed to the inference that, whereas the threshold for the sensation of pain is uniform among men and women, individual reactions to pain and alarming experiences vary greatly. These reactions constitute the most apparent, and perhaps the most important, aspects of a distressing experience. The pain sensation can be clearly dissociated from the reaction to it. For instance, when morphine sulfate is administered during pain, pain usually continues to be experienced, but the characteristic fight-flight anxiety reaction pattern is significantly altered.

It was considered desirable to demonstrate in quantitative terms some aspect of this reaction to pain as contrasted with pain sensation. One of the simplest components of the "alarm" reaction was used for this purpose, namely, the change in electrical resistance of the skin (71, 493, 490, 435). The sudden drop in the electrical resistance of the skin following exposure to a stressful situation (260, 259, 95) is a sensitive indicator of the activity of the sympathetic nervous system (496, 104, 362, 379) and has been demonstrated to be of generalized, not merely of local, character (70, 379). The peculiarity of sweating on the palms, soles and in the axillae has been firmly established (258, 261) as being related to psychological and sensory processes rather than to body temperature regulation. Arguments have also been advanced for the specific value of sweating in these areas as part of the mechanism of preparedness in terms of greater surety of grip (254, 94).

Because alcohol is so common and ancient a means for reducing anxiety, and because of its prompt and considerable effect in raising the pain threshold, the influence of this agent upon the threshold of the "alarm" reaction was ascertained.

Pain and Response Thresholds

The forearm and palmar surface of the middle finger were connected to a Wheatstone bridge through electrodes in contact with the skin. The resistance between these points was measured. Thermal radiation was then applied for three seconds to a 1.5 cm.^{2} area of blackened forehead of the subject. Through repeated exposures the intensity of the radiation was altered until the minimal intensity was found which would cause the galvanometer needle to swing sharply across the scale immediately following the application of the stimulus. This amount of radiation was called the threshold of the "alarm" reaction. For comparison, the pain threshold was also determined on the same skin area.

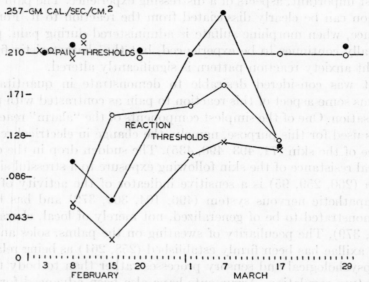

FIG. 83. A COMPARISON OF THE PAIN THRESHOLDS WITH THE "ALARM" REACTION THRESHOLDS IN 3 SUBJECTS, UNDER CONTROL CONDITIONS

The ordinate = the intensity of stimulus, i.e., the amount of heat in gram calories per second per square centimeter. The abscissa = the date of the observations. Note the variability of the reaction threshold as compared with the stability of the pain threshold. ×, J. D. H.; ●, H. G. W.; ○, H. G.

The amount of thermal radiation necessary to evoke this "alarm" reaction was widely variable from day to day in the same individual, and from individual to individual in the three persons intensively studied. It was sometimes as little as 27 mc./sec./cm.[2] which was about fifteen per cent of the energy required to evoke the sensation of pain (see fig. 83). When 40 cc. of 95 per cent ethyl alcohol was administered to the subjects of this study, their thresholds for the "alarm" reaction were observed to be elevated

within ten minutes after ingestion of the alcohol (fig. 84). In each
of the three subjects the level of the maximum elevation of the

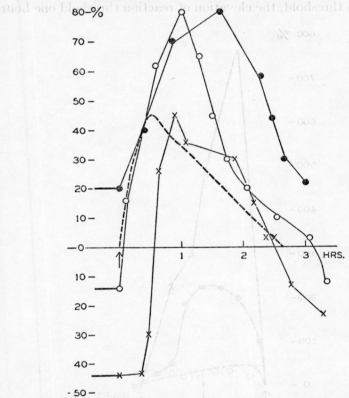

FIG. 84. THE EFFECT OF 95 PER CENT ALCOHOL, 40 CC., ON THE THRESHOLD OF
THE "ALARM" REACTION

Each point represents the per cent deviation of the threshold of the "alarm"
reaction from the control level of the pain threshold. The per cent deviation
of the control level of the individual threshold of the "alarm" reaction from the
control level of the pain threshold, is indicated by short heavy horizontal lines.

The ordinate = per cent deviation above and below the control level of the
pain threshold as zero. The abscissa = duration of effect. The broken line represents the average effect of 40 cc. of 95 per cent alcohol on the pain threshold.
×, J. D. H.; ●, H. G. W.; ○, H. G.

threshold for the reaction significantly exceeded that of the maximum elevation of the threshold for pain. In other words, after
alcohol more energy was required to evoke the reaction than to

evoke threshold sensation of pain. Thus, in subject H.G., whose control reaction threshold before alcohol was fifteen per cent below pain threshold, the elevation of reaction threshold one hour

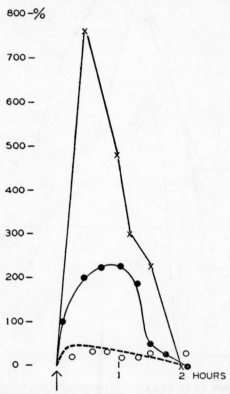

FIG. 85. THE EFFECT OF 95 PER CENT ETHYL ALCOHOL, 30 CC., ON THE THRESHOLD
OF THE "ALARM" REACTION

The ordinate = the per cent elevation of the threshold of the "alarm" reaction above its control level as zero. The abscissa = duration of effect. ×, J. D. H.; ●, H. G. W.; ○, H. G.

after ingestion of the alcohol was approximately 50 per cent above the elevated pain threshold. In another series of experiments, the threshold of the "alarm" reaction as measured by the galvanic skin response in one instance was raised 780 per cent above its own control level after 30 cc. of 95 per cent alcohol. This elevation was 85 per cent above the control level of the pain threshold. With this amount of heat, blistering of the skin occurred (see fig. 85). Two other subjects had only moderate elevations of reaction thresholds on this day.

COMMENT

Alcohol has an immediate and dramatic effect upon the threshold of the "alarm" reaction. The effect upon this threshold outlasts the effect on the pain threshold. Thus, there is afforded a demonstration of the distinction between the sensation of pain and the reaction pattern to pain.

Such a dissociation of pain sensation from pain reaction is of importance in evaluating the therapeutic action of analgesics (7). Some agents, such as the salicylates, affect chiefly the pain threshold, while others, such as the opiates and alcohol, affect also the reaction pattern. Suggestion, reassurance, and confidence also influence the reaction pattern, and account for the enormous individual variations in the threshold for the "alarm" reaction.

It is to be noted that this "alarm" reaction commonly set off by pain may, and frequently does, follow a completely innocuous stimulus. This would account for the observations frequently made on patients, namely that non-painful as well as painful stimuli cause similar reactions; that on different days, patients react differently to the same stimulus, painful or not (78, 76, 75, 383).

The Magnitude of the Galvanic Skin Response as Related to Pain Intensity

As a further step in the investigation of the relation of pain to the "alarm" reaction, a study was made of the effectiveness of various intensities of pains of short duration in evoking greater or lesser degrees of reaction.

The "galvanic skin response" was again selected as an index of the reaction to pain.

Four normal adults were subjects for the study, two males, H & F, and two females, M and W. Three of the subjects, H, M and F were present at the beginning of the study and the fourth, W, entered two months later.

The experiments were conducted in an average-sized room in

which the temperature could be controlled as desired (476), and were carried out daily, six days a week, for a period of six months, except for occasional lapses of a few days' duration.

Painful sensations were induced by a three-second exposure to thermal radiation on the blackened skin of hand, face or forearm. The galvanic skin response was recorded from two rectangular silver-silver chloride electrodes which were placed on the palmar surface of the index and middle finger. A sodium chloride paste was used to make contact. The electrodes were 5 x 1.2 cm. in size, and covered most of the palmar surface of the distal phalanges and part of the proximal phalanx. Insulating tape at the proximal end of the electrode insured uniform size of the skin area in contact with the electrode or electrolyte during the procedure. The usual time required for an observation, about twenty to thirty minutes, was too short for significant evaporation of the paste (40). The recording instrument was a modified vacuum tube voltmeter in series with an amplifier and graphic ammeter. The subject received three volts D.C. through a 200,000 ohm resistor in series, so that only a small current was flowing in the circuit and it remained essentially constant despite changes in skin resistance.

Measurement of the galvanic skin response was carried out as follows: The resistance was determined at the outset of the experiment and during a ten-minute rest period that followed. The resistance level before each stimulus, and the level to which the resistance dropped after the stimulus, were recorded. The magnitude of the galvanic skin response was computed as percentage change, thus:

$$G = \frac{\Delta R}{R} \times 100$$

where G = galvanic skin response,

    ΔR = observed change in resistance from the resting level following painful stimulation,

    R = resting level of resistance before the painful stimulus.

In general, by this method of computation, G was not dependent upon the initial resistance level (174, 173). The drop in resistance following a painful stimulus was rapid and there was no difficulty in identifying this change from the slower changes which followed.

OBSERVATIONS: SERIES I

Figure 86 shows the arrangement of apparatus and investigators for the first series of experiments. The pain threshold was determined as described in previous chapters, and the subject was allowed to relax undisturbed until the resistance reached a steady level before exposing him to painful stimuli. During the earlier

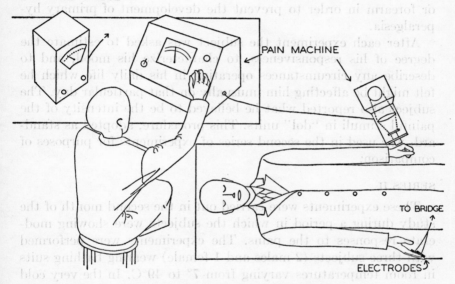

RESISTANCE BRIDGE

PAIN MACHINE

TO BRIDGE

ELECTRODES

FIG. 86. EXPERIMENTAL ARRANGEMENT FOR OBSERVING THE GALVANIC SKIN RESPONSE TO GRADED INTENSITIES OF PAIN

part of the study this waiting period occasionally lasted as long as 45 minutes. However, as the procedure became a matter of routine the period in which a level was reached was almost always ten minutes, more or less. Thus an arbitrary limit of ten minutes fixed (364, 363, 365).

When equilibrium had been established a series of stimuli from the dolorimeter was given in order of increasing intensity. The first of these was merely a clicking of the shutter without thermal radiation. Then stimuli calculated (see Chapter VII) to induce threshold, two-, four-, six-, and eight-"dol" pains were given. After the painful stimuli had been given the pain threshold was again measured. Between every two stimuli the resistance was allowed to return to a value approximating the previous resting level. In the initial experiments after large responses to high intensity pains this return required from ten to twenty minutes. However, after a few experiments the resistance returned and leveled off within one to three minutes, even following large responses. Each stimulus was applied to a different area of the skin on the back of the hand or forearm in order to prevent the development of primary hyperalgesia.

After each experiment the subject was asked to estimate the degree of his responsiveness, to characterize his mood, and to describe any circumstances operating in his daily life which he felt might be affecting him unusually on that particular day. The subject also reported what he believed to be the intensity of the painful stimuli in "dol" units. This procedure, adopted as standard, was used in the second series of experiments for purposes of comparison.

SERIES II

These experiments were carried out in the second month of the study during a period in which the subjects were showing moderate responses to the pains. The experiments were performed with three subjects (2 males and 1 female) wearing bathing suits in room temperatures varying from 7° to 49°C. In the very cold atmospheres the subjects were shivering and uncomfortable. Special care was taken to make sure that the proper intensities of pain had been perceived (see Chapter IV). Also, the ability of the subject to give a full galvanic skin response was ensured by noting the amount of resistance change following several deep breaths (138, 46). Similar precautions were taken in the hot environments.

SERIES III

The third series of experiments was begun about 130 days after the initial experiment of the first series, during a period in which the subjects were having little or no galvanic skin response to any of the stimuli, even the most severe pains causing less than four per cent change. The responses of subjects H and M had thus been "adapted" for ten days, and of subject W for sixteen days. Efforts were thus directed toward finding circumstances under which the galvanic skin response would return. Seven more or less distressing situations were employed. The first of these was one ne-

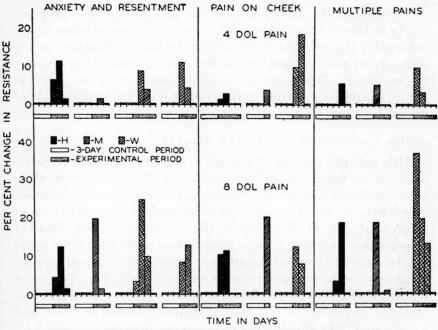

FIG. 87. THE EFFECT OF SITUATIONS OF INCREASED ANXIETY UPON THE RESPONSIVENESS TO PAIN

cessitating the hurried preparation of material for an important lecture by subject H (fig. 87, black column, first section). The second situation was produced by precipitating a quarrel between two subjects, M and W (hatched and first cross-hatched columns, respectively, first section, fig. 87). The third involved a criticism of subject W (second cross-hatched columns, first section, fig. 87), and the last four were created by altering the experimental procedure so as to increase the anxiety of the subjects. These were: stimulating an area on the face instead of on the hand or arm;

stimulating simultaneously four areas on various parts of the body; presenting pains in random order rather than in order of increasing intensity; and inducing a continuous mild pain by means of pressure on the arm during the period of testing.

RESULTS

Throughout the study, whether the painful stimuli were given singly in known or random order, or on one or several sites simultaneously, the subjects were definite in their estimation of the intensity of pain in "dol" units and were almost always correct (± one "dol"). There can be no doubt that during the period of study, accurate estimation of pain sensation in "dol" units did not diminish.

SERIES I. RESPONSE TO PAINFUL STIMULI

Although the pattern of change in the galvanic skin response over the six-month period was similar in all four subjects, there were significant individual differences. For example, the responses of subjects W and F diminished more rapidly than did those of subjects H and M. The day to day variation in magnitude of response was marked in each subject and these variations could not be correlated with the subjects' reports of degree of responsiveness, mood, or circumstances in their daily life. The most marked change during the first few months of the experiment was that the responses to the painful stimuli became of lesser and lesser magnitude. Finally, the response disappeared entirely. This process has been called "negative adaptation" or "habituation" and to quote Darrow, "If there is any single observation in galvanic studies which is more characteristic than another it is that the stimuli become progressively less effective with repetition" (94). Other studies, however, have covered a period of days and showed only the tendency toward a decrease in the magnitude of the response without demonstrating its complete disappearance. This adaptive process was noted in the experiments of Davis using noise as the stimulus, and in the experiments by Blatz using the collapse of the subject's chair, and in many others (98, 42).

In the present studies the period of adaptation is defined as the interval, measured in days, beginning with the first experiment and ending when there was less than four per cent galvanic skin response to all pains in five successive experiments. This period was of variable length, being 122 days for subject M, 120 days for subject H, and 26 days and 16 days for subjects W and F, respectively. Subject F had generally small galvanic skin responses

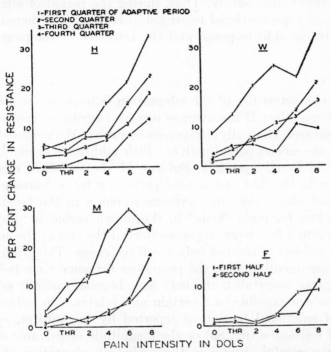

FIG. 88. RELATION OF THE AVERAGE VALUES OF THE GALVANIC SKIN RESPONSE TO THE INTENSITY OF THE EXPERIMENTAL PAINS DURING THE PERIOD OF ADAPTATION

even at the beginning of the study and at the end of 100 days his responses had completely disappeared. Minimal responses (one to three per cent) were observed in the other subjects even during the experimental period following adaptation.

For the purposes of analysis the period of adaptation for each individual was divided into quarters and the galvanic skin response to the various stimuli were averaged for each quarter. Figure 88 represents the average galvanic skin responses for each of the four quarters (designated by 1, 2, 3, and 4), plotted against the intensity of pain in "dols" by which they were elicited. The process of adaptation in all subjects was the diminution in response, first to the non-painful stimulus, next to stimuli evoking threshold pain, and then to stimuli evoking two, four, six and eight "dols" successively. Thus, during the period of adaptation there was a proportional relationship between the magnitude of the galvanic skin response and the intensity of the pain experienced.

COMMENT

The characteristics of the adaptation differed in the four subjects. For subject H the average response during successive quarters decreased gradually. Responses of subject W decreased markedly in the second period with but little additional decrease in the third and fourth quarters. Subject M showed little change in response in the first and second periods, a large decrease in the third and about the same average response in the fourth. The high values for eight "dols" in the fourth period in subject M were due to a few large responses toward the end of the adaptive period. Subject F showed only small responses. This subject had been experimenting with the procedure for some time before recording was undertaken and may have become partially adapted.

It was not possible to ascertain any relationship between the state of emotional tension as reported by the subject, and the level of resistance (fig. 89) or the magnitude of galvanic skin response to painful stimuli in the period of adaptation (fig. 88). Graphs of the averages of the galvanic skin response in the experiments in which the subjects reported states of tension are not significantly different from those shown in figure 88. This suggests that if a relationship exists between the daily emotional state as reported by the subject, and the galvanic skin response to pain, either it was obscured by the adaptive process or the individual was not aware of the states which influence this response to the pains. At the end of an experiment the subjects were unable to judge whether they had responded or to what degree they had responded to the experimental pains.

The observations on adaptation are explained if we consider the reaction to the pains as indicating the degree of threat evoked in the subject by the pains. Initially the entire procedure contained for the subjects an element of danger, as indicated by the large reactions occurring with all the pains, and, indeed, with the mere clicking of the shutter (see fig. 90, comparing the reactions in the

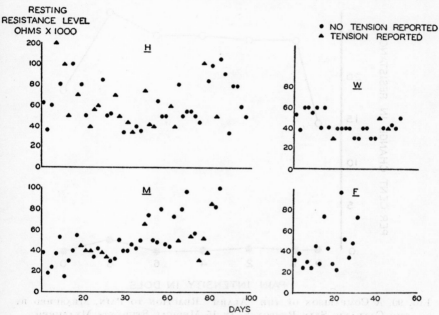

FIG. 89. RESTING RESISTANCE LEVELS PRIOR TO STARTING OF PAINFUL STIMULATION

initial experiment on fifteen medical students with those of the adapted subjects). As the experiments were repeated the threat content of the stimuli diminished, first for the lesser and then more gradually for the greater pains. In this sense we can say that the intensity of pain bears a predictable relationship to the magnitude of reaction. Such a correlation may explain partly why sensation of and reaction to pain have been confused for so long a time. Actually the most widely accepted clinical index of the intensity of pain experienced by a patient is the patient's reaction, and it can be seen from the above evidence that under certain circumstances this reaction can be trusted. However, after adaptation to a chronic pain or in situations in which the individual is anxious, reactions are often misleading and measurements of pain intensity give more accurate information as regards the intensity of pain being experienced. Merely questioning or observing the

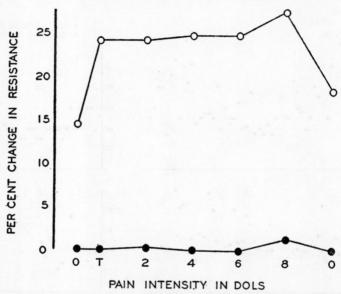

Fig. 90. A Comparison of the "Alarm" Reaction to Pain, Measured by the Galvanic Skin Response, in 15 Medical Students Measured for the First Time (O), and in 4 Adapted Individuals (●)

stolid, unperturbed patient on the one hand, or the complaining, excited patient on the other, may lead to faulty estimation of pain intensity.

The importance of adaptation in the broad sense is obvious in that it provides a necessary flexibility to the organism in its struggle for survival. Otherwise, the reactions to symbols of danger would be overwhelming to the individual, could not security be attained through rapid adaptation. On the other hand, too much adaptation to pain or to other forms of actual threat might lead to disaster. For example, blistering is sometimes induced by sustained thermal radiation evoking not more than two-"dol" pain to which adaptation is prompt. Failure to react to such a painful warning would jeopardize the integrity of the individual. In other words, while adaptation to threatful situations serves to "protect" the individual by augmenting his flexibility, it may actually en-

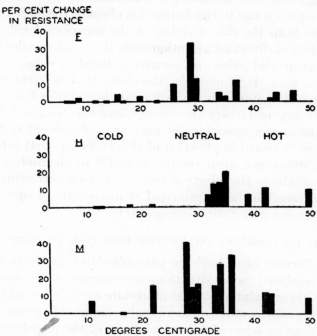

Fig. 91. The Influence of Heat and Cold upon the Responsiveness to Pain

danger him by making him sluggish under conditions where alertness is required.

SERIES II. THE EFFECT OF EXTREMES OF ENVIRONMENTAL TEMPERATURE UPON REACTION TO PAIN

Figure 91 represents the galvanic skin response to the six-"dol" pain in air temperatures from 7° to 49°C., for subjects F, H and M. Although the responses were variable there was a definite tendency for the peak responses to occur near the comfort zone with diminishing responses as the extremes of temperature were approached. This occurred also in the response to pains of other intensities.

COMMENT

It is suggested that the effect of cold and heat in reducing the response to pain is due to the distracting effect of the large barrage of impulses from the skin arriving at the conscious level. These had the effect of diverting attention from the much smaller threat of the experimental pains and thereby reduced or eliminated the response to pain. It is possible, therefore, that whereas certain types of stressful situations may summate in so far as their threat content is concerned, there are others whose effects cancel. In this instance the strong sensations of heat or cold reduced responses to the pains. A broad implication of this finding is that intensely absorbing situations, even though stressful in themselves, may reduce or eliminate the effects of reaction to other stressful situations. It is possible that a principal characteristic of such situations is intense sensory stimulation (141).

SERIES III. FACTORS ENHANCING THE RESPONSE TO PAIN

In the efforts to bring back the galvanic skin response to experimentally produced pains, situations were sought which would increase the threat content of the procedure or which would make the experimental routine otherwise obnoxious. All seven of the test situations so selected caused a return of the response to the pains in subjects H, M, and W, but none had any effect upon subject F.

In figure 87 are represented the galvanic skin responses to the four- and eight-"dol" pains in subjects W, H, and M in ten typical experiments involving five situations. At the left in the figure are shown experiments done during periods of anxiety and resentment. The experimental periods were not selected as periods during which the subjects themselves were conscious of tension. Prior investigation of the reports revealed that the subject's own feelings of tension did not bear a predictable relationship to the presence or absence of the galvanic skin response. Actually, the periods were chosen to coincide with certain activities which are generally associated with tension. The first set of bars in figure 87 represents a moderate return of response, with rapid adaptation as the tension eased, shown by subject H in association with the preparation of material for a scientific meeting. The second situation in this first group of experiments is illustrated by the return of response in subject M when subject W was asked to create animosity between them. In the second day of this experiment, when only small responses were observed to the eight-"dol" pain, subject M confessed to having become aware of the hoax. This task greatly distressed subject W and she evidenced an even larger return of reaction, as shown in the next group of bars. Subject W also shows a moderate return of response, as illustrated by the fourth set of bars, when she was questioned about behavior toward another member of the group.

The second set of experiments in figure 87 represents the return of response for subjects H, M, and W when the painful stimuli were applied to the cheek rather than to the hand or arm. Adaptation occurred in subjects H and W in three repetitions. Subject M was available for only one experiment.

The third set of experiments represents the return of response in subjects H, M, and W when the area exposed to radiation was successively increased by simultaneous irradiation of two, three, and four skin areas. Increasing the area exposed does not result in an increase in the intensity of the pain. The stimuli were induced in both hands and forearms. The response returned to a moderate degree in subject H and M and to a greater degree in subject W. Adaptation occurred here, too, since despite continued increase in size of the area exposed to noxious stimulation, the response was least in the last experiment, that with the largest area.

Absence from the experiment for four to six days during this period did not result in return of the responses, but after an interruption of one month moderate responses recurred.

COMMENT

In the period when adaptation had been achieved, i.e., when pains in the standard procedure were ineffective in calling forth a response, these same pains, if evoked under certain other conditions, were again evaluated as threatening and responses were then elicited. All of the above described changes from the standard experimental routine were of a type which one would expect to increase the subject's anxiety about the experimental pains. The "anxiety potential" of the situations described was small and adaptation to them occurred rapidly. It is conceivable that other situations could be more serious and that adaptation might not occur; indeed, the individual might return to the condition of large responses even to the shutter click.

During the period of adaptation marked swings in the magnitude of response to the pains were observed, but these could not be correlated with the individual's statement of his feelings during the series of experiments. This failure is probably due more to the subject's inability to evaluate his emotional state than to a true lack of association. Indeed, it is apparent that the degree of responsiveness during the third experimental series was a more reliable index of the degree of emotional tension than was the subject's report.

The results of the experiments in Series III stand in striking contrast to those of Series II, experiments at various air temperatures, in which the reaction diminished as the stress put on the body increased. The differences between these two situations offer interesting material for speculation about the elements which result in an increase, and those which result in a decrease in the "alarm" reaction to pain. In Series III the predominant change had been in the affective state of the individual; he was unable to institute behavior appropriate to this feeling and there were no other disturbing sensory stimuli save the pains. In Series II the predominant change had been the presence of many disturbing sensory stimuli, and the body had begun to institute protective reaction (heat regulation).

The fact that anxiety as determined clinically increases the level of physiologic response has often been demonstrated (304). This "reinforcing action of anxiety" is thought by some to be useful to the organism in avoiding the threatening stimulus (319). On the other hand, the ability of the organism to focus upon the most

threatening of a number of conditions, to the temporary exclusion
of the others, is of doubtful advantage, and accounts for the suppression of the reaction to the experimental pains in the presence
of high intensity heat or cold. This is comparable to the lack of
spatial summation in pain sense itself, and demonstrates a safety
device which prevents the overwhelming of the individual by an
overabundance of emotional reaction to the many simultaneous
threats in the environment.

HYPNOTIC SUGGESTION OF ANALGESIA

Recently there has been a revival of interest in hypnotically
induced anesthesia, particularly in the fields of obstetrics and
dentistry (56, 478, 163). This aspect of hypnosis is especially interesting because it can now be quantitatively investigated. Bramwell's review (55) of studies on hypnosis includes the literature
up to 1930, and Hollander's discussion (219) covers the clinical
aspects of the method.

Studies have been made of the influence of hypnotic suggestion
of anesthesia upon the galvanic skin response, change in heart
rate, respiration and vasomotor reactions following a painful stimulus. However, aside from observations made on one subject (490)
placed in "shallow hypnosis" in which suggestion of anesthesia
raised the pain threshold by 40 per cent, no quantitative study
has been made of the effects of such suggestion upon perception
of noxious stimuli or of the reaction to such stimuli.

Using the technique described in the previous section, experiments were done on seven normal subjects, four females and three
males. The procedure was carried out first in the non-hypnotized
state; hypnosis was then induced, using visual fixation and suggestions of heaviness of the eyelids. Involuntary closure of the lids,
with inability to reopen them, was considered the initial stage of
the light trance. Depth of trance was estimated at each session
using criteria other than anesthesia. In general, the criteria were
those of the Davis "Hypnotic Susceptibility Test" as described
by Friedlander and Sarbin (137). Phenomena of the light trance
were held to include catalepsy of lids, limb catalepsies, involuntary rigidity of limbs, inhibitions of voluntary movements,

and automatic movements. Those for medium trance included partial post-hypnotic amnesia, response to simple post-hypnotic suggestions, and hallucinations of heat and cold. Criteria for deep trance included ability to open the eyes without affecting the trance, production of visual and auditory hallucinations, complete post-hypnotic amnesia, and post-hypnotic hallucinations.

At each session, after hypnotic suggestions of anesthesia had been made, the noxious thermal stimuli were repeated in the same order as in the control period, and the galvanic skin response was measured. While still hypnotized, the subject was asked to give his impressions of the sensations evoked by the stimuli according to the "dol" scale. If pain had been perceived, an attempt was made again to measure the pain threshold, and the subject's ability to discriminate between stimuli of various intensities was noted. The subject was then awakened and asked to tell what he remembered of the hypnotic experience, particularly with regard to the stimuli perceived.

Every effort was made to keep the experimental conditions standardized. No talk was permitted except for hypnotic suggestions and the questioning of the subject. For control purposes the periods of hypnosis and waking were occasionally reversed, but no changes were observed due to such inversion of sequence. A few experiments were conducted in which suggestions of hyperesthesia were made.

RESULTS

A general summary of the results is to be found in table 18. The subjects are listed from one through seven on the basis of the average estimated depth of hypnotic trance achieved in each. Each subject's sensations during the control period were compared with sensations following identical stimuli during the hypnotic peroid at each session. Similarly, the galvanic skin response to each stimulus in the control period at a given session was compared with the response to the identical stimulus during the hypnotic period.

In order to express quantitatively the effects of hypnotic suggestion of anesthesia upon pain sensation it is desirable to define conditions of analgesia and hypalgesia. By *analgesia* is meant the state in which none of the noxious stimuli administered are reported as painful. *Hypalgesia* is used to refer to a state in which noxious stimuli are reported as less painful than would be expected on the basis of reports of the same subject regarding the same stimuli in control (i.e., normal) situations. Hypalgesia can thus be measured in "dols" as the difference between the reported and expected pain intensities expressed in "dols". Hyperalgesia can be similarly expressed in "dols", but analgesia, as it is a maximal state, cannot be measured.

TABLE 18

Effect of hypnotic suggestion of anesthesia on pain sensation and on the galvanic skin response to pain

SUBJECT NUMBER	NUMBER OF OBSERVATIONS	DEPTH OF TRANCE	PAIN PERCEPTION	PER CENT REDUCTION OF GSR	DEGREE OF CONFIDENCE
1	28	Light	Unchanged	26	.05
2	118	Light	Hypalgesia, 0–2 "dols"	64	.01
3	48	Light	Hypalgesia, 0–4 "dols"	49	.01
4	92	Light	Hypalgesia, 0–6 "dols"	55	.01
5	100	Light Medium	Hypalgesia, 5 "dols". Analgesia	67	.01
6	50	Medium Medium	Hypalgesia, 5 "dols". Analgesia	57	.01
7	42	Medium Deep	Hypalgesia, 6 "dols". Analgesia	62	.01

To determine whether the galvanic skin responses following hypnotic suggestions of analgesia differed significantly from those in the control period, averages and standard deviations of the responses were calculated from the data on each subject, using the responses to identical stimuli administered in hypnotic and control periods. This procedure eliminated any possible effects due to "adaptation". Average differences thus determined indicated that the reduction in response after hypnotic suggestion was definitely related to some aspect of the hypnotic situation rather than to the operation of chance factors in the experiment. As noted in the table, alterations in pain threshold were variable from subject to subject and in the same subject at different sessions. A rough correlation of the extent of analgesia produced with the depth of trance was possible.

SUBJECT 1

At each session this subject reacted to the induction of hypnosis with anxiety accompanied by increased pulse rate, respiratory rate, and cardiac thrust, described also by Schneck (385). It is noteworthy that on every occasion this subject achieved only a light trance, and never showed evidence of analgesia or hypalgesia; indeed, on several occasions, he reported a higher intensity of pain from stimuli in the hypnotic state than in the control period. Nevertheless, there was a definite reduction in the galvanic skin response to the pains during the period of hypnotic suggestion of analgesia.

SUBJECT 2

Figure 92 indicates that this subject sensed all the stimuli as painful in spite of the hypnotic suggestion of analgesia, although a progressive degree of hypalgesia for the more intense stimuli was observed. In five sessions, attempts were made to re-measure her pain threshold before terminating hypnosis. In two of these the threshold was unchanged and her reports were reproducible and consistent with those given in the waking state according to the routine procedure. In a third session, the threshold was found to be elevated fifteen per cent although her reports of the stimuli above threshold would indicate no hypalgesia. In the remaining two attempts, the reports on re-measuring the pain threshold were quite variable. Also, during these two sessions, the subject could not discriminate between stimuli of widely different intensities. For example, she reported a thermal stimulus of 300 mc./sec./cm.^{2} (normally evoking four "dols") as "one dol", but 275 mc./sec./cm.^{2} (three "dols") as "almost two". Thus, the subject's ability to discriminate among stimuli of different intensity was diminished by the hypnotic suggestion.

On one occasion hyperalgesia of the left arm was suggested. In spite of this, no galvanic skin responses were obtained to noxious stimuli administered in the usual order during the trance, although significant responses had been obtained during the control period. On the other hand, the subject winced when a stimulus normally evoking a four-"dol" pain was given, and withdrew her arm from the aperture of the dolorimeter, remarking, "He made my arm red, flushed and painful." During this trance pain discrimination, as judged by re-measuring the pain threshold under hypnosis, was

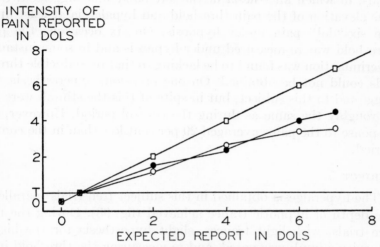

FIG. 92. INFLUENCE OF HYPNOTIC SUGGESTION OF ANESTHESIA UPON PAIN PERCEPTION

Hypalgesia was produced for more intense pains with no alteration in pain threshold. Subject 2: □, control; ●, average of first 5 experiments; ○, average of last 5 experiments.

not affected. Thus, suggestion of hyperalgesia failed to increase the threat content of the stimuli although it did condition the overt responses of the subject.

SUBJECT 3

This subject gave somewhat variable reports during the control periods. Hypalgesia as a result of hypnotic suggestion was more marked in the first two sessions (see table 18). Adaptation of the galvanic skin response to the experimental pains was very rapid, with the responses in the non-hypnotic state becoming very small. Nevertheless, the responses to pain following hypnotic suggestion were on the average reduced to less than half of those in the control period.

SUBJECT 4

During the first three sessions, this subject, like subject 1, reacted with anxiety to induction of hypnosis. In seven of the nine trials, in which anesthesia of the left hand was suggested, there was elevation of the pain threshold and hypalgesia at least up to the six-"dol" pain under hypnosis. On six occasions the pain threshold was re-measured under hypnosis and in some instances discrimination was found to be lacking so that reproducible thresholds could not be obtained. On one occasion, hyperesthesia was suggested to this subject, but in spite of this the stimuli were felt as roughly the same as during the control period. However, the response to the pains averaged 29 per cent less than in the control period.

SUBJECT 5

The hyperalgesia obtained in this subject (ten trials) paralleled the depth of hypnotic trance achieved (fig. 93). During the first five trials, with light trances, slight hypesthesia for the higher intensity stimuli was noted, and re-measuring the threshold indicated that there had been a significant elevation. None of the administered stimuli was perceived as painful in the sixth and seventh trials when a medium trance was achieved. In the last three trials, the depth of trance was somewhat lighter and the higher intensity stimuli were again perceived as slightly painful. This subject, when successful suggestions of anesthesia were made during the two medium trances, gave no galvanic skin response to any stimuli up to 300 mc./sec./cm.^{2} (evoking a six-"dol" pain in the control period).

SUBJECT 6

In only one of the five trials did this subject perceive any of the noxious stimuli administered during hypnosis. In this one he reported the stimuli evoking six- and seven-"dol" pain in the control period as "two dols". On one occasion during the period of hypnotic analgesia, there was no galvanic skin response to five stimuli ranging up to 330 mc./sec./cm.[2] (eliciting a seven-"dol" pain in the control period).

SUBJECT 7

In the first experiment, following the suggestion of anesthesia, this subject perceived a stimulus as "threshold" which had caused

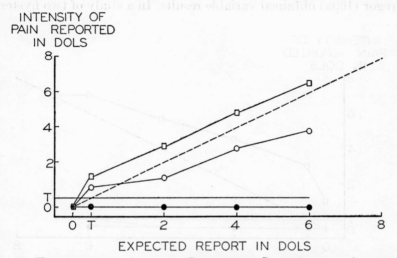

INTENSITY OF
PAIN REPORTED
IN DOLS

EXPECTED REPORT IN DOLS

FIG. 93. HYPALGESIA AND ANALGESIA PRODUCED BY SUGGESTIONS OF ANALGESIA
IN LIGHT AND MEDIUM HYPNOTIC TRANCES RESPECTIVELY
Subject 5: □, control; ○, average of experiments in light trance; ●, average of experiments in medium trance.

a six-"dol" pain before hypnosis. In the remaining three experiments she perceived no pain from any of the stimuli during the hypnotic trance. She was judged to be in a medium trance on the first occasion and in a deep trance on the last three. These results are illustrated in figure 94.

COMMENT

A number of investigations have been reported on the galvanic skin response to painful and other stimuli during hypnosis, but there is disagreement as to whether or not hypnotic anesthesia alters this reaction. Moravcsik (315) in one, and Georgi (147) in three subjects, found that stimulation of hypnotically anesthetized areas evoked no response. Peiper (335), Prideaux (346), and Prince and Peterson (347) reported opposite observations. In hysterical anesthesia, often thought to involve the same mechanism as hypnotic anesthesia, Veraguth (444), and Prideaux (346) found that stimulation of an "anesthetic" area gave normal responses; Gregor (169a) obtained variable results. In a study of two hysteri-

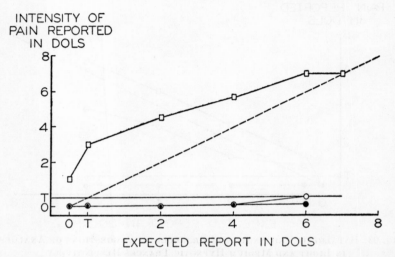

FIG. 94. ANALGESIA RESULTING FROM HYPNOTIC SUGGESTION OF ANESTHESIA
Subject 7: □, control; ○, first experiment; ●, average of 3 experiments

cal patients, Levine (273a) noted that a galvanic skin response was present following stimulation of anesthetic cutaneous areas in both the hypnotized and non-hypnotized states. He also noted that hypnotically induced hallucinations of a needle-prick produced such a response. The presence of this reflex to define hysterical anesthesia or malingering, as differentiated from anesthesias of organic origin, has been described by Winn (475), Golla (159), Myasischev (325), Sears and Cohen (394), and Redlich (356). In none of these studies was a systematic attempt made to measure the magnitude of the change of skin resistance under different conditions. Such measurements were made by Sears (393) in a study of seven male subjects who were capable of deep trance, with complete anesthesia and post-hypnotic amnesia. Measurements revealed that the galvanic skin response, while present, was on the average decreased by 20 per cent following stimulation of the anesthetized limb compared with the response to the same stimulation in the waking state. Sears also found that hypnotic anesthesia greatly reduced the pulse variability and practically eliminated the facial flinch and respiratory reactions to pain. Separate controls in the waking state indicated that attempted voluntary inhibition of the galvanic skin reactions to pain were ineffective in reducing the response. A subsequent study by Dynes (105) on seven subjects under hypnotic anesthesia in deep trance confirmed in general Sears' results regarding the cardiac and respiratory changes, but he observed the galvanic skin response to be little "influenced", showing only "a slight decrease as compared with the normal". Brown and Vogel (61) studied three subjects in deep hypnosis with the Darrow Photopolygraph. In contradiction to the results of Sears, as confirmed by Dynes, they concluded that quantitative changes in galvanic skin reactions to painful stimuli were not reliable indicators of the pain experienced, and that suggested analgesia in the hypnotic state did not abolish such physiological reaction to pain. While they inferred that imagination in the waking state might be as effective as hypnotic suggestion in influencing these reactions to pain, they found that hypersensitivity suggested during hypnosis could markedly increase these reactions. Doupe, Miller and Keller (102) studied vasomotor reaction to pain, and drew attention to the fact that reinforcement of suggestions of anesthesia during the course of experiment made for a more effective inhibition of these reactions. They made rough distinctions between "moderate" and "severe" painful stimuli by pin pricks, finding paradoxically that hypnotic anesthesia was more effective in inhibiting reactions to "severe" pain than to "moderate" pain.

In the present experiments, as a result of hypnotic suggestions of anesthesia, and depending upon the depth of hypnosis, the following effects on pain sensation were observed at one time or another in the seven subjects:

1. No alteration of pain perception;
2. Hypalgesia for higher intensity stimuli without elevation of the pain threshold;
3. Elevation of the pain threshold and hypalgesia;
4. Anesthesia for all stimuli administered;
5. Lack of ability to discriminate between noxious stimuli of various intensities.

The progression of effects 1 through 4 appears to be related to the depth of the trance. The third effect was observed in a majority of trials. The threshold elevation (10 to 30 per cent) in light trances is roughly the same as that which can be produced by suggestion to the non-hypnotized individual (190), but in deeper trances the effectiveness of hypnotic suggestion is much greater (50 to 100 per cent). The fifth effect was variable, and was seen only in conjunction with the third effect. It is described as a separate phenomenon because the lack of ability to discriminate between stimuli of markedly differing intensities was clearly observed only when re-measuring pain thresholds. In actuality it may merely represent a facet of altered pain perception, and the variability of its appearance may be related to the variable psychological state of the subject. The hypnotic trance is not a static state as it is influenced by the many internal and external stimuli which constantly affect the subject. For example, repetition and reinforcement of suggestions of anesthesia during hypnosis is an important though variable factor. There appeared to be varying depths of trance within a single twenty-minute session, and there was certainly a variability in depth of trance from one session to the next. The gross classification of depth of trance serves only as a general guide. The personality of the individual subject also played an important role. Thus, in subject 3 there was a decreasing effectiveness of the suggestions of anesthesia in successive hypnotic sessions, whereas subjects 2, 4, and 7 showed the opposite trend. Subject 5 achieved medium trances twice, and on these two occasions complete anesthesia was observed. Yet, on three subsequent occasions the trance was not as deep, and hypalgesia was variable, although greater than in the first five sessions. In those subjects who demonstrated complete anesthesia for stimuli up to 355 mc./sec./cm.² it is possible that stimuli of higher intensities (normally eliciting eight- to ten and one-half-"dol" pains) might have been perceived. Such stimuli were not used in this study because of the skin damage which they invariably produce.

The galvanic skin response provides a relatively simple measurement of autonomic response to the threat of pain. Review of the literature reveals no evidence that the hypnotic state per se affects this response. Controls in the experiments by Sears indicate no influence of hypnotic trance alone upon the galvanic skin response and this is borne out by the observations of Brown and Vogel. A single experiment on one subject was done at the beginning of the present study, and the induction of medium trance with no suggestion of anesthesia had no effect upon the galvanic skin response.

The experimental results leave no doubt that hypnotic suggestion of anesthesia diminishes the galvanic skin response to pain. This is related to, but not entirely dependent upon, the effectiveness of the suggestion of analgesia. Thus, we see that subject 2, with only a moderate hypalgesia, had the response to pain diminished by 64 per cent, while subject 6, with anesthesia on nearly all trials, had a reduction of response of only 57 per cent. It is particularly interesting that subject 1 exhibited a reduced response to pain of 25 per cent due to hypnotic suggestions which apparently had no effect at all upon his pain perception, and which even seemed to make him anxious. Toward the end of the experiment attempts were made to restore the response, or to increase it over the control levels, by suggesting hyperesthesia. Such suggestions were couched in terms of increased sensitivity of the skin due to sunburn or scalding. Three subjects in light trance were studied in this respect, and all trials were unsuccessful, indicating an inability to increase the threat content of the experimentally induced pain in these subjects.

It is important to note that on fourteen occasions hypnotic anesthesia led to a complete disappearance of the galvanic skin response to all stimuli during a given session. This lack of response with hypnotic anesthesia suggests the need for caution in the use of the galvanic skin response for distinguishing between hysterical anesthesias and those due to gross anatomic defects. The galvanic skin response is related to the meaning of the situation to the subject rather than to the intensity of noxious stimulation or of pain.

DYNAMIC REACTIONS TO PAIN

Chapman et al. (79), using radiant heat applied to the forehead as a painful stimulus, evaluated a wince response characterized by contraction of the eye muscles at the outer canthus, as evidence of reaction to pain. They found that "neurotic" patients and excessively anxious or overalert persons displayed, in general, a lower threshold for reaction than did "control" individuals (80). The older observations of Libman (284), who recorded patients' complaints following manual pressure upon the styloid process, support this view. Also, Hollander (220) who used a cheese grater pressed into the arm by a blood pressure cuff as a means of producing pain, observed that overanxious individuals complained of pain at a lower cuff pressure than did more tranquil persons. These components of the pain experience include feeling states and represent the individual's response to a pain sensation based on his own past experience and inborn peculiarities.

Some of the visceral reactions associated with pain, if sustained, may damage the organism. For example, Wolf (479) has demonstrated that induced pain may be associated with a decrease in urine output and kidney blood flow. The resultant ischemia is of little importance to the healthy kidney, but in an organ severely damaged by disease, a transient decrease in kidney circulation as a sequel of noxious stimulation has resulted in irreversible changes and death (480). Also, Gold, Kwit and Modell (153) have shown that induced pain is associated with alteration in heart function as indicated by the electrocardiogram. Again, such changes, although of little importance to the healthy heart may be of dire significance to one already functioning poorly.

The bodily reactions to pain mentioned above are both superficial and deep, local and widespread, and may include at one time or another all bodily structures and functions. These major adaptive and protective mechanisms are integrated into elaborate systems including complicated emotional and feeling components and altered behavior. They appear to fall into two categories: a) those that mobilize the animal to fight by offensive or defensive action, or for flight from the site of danger; and b) those that immobilize as a defensive measure when fight or flight seems impossible. Hence, it is evident that a part of any system of the organism may exhibit either hypo- or hyperdynamic responses. The final integrated pattern of these responses will depend upon the nature of the danger and the temperament and experience of the individual involved, and on his physical and psychological state at the time of the assault.

Such reactions involve many facets of integrative function and are exhibited as well in the attitude of the subject toward the assault or threat. For example, pain induced in two subjects by means of thumb screw pressure applied about the head, was associated with diametrically opposite responses in the large bowel. A hypodynamic response with pallor of the colonic mucous membrane and decline of motility was exhibited by one of these individuals. In contrast, the second exhibited hyperdynamic response of the large bowel. However, it is known that an isolated hypodynamic response in one organ may be part of the overall integrated pattern of hyperdynamic response for fight and flight. Thus, the blood may be forced from the viscera into the periphery where it is available for the support of both muscular and nervous activity. Indeed, the first of these subjects resented what was being done to him and showed by his behavior a general pattern of mobilization for defense, i.e., restlessness, combativeness, and vindictive utterances. In contrast, response in the bowel of the second subject was a part of his pattern of general immobilization with a concentration of blood in the viscera. This subject exhibited extraordinary passivity—a resigned acceptance of what he supposed was expected of him—and indicated by his utterances, his feelings of being "whipped" and defeated, and his attitude of futility about taking steps to avoid his plight. Thus, the paradoxical nature of the hyper- and hypodynamic response of any part of a reaction pattern can only be understood in terms of its contribution to the integrated pattern for mobilization or immobilization as the case may be.

A further example of the fact that the effect of pain is dependent upon the state of the subject and the meaning of the assault is exemplified by the studies of Stevenson and Duncan, as quoted by Wolf et al. (484). Pain was induced in a given individual on two occasions by immersing her arm in ice water (the "cold-pressor" test). On the first occasion, when, during certain adverse life experiences, she felt hopeless and desperate, the vascular response was hypodynamic in nature; whereas, on a later occasion with the same test stimulus, when she felt cheerful and confident, she presented the more usual hyperdynamic reaction. Also, the degree of rise in blood pressure to the same noxious stimulation was shown to be intimately related to the meaning of the assault. Thus, a man who suspected that the degree of his response to placing his hand in ice water would determine whether or not he was to undergo a major surgical operation, exhibited a striking pressor response; when, subsequently, the procedure held for him less serious implications the pressor response was small or absent.

Despite considerable divergence of opinion concerning the relation of awareness of the meaning of a threat to the concurrent bodily reaction, perhaps some unification is nonetheless possible at this time. Thus, one group of investigators emphasize that only through a knowledge of unconscious processes can one interpret the changing patterns of response of the organ being studied (305, 495). Implied is the view that only through the application of special procedures and concepts is the true state of the unconscious revealed, and inversely that conflicts and feelings of which the subject is conscious are not relevant to, or, indeed, are misleading in attempts at the correlation of bodily reactions, stimulus situations, and emotions (313).

The view best supported by observations of the galvanic skin response, of gastric function, of cardiovascular and voluntary muscular responses, is that the stimulus that has the most significance or is most threatening for the individual is the one most effective in eliciting the response. This effectiveness does not seem to depend upon whether or not the conflict be consciously recognized or not. Since important conflicts are more likely to be repressed into unconsciousness than less important ones, the view that "only" through knowledge of unconscious processes can one interpret bodily reactions is often supported. However, it would appear to be more profitable at this time to emphasize basic significance of the threat or assault to the individual rather than his degree of awareness of his state at the time.

In addition to life experience and attitude of the subject as factors in defining whether the response be hypo- or hyperdynamic in any given part or system, further distinction may be made in terms of the site of noxious stimulation. Quite commonly superficial noxious stimulation incites patterns of mobilization of a fight or flight nature, for example the effect of a snap of the tip of the whip on a horse's shoulder or the slapping of a man's face. In such situations, cardiovascular responses are of the accelerator-pressor type and both horse and man are induced to increase speed and force of muscle contraction. Inversely, noxious stimulation arising from the viscera or deeper somatic structures such as from an abdominal blow, injury to the testicle, or after coronary occlusion, commonly incites immobilization patterns and reactions associated with hypodynamic responses. Gastrointestinal patterns are of the ejection or rejection type and body movements cease or there are weak muscular contractions. But even these reactions are not independent of their meaning to the individual and may not be thought of only in terms of site of the noxious stimulus.

Various body systems and functions have been investigated, which, however, cannot be discussed in detail here (495, 221, 165). As might be anticipated from the foregoing discussion, the reactions to noxious stimulation and pain studied and reported upon are not always in agreement. This would seem in part to represent a difference in the circumstances under which a given noxious stimulus is applied and differences in the meaning of such assault to the subject. This meaning depends upon the basic nature and previous conditioning or experience of the subject. A striking example of the conditionality of response is seen in skeletal muscle participation in the reaction to noxious stimulation. Thus, Lewis and Kellgren (280), and Simons, Day, Goodell and Wolff (403) were able to show that in response to the noxious stimulation of skeletal muscles and adjacent tissues, certain more or less local or segmental reflex contractions of skeletal muscle occurred. It was suggested that these were akin to those exhibited by the abdominal musculature in the general region of an inflamed peritoneum about a ruptured appendix or to the muscular contraction producing the head tilt in a patient with a posterior fossa brain tumor syndrome. Depending on the nature of the individual and of his state at the time, these muscle contractions may be more or less widespread, or circumscribed.

Harell et al. (192) on repeating these experiments in man could not discern disturbances in action potential in the skeletal muscles in the neighborhood of the injured tissues. It is conceivable that the difference in observation is the outcome of emphasis of the experimenter. Simons et al. made no attempt to curb or inhibit the reactions of the experimentally injured individuals and merely measured in terms of action potential those disturbances in skeletal muscles in the general neighborhood of the injury. Harell, more interested in limiting reactions, did much to induce calm, tranquility, relaxation and cooperation, factors which may have exerted an inhibitory effect or at least curbed the spread of excitatory effects.

The experiments of Simons et al. were, therefore, repeated under somewhat different circumstances (494). In this second series of experiments action potentials were recorded from precisely the same areas as before, namely from the muscles of the head, neck and shoulders. However, the subject was instructed first to assume any position or posture that seemed to occur naturally to him; then to attempt to relax completely all of his skeletal musculature, inhibiting any muscle contraction of which he was aware. Further, his position was adjusted by an assistant so as to promote muscular relaxation. When pain of moderate intensity was induced by thumb screw pressure upon the scalp, high frequency muscle action potentials of large amplitude were noted. Under the first set of circumstances, there was, as in the original series of observations, electromyographic evidence of muscular contractions, which spread as the intensity of the pain increased and persisted. After the induced relaxation of the subject further recordings were obtained. Practically all action potentials had disappeared. Observations were also made after noxious stimulation of the head by the intramuscular injection of hypertonic salt solution. Again, after the initial exhibition of violent action potentials, the inhibition of the latter was readily demonstrable by suggesting relaxation and by "positioning" the subject. These observations, therefore, support both those made originally by Simons et al., and Harell et al., and indicate that muscle spasm does occur in reaction to noxious stimulation but that it may be modified by suggestions that alter the emotional attitude and by the adjustment of the bodily posture of the subject.

Some individuals who are extremely apprehensive and conditioned by early life experience to overreact or to react diffusely, can become especially alert on noxious stimulation of any part and exhibit widespread response of skeletal muscle contraction, notably in the head, back, and legs. Others, not so alerted to danger, respond locally if at all. Moreover, the especially overalerted individual may, through the persuasive influence of some trusted person, lose his overalertness and exhibit rather less response. It thus becomes apparent that noxious stimulation in itself capable of evoking responses, may, especially when it gives rise to a sensation of pain, assume a special symbolic significance and evoke widespread protective and adaptive responses based on conditioning factors obviously involving highest integrative functions. These may either augment the local response or inhibit it.

ASSOCIATIVE REACTIONS TO PAIN

Pain-Dependent Sexual Patterns

It has been amply demonstrated in laboratory animals that pain can be used as a basis of conditioning. Thus, when previously coupled with feeding, electrical stimulation causing withdrawal of a leg may thereafter initiate digestive secretions (285). It therefore became evident that painful sensation may be intimately linked with important drives and needs to such an extent, perhaps, as to become essential to the initiation and fulfillment of a pattern. It is further likely that sexual activity and pain can be similarly linked.

These considerations may be relevant to the topic of sadism and masochism in man. Certain individuals have so linked their sexual activity with the experience of being painfully stimulated that pain becomes either an essential or at least a much sought for aspect of the sexual act. The study of patients in whom this pain-dependent sexual behavior has become a serious personal and social problem lends support to the view that a linkage early in life of noxious and painful stimulation and sexual activity may be the foundation of such pain-dependent sexual patterns.

Thus, Rado (349) infers from an extensive study of a group of such patients that during the period of development of sex appetite, when the parent attempts to deter the child from sex activities by threats or punishment, the sexual activity becomes conditioned to such pain. Orgastic arousal then becomes difficult or impossible without first experiencing the torture of being afraid or actually being painfully punished. Rado further finds that when rage as a result of frustration or induced pain is thus linked with sexual excitement, subsequently such an individual may feel the need to inflict pain on the mate with appropriate co-suffering to fulfill the requirements necessary for orgastic satisfaction.

He suggests that a person exhibiting conspicuous sadism or masochism with awareness of the subject of his needs and a willingness to dramatize them is relatively infrequent in comparison with the number of persons in whom a similar linkage exists without awareness by the subject or without serious consequences.

POSITIVE REACTIONS TO PAIN

The linkage of sex appetite and pain sensation is not the only example of conditioning of pain with basic needs. Indeed, the pain experience, especially in certain cultures, becomes an essential ingredient of adjustment. The ways in which this is accomplished by an individual may include a number of the patterns of reaction touched upon in the following paragraphs. For purposes of clarity, the patterns are appraised as more clearcut than they are usually encountered, but extremes of any one of these patterns do occur.

Depending on the individual's nature, past experience, and conditioning, pain sensation per se or threat may elicit any one or a combination of reactions presented below. These are epitomized and listed to indicate the variety and distinctiveness of such patterns. It is not implied that the list is a complete one.

a. Some persons complain of pain when, indeed, no pain is experienced. The individual perceives non-noxious stimuli which in the past have often been forewarnings of pain, and makes the necessary adjustments for avoiding it, i.e., bodily sensations such as fullness in the substernum in those subject to attacks of angina pectoris, of fullness in the head in those who frequently have vascular headache. That is, when questioned, or given examples of painful and non-painful sensory experiences, they readily discriminate between them and identify their sensations as non-painful. Also, some especially conditioned and anxious persons complain of pain in anticipation of being noxiously stimulated. The reaction, under these circumstances, is to the numerous afferent impulses other than those of a painful nature that accompany or precede a previously painful sensation to which the subject has become excessively responsive. Examples are children who "cry before they are hurt" and adults who because of the death from coronary occlusion of a member of the family or a friend now complain of pain from substernal sensations previously experienced as non-painful.

b. Pain is perceived and the individual makes adjustments to retard its development and, moreover, takes steps to avoid future exposure to the source of noxious stimulation. This occurs when the overall experience, including the pain, is not sufficiently satisfactory or rewarding to justify repetition of the pain endured.

c. Prolonged, low intensity pain is perceived and the individual, recognizing that there is no immediate danger connected with such pain (regardless of the source of noxious stimulation) learns to tolerate and accept the pain as an aspect of day-to-day living which can readily be endured and which on the whole carries with it less discomfort or disability than those procedures or agents designed to eliminate it. Conversely, because of inherent qualities or earlier conditioning, some individuals overreact to low intensity pain. Under these circumstances, a low intensity pain may induce responses more commonly associated with higher intensity pain, including feelings of alarm, panic, desperation, and conspicuous complaining.

d. The individual perceives pain pressed upon him by life circumstances, recognizes its high intensity and destructive nature, yet accepts and tolerates it because the experience is considered worthwhile by the individual. Examples are the pain of childbirth and pain from torture designed to elicit information of value to a military enemy (355, 473, 204, 161).

e. The individual induces painful states as incidental to the purpose of gaining prestige, social approval, winning a mate, or to achieve a prescribed bodily appearance, form, grace, or skill, i.e., pain induced by tight garments, shoes, coiffures, hair plucking, postures, gaits, plastic surgery; hunger pain endured to reduce weight to acquire the fashionable or youthful figure or appearance; pain from sunburn; painfully cold feet from sheer stockings and light shoes; puberty rites, ritualistic body scars.

As a corollary to this, the individual may actually select a certain course of action which brings with it a painful sequel, because the end or goal attained justifies the cost; for instance, a child, repeatedly humiliated by his mother in the presence of "outsiders", in turn humiliates her in the presence of a guest, realizing this will bring a "spanking" but the achieved vengeance makes the pain to be experienced worthwhile.

f. Life adjustments may be made because of desirable individual and social goals which bring with them bodily changes in themselves painful, but because their nature is understood by the individual, and since the goals are considered worth achieving the price is paid with pain. This pain is accepted and tolerated until excessive in intensity or duration, i.e., vascular headaches in striving, ambitious people may be the result of stressful life patterns which, when understood as the price of certain desirable ends, are accepted with patience.

g. Careers are chosen which may bring with them a high risk of painful experience, but which because of the prestige they carry or the zest, thrill, or excitement they induce, or the money they bring, are considered worthwhile and are tolerated; for example, being an explorer, an automobile racer, prize-fighter, etc.

h. The individual pursues, develops or induces low-intensity painful experiences because of the zest, excitement, or satisfaction of "full living" they induce, as with the use of snuff, pepper, "needle" baths, vigorous massage, cold showers, and ice water bathing.

i. Pain may be the complaint of persons who use the word as the equivalent of feeling states which may or may not be associated with the sensation of pain, i.e., misery, suffering, depression, feelings of hopelessness, and frustration. Such a response may not be in the nature of a delusion or hallucination, but the use of the term "pain" in connection with it more correctly presents a semantic difficulty in which no discrimination has been made between a feeling state stemming from one type of disagreeable experience and that from another, or even from pain itself.

j. Because of feelings of morbid guilt stemming from unacceptable attitudes involving hostilities, convictions of cowardice, or unworthiness, some persons feel more tranquil or satisfied when they are enduring pain. This may be self-induced, by exposure to cold, sleeping on a hard bed or sleeping board, or, in extreme instances, self-mutilation. On the other hand, the pain may be induced through the agency of others, i.e., the child may seek punishment or a "whipping" by a parent; an aggressive adult may initiate a quarrel with an overpowering opponent in order to be beaten by him; a nagging dissatisfied wife may take steps to provoke blows from an angry husband.

As a corollary of the above, feelings of guilt for whatever reason may cause some individuals to endure pain from bodily disease with unusual patience and fortitude, and induce tranquility in such persons, not present during periods of bodily health and well being. For instance, abdominal cramps in a patient with ulcerative colitis may be accepted with unusual patience.

It is not to be inferred from the above that pain is considered pleasant under circumstances in which it is preferred. It is a more profitable point of view to consider that painful conditions are among those that may be preferred relative to other alternatives. Although the hedonistic doctrine holds that individuals, by their choice among possible courses of action, try to maximize pleasure (23), this concept does not exclude the relative nature of such choices. Thus, as brief episodes of moderately intense pain or prolonged periods of low intensity pain can be sustained well enough, the individual may, under certain conditions, prefer pain to some other situation.

PAIN AND CULTURAL EMPHASIS

In some cultures, pain and the endurance of pain are looked upon as desirable disciplines and worthwhile experiences. Thus, because of the pain and suffering endured by Christ, certain Christians, in an attempt to identify themselves with the "Savior" or "God", or in an attempt to establish an ideal of Christian practice as they view it, embrace pain when it spontaneously occurs with disease (to "bear one's Cross"), or induce it by self-chastisement, i.e., "stigmata" in religious zealots.

The experience of pain in an individual, regardless of how induced—accidentally, self-inflicted, or spontaneously occurring from disease—may bring with it a highly developed response in certain cultures by which the sufferer is "protected" or "cared for". The individual who cannot express his need to be cared for when free of pain, because of cultural demands of self-reliance, initiative, and independence, finds himself in a socially or culturally acceptable position when he is experiencing pain. Thus, being "disabled" allows of or even puts a value upon being dependent and willing to be cared for. Indeed, he may even be disapproved of if he is seen to be impassive, "uncooperative", or a "poor patient". Under such circumstances the ideal behavior becomes one of almost complete passivity in which the individual remains immobile, allows himself to be fed, turned, and bathed. His creative work and occupational satisfactions are denied him, he is allowed no decisions, and may assume no responsibilities. Such a pattern has been rationalized as an attempt on the part of the culture to remove all burdens from the "sick" individual ostensibly fighting for his life.

It thus follows readily that some individuals with more need of support than the culture will allow to be exhibited in ordinary day-to-day living, will find in "pain" a suitable means for fulfillment of deeply felt needs. The pain experience will then be embraced as a way of life since it brings with it larger rewards than a state of freedom from pain.

As a corollary of the above, pain, regardless of how induced, may be a more acceptable sensation and experience than some other already existent variety of adaptation. Thus, anxiety, emotional tension, and asthenia, more or less overtly manifest, may be less satisfactory states than low intensity pain from a wound or lesion. Pain from wounds of battle may then actually be far more acceptable than the sustained anxiety and fear induced by battle conditions, i.e., "combat fatigue".

Pains experienced in certain parts of the body are culturally more acceptable and bring with them greater sympathetic response than others. Pains from the genitalia, rectum, and anus, or pain resulting from a fall on the podex do not evoke the sympathetic response that do pains from the extremities, from the chest, or even from the abdomen. Hence, pains of minor intensity from certain regions of the body are complained of more than others, and may, therefore, be more conspicuous when pain has been incorporated as a way of life.

Imposing independence on children before they are ready, long standing deprivation, notably of love and affection in infancy and childhood, may become linked with the pain experience, making it acceptable or even attractive. It may be a means of evoking from a parent, a spouse, a parent-surrogate, or a cultural group that support or regard which have long been withheld or reluctantly doled out.

In earlier chapters the close and highly predictable relationships of pain sensation and certain bodily reactions to noxious stimulation have been discussed. This chapter has been concerned with the variable dependence of the reactions to pain upon pain intensity, or, indeed, upon the presence of pain. Reactions to pain, however, form a proper category because they are characteristically associated with pain and are initiated by pain. Included in this reaction group are conscious and partly conscious, purposeful and non-purposeful behavior patterns. The partly conscious reactions are the most easily studied under laboratory conditions and as typical of this group the psychogalvanic skin response was studied under a variety of conditions. Although initiated by pain, this response can be shown to be dependent, within limits, upon the threat which the pain signifies to the individual rather than

TABLE 19

Analysis of the effects of noxious stimulation

A. Reactions *not* dependent on consciousness (nociception)
    I. Effects at site of tissue damage
        Inflammation
        Cellular death
        Electrical potential changes
    II. Integrated reflex effects
        Pilomotor
        Skeletal muscle contraction
        Gastrointestinal
        Sudomotor
        Neuro-endocrine
        Humoral
    III. Local lowering of threshold for noxious stimulation and heightened central excitatory state

B. Reactions *involving* consciousness—"The pain experience"
    I. Pain sensation
      1. Dimensions
        a. localization; site; extension—movement
        b. quality—burning, aching, pricking
        c. intensity—threshold to $10\frac{1}{2}$ "dols"
        d. temporal aspects—duration, frequency, rhythmic, pulsatile, diurnal, seasonal, periodic
      2. Modifying factors
        a. Admixture of other sensations—pressure, fullness, tightness, numbness, heat, cold, etc.
        b. factors increasing and decreasing intensity—primary and secondary hyperalgesia
        c. factors modifying site, quality, and temporal aspects
    II. Feeling, mood, attitude, bodily and behavior reactions to pain sensation
      1. Individual and cultural factors conditioning reactions to pain sensation (past life experience)
      2. Agents and procedures altering reactions to pain sensation
        a. analgesics and other pharmacodynamic agents
        b. suggestion, distraction, hypnosis
        c. life setting of the pain sensation (concurrent adaptation problems)
        d. reversible and irreversible alterations in brain function
          a. sleep
          b. brain injury

upon the intensity of pain per se. The reaction threshold, measured by the minimal intensity of thermal radiation which will evoke it, is more variable than the pain threshold and is more easily affected by analgesic drugs, hypnosis, laboratory conditions (room temperature), and the subject's attitude and emotional state. Feelings of relative tranquility are associated with a rise in the reaction threshold, and, inversely, feelings of anxiety are associated with a lowering.

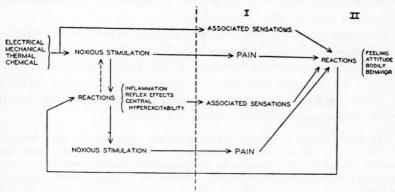

FIG. 95. INTERPLAY OF RESPONSES TO NOXIOUS STIMULATION NOT DEPENDENT UPON CONSCIOUSNESS AND REACTIONS INVOLVING CONSCIOUSNESS, AS AFFECTING THE PAIN EXPERIENCE

A (left of dotted line): responses not dependent upon consciousness. B (right of dotted line): reactions involving consciousness.

The hypo- and hyperdynamic nature of many of the reactions to pain were noted as contributing to processes of adaptation and re-establishment of homeostasis (397).

Pain is an important factor in conditioning behavior, in forming sex patterns, and may shape religious rites. Also, individual and cultural attitudes toward pain may constitute the dominant component of suffering in those with disease.

From the data of this and preceding chapters it is possible to outline in more detail the components of the pain experience and their interrelationships (table 19). In the outline, noxious stimulation is shown as evoking two major reaction groups, those not dependent upon consciousness, or nociception, and reactions involving consciousness, the pain experience. Many of the subdivisions of this outline have been the topics of experimental investigation and the details of the experiments have been presented in this and previous chapters. At first glance, it might seem as if the outline contained a list of functions of all physiological and mental life. However, the integration of the effects of noxious stimulation can be related in a definite pattern to the pain experience from evidence already presented. Diagrammatically the effects can be represented as connected by arrows to represent the direction of the action (see fig. 95).

The representation has practical as well as theoretical value as it indicates methods of approach for the control of pain as well as the pattern of responses involved in the pain experience. Such a concept is especially useful in the understanding of the action of analgesic agents, as a relatively small portion of such action involves suppression of pain sensation per se.*

* In this chapter, in attempting to penetrate more deeply, such words as "psychogenic", "hysterical", and "illusory", in describing pain, have been avoided, though not the phenomena they represent. Several reviews have been expressed in these terms, but especially entertaining is that of Macdonald Critchley (89a).

Chapter XII
PAIN SENSATION AND REACTIONS AS AFFECTED BY CEREBRAL DAMAGE

Vision, hearing, touch and other sensations as well as motor activity have been elicited by stimulation of special cortical areas, and thus the cortical representations for these sensations are known. Pain does not result from direct electrical stimulation of the cerebral cortex of intact healthy persons (338), although such stimulation of appropriate parts of the post central gyrus of patients with "painful" phantom limbs may augment or induce the characteristic sensations of which they complain (117a). Thus, a special center for pain perception has not been discovered, and it seems likely that the integration of pain sensation involves much of the thalamus and cerebral cortex. Indeed, patients suffering from intractable pain have been relieved by surgically damaging the cerebral cortex. Whether this relief was the result of reduced pain perception or alterations in reactions to pain was not at first clear.

Van Wagenen (442) was the first to note the effectiveness of prefrontal lobotomy for the relief of intractable pain. In 1942 and during the next few years Freeman, Watts and associates (134, 135, 136, 456, 455, 457) described a group of patients in whom intractable pain was relieved by bilateral lobotomy. These early observations were confirmed by Falconer (119) and by Koskoff and his associates (244).

Prefrontal lobotomy, either unilateral or bilateral, is performed by transecting the cerebrum in a plane identified by the coronal suture and the sphenoidal ridge and just anterior to the lateral ventricle. It is estimated that Brodman areas 8, 9, 10, 11, 32, 46, and 47 are isolated by these procedures (136). A series of fifteen brains has been examined post-mortem from one hour to one year after lobotomy by Freeman and Williams. Three were characterized by massive postoperative hemorrhage but in the other specimens (mostly from patients who had died of cancer) interruption of the thalamofrontal radiation with retrograde degeneration in the nucleus medialis dorsalis of the thalamus was characteristic of the operative lesion. Obviously, depending upon whether the section is more or less anterior and more or less deep, greater or lesser brain damage will ensue from the operative procedure. Therefore, considerable variation in effect may be anticipated.

Poppen and Dynes (343, 106) performed bilateral frontal lobotomy on eighteen patients and noted that "the results were more favorable in patients with metastatic malignant disease than any other group." This may possibly be related to the fact that in the first group symptoms had existed for an average of only 2.2 years, as contrasted with 12.8 years for the group without malignant disease. These authors state that "Certain patients with metastatic malignant disease never again complained of pain in the few remaining months of life. This, however, was the exception and not the rule. Most patients with metastatic malignant disease continued to complain of pain if asked if they had pain; however, if no comment was made to them and no questions were asked, they would not spontaneously complain of pain after lobotomy." As has also been noted by other observers, the procedure apparently attenuated the patient's anxiety and fear of and concern for impending death. In those who did not spontaneously complain of pain it was not necessary again to resort to the use of narcotics.

Scarff (380) performed unilateral prefrontal lobotomy on 33 patients with intractable pain, who were studied for periods ranging from one to ten months following operation. The results obtained were said to be as satisfactory as those obtained with bilateral lobotomy. Scarff (380) at the same time observed that abrupt termination of the use of narcotics, on which some of these patients had become dependent for the relief of pain prior to operation, was not followed postoperatively by the usual withdrawal symptoms. Preoperative pain in these patients was due to a variety of pathologic processes, such as carcinoma of the tongue, jaw, pancreas, metastatic carcinoma of long bones, metastases to the spine, trigeminal neuralgia, aneurysm of the thoracic aorta, and advanced arthritis. The results in 22 were "completely satisfactory". In five patients, the results were unsatisfactory. In three patients of the group with poor results, immediate relief of pain was later followed by return of pain. Scarff (381) later reported on a larger series of 58 patients with approximately the same results.

The particular "psychometric" tests applied to patients of this group before and after operation failed to reveal any alteration in intellect or personality. As with the patients studied by Poppen and Dynes the usual withdrawal symptoms in patients who had been addicted to the use of drugs for the relief of pain were absent.

Comparable results in the management of intractable pain have been observed following "topectomy", a procedure characterized by attempts to remove specific brain areas. Le Beau and J. Gacheo (264, 265) operated upon 25 patients with intractable pain by removing the rostromedial portions of areas 9, 10, and 46. The patients were followed for periods up to 23 months. In four, the "pain" was in no way influenced. Bilateral topectomy was effective in relieving causalgia of 25 year's duration in one, and of seven month's duration in a second patient.

Riechert (367), on the basis of his experience with patients with intractable pain and from operations performed under local anesthesia while the patient experienced intractable pain, noted that cutting the thalamofrontal tracts differentially or progressively reduced the area of pain. It was inferred that cutting portions of the thalamofrontal tracts, principally those leading to the median basal orbital part of the brain, was related to the altered pain.

Freeman and Watts, as a result of a study on therapy of painful conditions by means of transorbital lobotomy, concluded that "generalized pain and distress can be alleviated more readily than pain due to direct involvement of nerve trunks" (131).

MEASUREMENT OF PAIN THRESHOLD AND PAIN INTENSITY BEFORE AND AFTER PREFRONTAL LOBOTOMY

A series of 38 prefrontal lobotomies [performed by Dr. Bronson Ray in the New York Hospital] on patients with intractable pain was selected for study. This group included patients with: metastases from tumors of the breast and of the bronchus; pheochromocytoma; Hodgkin's disease; radiculitis; tabes; phantom limb; and atypical facial neuralgia. Either unilateral (25 patients) or bilateral (thirteen patients) lobotomy was performed. During periods of from one month to several years postoperatively, patients were studied in terms of whether or not they were relieved or free of pain, or whether or not they said they experienced pain when asked about it. These inquiries indicated that following the operation four patients had no pain whatever, three of these following unilateral operation. Fifteen other patients offered no spontaneous complaints but when asked replied that they were experiencing pain but that it no longer "bothered" them. Eight of these had had bilateral operations. Following bilateral operation two patients had spontaneous complaints of pain in addition to complaints on inquiry, but the pain was of lower intensity than before. The remaining seventeen showed no change as regards complaints of pain. Fifteen of the latter had had a unilateral lobotomy. In short, in 21 out of 38 persons, following lobotomy, some relief of pain appeared to have been achieved in some way; of these, seventeen admitted experiencing pain only when asked; four had no pain at all.

There was no evidence from these studies that painful states from one structure or region of the body were modified either more or less than those from others. Also, there was noted no significant difference in effect whether the pain stemmed from a structure deep or superficial, visceral, or "somatic". In no instance was the spontaneous pain for which the procedure had been done increased as a sequel of the lobotomy. Occasionally, however, there was noted a widespread hyperalgesia of the skin which persisted for some hours after the surgical procedure.

None of the patients with unilateral operative lesions in this group showed evidence of serious disorganization of personality. Following bilateral lobotomies, all had changed more or less in personality integration. In one, serious disorganization of personality followed and in two others less serious changes were noted.

Despite efforts to define the areas destroyed in precise anatomic terms, it was often extremely difficult to know what had been destroyed even though one described where the knife had cut. Brain damage is often diffuse. However, in each patient an estimation was made of the amount of brain damaged by the operative procedure. This was relatively easy when sections were made bilaterally, and difficult when made unilaterally.

Following the development of methods of estimating pain intensity, a group of patients was studied before and after operation. Measurements were made of the pricking pain threshold, of the intensity of the intractable pain, and of the degree of hyperalgesia when this was a prominent feature of the patient's complaint.

Pain Thresholds

Measurements of pain threshold by the thermal radiation method were made on skin areas of the forehead and back of the hand in eight patients prior to operation. Care was taken to choose areas in which there was no evidence of hyperalgesia or other manifestation of disease. The average of all of these measurements was 206 mc./sec./cm.^{2}, with a standard deviation of ± 21 mc./sec./cm.^{2} This is a mean value within the normal range. As shown below the intensity of their spontaneous pain was of low order and did not appreciably affect the pain threshold.

Pain threshold measurements were made in ten patients post-operatively. In two patients the pain threshold was observed to be lowered immediately following operation. In one of these who was observed again two weeks post-operatively the pain threshold had returned to the pre-operative level. In three patients who had been measured pre-operatively the post-operative pain threshold was unaltered. In five patients who were not measured pre-operatively, measurements one week or more post-operatively gave pain thresholds within the normal range, 200 to 230 mc./sec./cm.^{2} The mean of all post-operative pain threshold measurements was 209 mc./sec./cm.^{2}, a value which is not significantly different from the pre-operative level. King (241) also reported slight lowering or no change of pain threshold in patients after unilateral prefrontal lobotomy for intractable pain.

Pain Intensity

In five patients it was possible to obtain measurements of pain intensity as well as of pain threshold before and after operation. Patients were chosen who were mentally clear and who would cooperate in the tests. Each subject was thoroughly instructed before the tests as regards the identification of the pain threshold and the matching of pain intensities. Measurement of pain intensity involved the patient's comparing the intensity of his spontaneous pain with that of a series of pains of increasing intensity induced on the skin with the dolorimeter. Pains of both lesser and greater intensity than that of the spontaneous pain were always included so as to "bracket" the intensity of the spontaneous pain.

All of the patients were females suffering from carcinoma of the breast which had painfully involved the head, neck or upper extremities. Four of the patients had unilateral lobotomies; one of these was studied eighteen months post-operatively when she returned to the clinic for further treatment for relief of her pain. One patient had bilateral prefrontal lobotomy.

When circumstances permitted patients were studied twice daily in the pre-operative period, at times in which the effect of medication was minimal. The pain threshold was measured as the first procedure during a testing session. Thresholds were measured on skin areas of affected parts as well as on contralateral unaffected parts and on the forehead. The intensity of the then existing pain was measured by presenting the series of suprathreshold stimuli on the forehead or on unaffected skin areas. The subject was then asked to recall the most intense and the least intense pains she had suffered during the preceding 24 hours from the diseased parts. These intensities were matched by pains induced with the dolorimeter and noted as the "maximum" and "minimum" pain intensities. An "average" pain intensity was obtained from the reported duration and intensity of pain.

When the part of the body concerned with the intractable pain was tender, pain threshold measurements were made in these skin areas. If these values were found to be markedly lower than those from the contralateral unaffected part, comparative measurements were made to determine the extent of the hyperalgesia. This was accomplished by applying a stimulus of "normal" threshold intensity to the affected skin and matching the pain thus produced with pains from suprathreshold stimuli on the "normal" or unaffected contralateral part.

PRE-OPERATIVE

A summary of spontaneous pain intensity measurements is included in table 20. In general, the pain was of low intensity with brief episodes of more intense pain accompanying a disturbance of a diseased part. However, at no time was any patient completely free of pain. These two factors characterized the pain picture in these patients. In two patients there was marked tenderness of the hand and arm with low pain thresholds.

TABLE 20

Intensity in "dols" of spontaneous pain—pre- and post-lobotomy measurements

PATIENT	PRE-OPERATIVE MEASUREMENT (IN "DOLS")			POST-OPERATIVE MEASUREMENT (IN "DOLS")								
				1st week			2nd week			18 months		
	Ave.	Min.	Max.	Ave.	Min.	Max.	Ave.	Min.	Max.	Ave.	Min.	Max.
1	2	T	4	1.5	T	2	0.5	T	0.5	—	—	—
2	0.5	T	2	0	0	0	0	0	0	—	—	—
3	3	T	6	T	T	2	—	—	—	—	—	—
4	T	T	T	T	T	T	T	T	T	—	—	—
5	0.5	T	1	T	T	T	T	T	T	—	—	—
6	(2–3)*	—	—	—	—	—	—	—	—	2	0.5	3.5

* As remembered.

POST-OPERATIVE

For comparative purposes, the intensity measurements of spontaneous pain for all patients are included in the table in the same form as for the pre-operative measurements. The studies were carried out daily as long as the patients were available. These results show:

a. In only one patient was the intractable pain completely eliminated.

b. In four out of five patients the pain was reduced on the average and in maximum value. However, they were at no time pain free.

In order to illustrate some of the effects brought about by the operation the pain charts of two patients are included. In figure 96 are shown the measurements on patient #1 (see table) of pain intensity and pain threshold before operation and during the two weeks following. Although this patient was operated on bilaterally the pain was reduced but not abolished. A serious alteration in personality occurred in this patient, but in spite of it her reports as to pain threshold and pain intensity were reproducible. She had no areas of superficial tenderness.

The next two charts (figs. 97 and 98) are those of patient #3

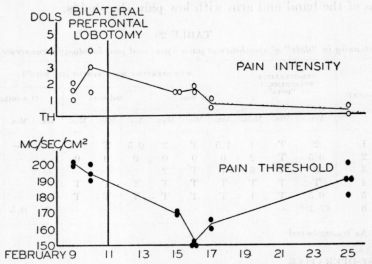

Fig. 96. Pain Intensity and Pain Threshold Levels Before and After Bilateral Prefrontal Lobotomy

whose pain arose from a swollen and tender left arm and hand. In figure 97 are shown the pain threshold measurements on the two hands before and after right prefrontal lobotomy. There was a slight rise in pain threshold in the normal hand following operation, but there was a dramatic disappearance of the tenderness in the swollen hand after operation. The pain threshold in this hand was increased almost 300 per cent following the operation.

In figure 98 are shown the pain intensity and degree of hyperalgesia before and after operation. Also, in this patient the pain intensity was measured before and after a procaine infiltration of the right prefrontal lobe before the operation. The spontaneous pain was eliminated for two days following the procaine and indefinitely following lobotomy. The marked *primary* hyperalgesia present before the operation was abolished for three or four days

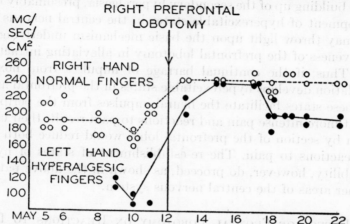

FIG. 97. PAIN THRESHOLD LEVELS ON NORMAL (O) AND DISEASED (●) FINGERS
BEFORE AND AFTER UNILATERAL PREFRONTAL LOBOTOMY
The marked rise in pain threshold indicates the elimination of the local tenderness due to primary hyperalgesia (see Chapter VIII).

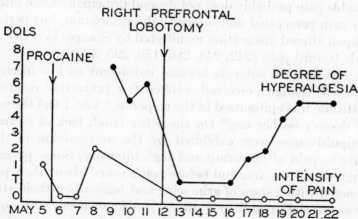

FIG. 98. PAIN INTENSITY LEVELS (O) FOLLOWING: a) PROCAINE INFILTRATION
OF PREFRONTAL LOBES, AND b) UNILATERAL PREFRONTAL LOBOTOMY
Degree of hyperalgesia in diseased fingers (●) before and after operation.
The increased tenderness in the postoperative period is due to the development
of secondary hyperalgesia (see Chapter VIII).

after the operation, but was gradually replaced by a *secondary* hyperalgesia which had almost the same intensity as the original primary hyperalgesia.

The building up of the secondary hyperalgesia, presumably from development of hyperexcitable states in the central nervous system, may throw light upon the basic mechanism underlying the effectiveness of the prefrontal lobotomy in alleviating intractable pain. Thus, if the continual barrage of impulses from noxious stimulation develops hyperexcitable states in the prefrontal areas, and these states facilitate the neural impulses from the periphery so that more intense pain and reactions to pain result, their elimination by section of the prefrontal lobes would reduce both pain and reactions to pain. The re-establishment of states of hyperexcitability, however, do proceed, as shown in the above patient, in other areas of the central nervous system.

The Effect of Frontal Lobotomy on Reactions to Pain, Including Attitude, Mood, and Behavior Patterns

The therapeutic effectiveness of frontal lobotomy for relief of intractable pain probably does not depend principally upon alteration in pain perception and intensity discrimination, but perhaps more upon altered integration manifested by changes in affect and attitude toward pain (242, 243, 286, 158, 295, 339).

The lobotomized subjects became indifferent to low intensity pain which, though perceived, evoked few protective reactions. The attitude was epitomized in the response, "Yes, I feel the pain, but it doesn't bother me." On the other hand, lack of restraint and impulsiveness were exhibited by the overreaction of these patients to pain of moderate and high intensity. Some patients, although ostensibly tranquil before being asked about their pain, overreacted with a show of grimacing and fears when their attention was focused upon it by a direct question concerning its quality and intensity. However, in the midst of such a show of suffering their extreme distractability was evidenced by the fact that a diversion induced a smile or even laughter.

Also, they exhibited a freedom from anxiety about pain, did not anticipate its occurrence and lacked an interest in recall and description of pain experienced in the past. Each painful experience was dealt with in its own terms as a fresh experience. They showed little concern about the implications of pain as regards damage to the body or threat to life. Also, the anxiety evoked by and associated with painful stimulation was much reduced. Indeed, these subjects exhibited in many ways, notably concerning the topic of pain, a flattened affect if not actual apathy. When noxious stimulation of high intensity was suddenly imposed upon them experimentally or by some surgical procedure, despite immediate vigorous reactions, these subjects promptly ceased to exhibit evidence of pain, "forgot" their recent experiences, and turned to the casual reading of a newspaper or idly looking about. Lack of complaint and failure to call attention to their plight and needs were striking. They failed not only to complain of their spontaneous pain but also of their needs, such as personal nursing care, need of urine bottle, bedpan, or the adjustment of an uncomfortable dressing. When incontinent of feces they were indifferent to the odor it spread about their persons and beds.

On the other hand, their freedom from pain and lack of anxiety about it were not coupled with any mounting interest in work or with plans for resuming their responsibilities. The impression was gained that patients previously well integrated who had been bilaterally lobotomized for pain exhibited more striking evidence of personality disintegration than did psychotic patients exposed to similar procedures.

It has been noted that the results of lobotomy as regards intractable pain are unpredictable. The impression has been gained from contact with patients that obsessive compulsive personality features are common among those with intractable pain and that anxiety is accompanied by bodily complaints especially if there be pain. Indeed, Rioch (369) noted that one patient, "relieved" of pain from cancer by prefrontal lobotomy, would again complain of pain when confronted with topics involving certain stressful interpersonal relations, to which he reacted with anxiety and would again become symptom-free when the anxiety was dispelled.

GENERAL COMMENT

Reactions to intractable pain following prefrontal lobotomy may be better understood if the overall performance of the patient is appraised. Brickner and others (57, 471, 309, 375, 411) have noted from studies of those who had sustained frontal lobe damage that behavior was impulsive and lacking in restraint, and that initiative and creative fantasy were usually reduced. Koskoff indicated that although performance of well known psychological testing procedures seemed not to be strikingly impaired, the creative capacities were dulled. There appeared to be an inappropriateness of response to a wide variety of stimuli and situations. Rylander (377) made an intensive study of a group of 32 lobectomized patients who had had frontal lobe tumors. His procedures included visits to the patients in their home environments, during which he interviewed the patient, his family, friends and associates. He applied tests for attention, memory, comprehension, abstract thinking, and configuration, and concluded that the emotional life of individuals suffering injury to the frontal lobes was dulled, although these individuals were subject to paroxysms of easily dispelled rage. They became tactless and distractible. They showed reduced ability to synthesize concepts, draw inferences, and make generalizations; their ability to think in abstract terms had deteriorated. They manifested defects in judgment, impaired retention and diminished rate of work. Persons who exhibited lively mood changes before operation, demonstrated euphoria, talkativeness and lack of inhibition following operative resection of a frontal lobe. Withdrawn, shut-in individuals became more shut-in and more secretive than before. Exaggeration of the basic features of the personality took place following injury to the frontal areas of the brain. These changes did not destroy the subject's ability to adjust to community life at some level but creative work abilities were markedly impaired. According to Scarff, unilateral lesions sufficient to eliminate the complaint of pain in those with intractable pain were compatible in some instances with highly ethical and responsible behavior.

It is evident from our studies that following prefrontal lobotomy for intractable pain there is not only a change in reaction to pain but a disturbance in perception as well. In about 10 per cent of such subjects this is striking at least for a time, if not permanently; in most who have experienced relief from spontaneous pain, it is evident to a slight degree. For example, a pain of low intensity from a bony periosteal metastatic lesion may no longer be perceived, whereas suddenly introduced cutaneous and deep noxious stimuli of higher intensity are perceived, at the usual intensity. Also an individual with such a disturbance may retain the memory of the intensity of the pain previously experienced from the metastatic lesions, i.e., he can identify experimental pains as more, less or exactly as intense as his previous pain. In other words, limited though it be, there is in most subjects following prefrontal lobotomy more or less disturbance in perception.

Further support for this view is the observation of Halstead (175) that dynamic visual field studies also demonstrate an alteration in perception in lobotomized patients. The dynamic visual field is that portion of the peripheral retinal field which can be made to yield a threshold visual impression at the same time that a form discrimination is being made in the region of the fovea. In the healthy person this dynamic visual field corresponds to the campimetric field. In it, a threshold visual impression in the order of time of 20 to 50 milliseconds may be appreciated, whereas in patients with lesions of the frontal lobe, there may be a constriction of the dynamic visual field even with exposures of objects up to 80 and 100 milliseconds. Thus in those who experienced prefrontal lobotomy, objects were not perceived in the peripheral fields with equal speed and accuracy, although the portions of the cerebrum primarily involved in visual perception are at some distance from the prefrontal lobes. Although not noted in all instances of lobotomy (505) such defects in the visual field were noted also by Bender et al. (29) who studied patients with more diffuse brain damage not directly involving the occipital lobes or visual pathways. These disturbances may be linked to those first observed many years ago. Persons after vascular or traumatic accidents involving the visual structures of the occipital lobe on one side of the brain may become for a time, totally blind. Gradually vision returns in the ipsilateral field and ultimately there remains only a homonymous hemianopia.

Additional evidence on the lack of high order of specificity as regards site of the lesion in relation to effect on pain comes from van Wagenen (443) who observed that in one instance a surgically made lesion in the temporal lobe was effective in the relief of a patient with intractable pain, and Horrax (222) noted "good relief from pain" in 2 out of 4 patients after excision of the postcentral cortex.

Chapman (75) investigated the "reaction" threshold in a group of 23 lobotomized patients and the ability to perceive pain 15 to 16 days post-operatively, and at intervals of 3, 6 and 12 months after lobotomy. These patients, in response to the thermal radiation, winced and pulled their heads away from the apparatus at significantly less intense stimulation than before lobotomy. The observations are in keeping with those made at the bedside where it becomes apparent that the removal of stitches and changes of dressings evoke even more vigorous reaction than similar noxious stimulation before lobotomy. It thus appears that frontal lobotomy has the effect of altering the response of the previous continuous influx of impulses from low intensity noxious stimulation without altering response to new or fresh or shortlived noxious stimulation. Thus, when suddenly moved or turned over, the patient, who until this time may have been relaxed and tranquilly resting in bed, may cry out vigorously with pain from bombardment of additional noxious impulses from his damaged bone and joint structure.

van Wagenen noted that what he calls the "after glow" of pain is shortened or absent after lobotomy (i.e., the pain experienced for a few seconds following firm compression of the Achilles tendon).

The concept that knowledge of intensity of spontaneous pain is of major importance in predicting whether or not a patient will feel pain after prefrontal lobotomy is upheld by an observation of Freeman (132). He reports that lobotomized women during labor accepted the first stage with a gay, cavalier manner, but during the second stage they vigorously overreacted, requiring special measures for their management in an obstetrical ward.

Bonner, Bobb, Sweet and White (47) studied a series of patients with intractable pain, as regards the effect of bilateral lower quadrant, bilateral, and unilateral lobotomy. These authors, too, have had the impression that the effects on the personality of these non-psychotic persons were graver than were those in psychotics. All of the patients in this series with bilateral extensive lobotomy demonstrated deterioration of personality. Those with bilateral lower quadrant lobotomy were apathetic. The groups with unilateral lobotomy demonstrated less serious disturbances, including apathy, inappropriate emotional response, less spontaneity in talking, longer latency in responding to prompting, decreased rate of speech, and, on the whole, a greater need of prompting to maintain verbal communication. There were seventeen in this group, and the effects as regards pain were "good" in twelve, "fair" in four, and "slight" in one.

In essence, there are a few features that stand out concerning the relationship of the frontal lobes to the sensation of and reaction to pain.

Firstly, it apparently makes no difference, as regards either of these features in patients with intractable pain, which frontal lobe, homolateral or ipsilateral, is injured. When pain is experienced in both right and left parts of the body the effect is equally great whether lobotomy is performed on the dominant or non-dominant hemisphere.

Secondly, patients having lesions giving rise to more or less sustained but low intensity noxious stimulation and low intensity pain are most likely to be benefited by prefrontal lobotomy.

Thirdly, the capacity to tolerate "intractable" pain without complaint or much reaction is increased after lobotomy. The effects observed as regards "relief from pain" and reduction of the complaints of pain appear, in general, to be related to the amount of frontal lobe damage induced. In the series of 38 patients, approximately 40% of those who had unilateral lobotomies obtained some relief, whereas 85% of those with bilateral operations were relieved. On the whole, there is less reaction to pain in those with more brain damage. On the other hand, it does not follow that major damage on both sides eliminates reaction to pain when the intensity of the pain is moderate or high. There is a recurrence of the complaint of pain when, because of progression of the disease, intensity of the pain increases. In brief, in appraising the effect of lobotomy on the pain experience there are two major variables; i.e.,

a. The intensity of the spontaneous pain experienced preoperatively by the patient. For a patient to be effectively relieved, the spontaneous pain must not be of high intensity.

b. The amount of damage to the brain done by the surgeon. Within limits, the specific area involved in brain damage seems to be of less importance than the amount of damage.

Fourthly, although the pain threshold may show temporary alterations, the average of the pain thresholds before and after operation is essentially the same.

Fifthly, reactions of patients to intractable pain are generally reduced, especially with pain of low intensity, although the "reaction threshold" as determined by wincing is not elevated and in many instances is actually lowered.

Sixthly, the intensity of "intractable pain" is reduced or eliminated in some patients, at least temporarily. States of primary and secondary hyperalgesia may also be temporarily abolished. These changes are not necessarily associated with any loss in ability of the subject to discriminate between noxious stimuli of different intensities.

Lastly, it would appear that any procedure which markedly alters or reduces reaction to pain and noxious stimulation has some effect on pain perception. This generalization is valid, regardless of whether the modifying factor be a chemical agent, the result of life experiences, or the result of injury to the brain.

From the neurophysiological point of view, these observations furnish a partial answer to the question, Which parts of the cerebral cortex are implicated in the perception of pain? Thus, pain of low intensity and long duration is affected by either infiltration of procaine into the prefrontal lobes or by surgical separation of these areas from the rest of the brain. However, as pain localization and discrimination are left unaltered by these procedures, the prefrontal areas of the cortex must be thought of as associated with rather than responsible for pain perception.

Inferences as to Mechanism

Impulses arriving from the periphery have their effectiveness within the nervous system modified by the prevailing state of the latter. Thus, for example, it has been found through studies of secondary hyperalgesia and itching that certain states of "hyperexcitability" exist in the cord at segmental levels. Noxious stimuli which are intense enough to excite peripheral organs, thus giving rise to impulses which reach the cord, may have their effectiveness augmented so that more intense pain sensation is experienced. It has been suggested that this is accomplished by a system of closed-chain neuronal circuits in which states of increased excitation are sustained by low intensity noxious stimulation at or even below the pain threshold. Such states of excitation can be terminated by blocking the source of the pathways of low frequency impulses. Once so interrupted, considerable time may be necessary for their re-establishment; indeed, they may not recur at all.

Similar circuits exist at suprasegmental levels and their excitatory states may be modified by certain agents, by life experiences, and through effects exerted by cerebral damage. The existence of such cortical hyperexcitability, dependent upon a minimal inflow of impulses from the periphery, need not alter pain thresholds. It is conceivable that the frontal lobe damage may exert an influence upon the thalamus and cerebral cortex in such a way as to interfere with dispersion of the effects of afferent impulses and thus to break up excitatory states which have been established by sustained low intensity noxious stimulation. Furthermore, lobotomy, in reducing such states of central excitement, would not prevent the perception of stimuli at the usual threshold levels. It would, however, curb or eliminate "intractable" pain dependent upon low frequency discharge by interference with the maintainance of such hyperexcitatory states within the cerebrum. The depressing effects of lobotomy on vision and the visual fields mentioned above lend support to this general view of the phenomenon, as does the observation of Rioch that the introduction of disturbing symbols revives the experience of pain from peripheral sources of low grade noxious stimulation.

As Livingston points out (287) one may postulate that these central excitatory effects, their gradual "building up" and "spread" over wide territories are a manifestation of long lasting pain, as though the central excitement were developing more and more of a "momentum". Exposing the individual to threatening circumstances or symbols may augment or inhibit the development of such "momentum"; frontal lobotomy curbs it.

Chapter XIII

THE EFFECT OF ANALGESIC AGENTS UPON PAIN

Though chemical agents have been used as analgesics for many hundreds of years, it is only within the recent past that quantitative methods for the study of pain have become available, thus making possible a more precise systematic study of the effects of such agents in man. The demand for better analgesics has increased steadily since the isolation of morphine from crude opium was effected by Friedrick W. A. Setürner in 1805 (398). As a result many new analgesics continue to appear for clinical trial in the hope of finding a morphine substitute which will have at least as strong a power to abolish pain but less potentiality for addiction (110, 410, 245).

One of the practical aspects of the study of pain sensation is the application of the methods in evaluating the effectiveness of means for relieving the sufferer. The search on a broad front for more effective analgesic agents has resulted in a group of drugs not chemically related, but having in common the power of reducing or abolishing the sensation of pain. Such lack of chemical relationship has impeded the study of the connection between chemical structure and analgesic potency (73). Though the literature on the effects of analgesics has grown steadily during the past decades, much disagreement still exists among investigators as regards both the facts of analgesic action and their interpretation (414, 491, 43, 99, 117, 125, 151a, 474).

The Characteristics of Analgesic Action

An analgesic may be defined as a substance which through its action upon the nervous system serves to reduce or abolish suffering from pain without producing unconsciousness. When a person experiencing pain is given an analgesic agent whose action affects some part of the neural apparatus, there are at least eight aspects of this effect which are factors in the evaluation of its usefulness. Some of these can be appraised quantitatively.

The first aspect is the pain threshold-raising property of the

325

analgesic agent, in the assay of which one can be reasonably precise, but which may not be the most important aspect of the therapeutic effect.

The second is the pain reducing property of the agent, likewise susceptible to measurement. Although this effect is often related to the pain threshold-raising property of the agent, it can change independently of the pain threshold.

A third effect is the property of the agent in curbing the influence of noxious stimulation either by direct action upon afferent nerves or upon central excitatory states at the segmental level. Painful contractions of smooth and skeletal muscles are sometimes effectively eliminated by the direct action of procaine upon afferent fibers or by the more central action of morphine. The sometimes massive, summated responses to noxious stimulation can be reduced or abolished by analgesics (127).

The fourth feature may be referred to as the capacity of the substance to change the attitude or mood of the subject in pain. Useful therapeutic effects in this category might be: promoting freedom from anxiety, mild euphoria or feelings of well being, or apathy. As commented upon in the previous chapter, central excitation heightened by the effects of adverse life events with accompanying feelings such as fear and anxiety, may further augment the intensity of pain. Consequently, reducing or abolishing such states may afford an important degree of relief from pain. Less desirable, however, and even dangerous, would be the stimulation of feelings of extreme excitement, depression, or hopelessness.

The fifth facet may be considered the agent's effect as a sedative and soporific, i.e., whether it induces relaxation and sleep, thus bringing about a state of "rest".

The sixth aspect is the evoking of so-called "side effects", chiefly of an untoward nature, i.e., whether it induces nausea, vomiting, diarrhea, or constipation and other non-painful but disturbing bodily changes.

The seventh factor is whether an agent's toxic effects, which jeopardize tissues or body functions, or even life itself, result from amounts that are near those required for therapeutic effect, thus imposing too high a risk when it is used. Coupled with the assets of an agent for inducing relief from pain there may exist a more or less serious potentiality for creating dependence, which may make its use fraught with danger.

Although the aspects of analgesic action just mentioned are conspicuous, there are other important ones such as tolerance, specific sensitivity, absorption into skin or gastrointestinal tract, rate of elimination, etc. (19). At this time it is not possible to make quantitative studies on all of them and the emphasis of this chapter is directed to factors one and two above.

Finally, and eighth, though perhaps not justifiably in a separate category, is the agent's total effect on the person experiencing pain. That is, does the individual "feel better" as a result of its administration? Is this state of better feeling purchased at too great a price in terms of the untoward side effects, and does it add to the general effectiveness of the therapeutic regimen prescribed for the patient?

Since many persons, miserable and frightened, "feel better" because of the symbolic significance of a pill, capsule, or injection regardless of pharmacodynamic action or lack of it (placebos), the total effectiveness of an agent must be more than the sum of the separate effects listed above. Also, many severely injured persons do not experience as much pain as the damage to their bodies and perhaps even lethal injuries might suggest (25). Hence, a relatively weak analgesic may suffice to achieve "relief" in such cases (236).

The sensation of pain can be affected by agents acting upon various parts of the physiological system involved in pain. These include the pain receptors and surrounding tissues, the conducting pathways (including the fiber tracts and the synaptic connections), the internuncial connections in the cord, and the afferent relay nuclei in the thalamus and the cortex (73). Agents which cause a reduction of pain by action upon the tissues surrounding the pain receptors are not generally considered to be analgesics. For example, ergot, which is effective in reducing the pain of migraine headache by its vasoconstrictor action, is not classified as an analgesic (167). In the same category are milk and alkalizing agents which abolish the pains of peptic ulcer, and atropine and calcium which relax painfully contracted smooth muscle.

METHODS OF STUDYING ANALGESIC ACTION

There are four general methods now in use for studying the degree of effectiveness of an analgesic agent. These are: 1) testing the effects of the agent upon the reaction of an animal to noxious stimulation (300, 111, 112, 474, 10, 196, 497, 197, 228); 2) the measurement of pain threshold-raising effect in normal human subjects (396, 321, 322, 8, 66, 74, 126, 130, 168, 183); 3) the measurement of pain-reducing effects of the agent both in normal humans with experimentally induced pain, and in patients experiencing pain spontaneously from whatever cause (191, 180, 230, 229). At the same time, untoward side reactions produced by the agent are evaluated. A fourth method is the statistical analysis of reports concerning "comfort" from patients following the administration to them of one or more analgesics or placebos (99, 236).

Actually, the first of these methods cannot be considered a study of pain sensation but rather of reactions to noxious stimulation. Much useful data has been obtained by using animals for the detection of possible analgesic effects of new agents and for testing their toxicity. Indeed, for this latter purpose animals are indispensible.

The authors (492, 491) have demonstrated the capacity of centrally acting analgesics to raise the pain threshold for all qualities of pain, and thus to produce superficial and deep hypalgesia. Also, Javert and Hardy have shown that the pain threshold-raising effect of an analgesic is not a necessary condition for reducing pain intensity (229). In a woman in labor apomorphine greatly reduced the intensity of labor pains but there was no cutaneous pain threshold-raising effect as measured by the thermal radiation method. This is an example of the third aspect of the action of an analgesic, i.e., by reducing the effects of noxious stimulation through depression of the motor apparatus within the segment involved (441). It is postulated that the effect of apomorphine in this instance is that of differentially reducing the intensity of the uterine contractions in the region of the internal os, so that fundal contractions are more effective though less painful (230).

Analyzing patients' reports of "comfort" is unquestionably the best available method of assaying the overall effectiveness of an analgesic in the relief of suffering. Due to the all-inclusive nature of a series of reports of patients little can be learned of the details of the effects produced by an agent. Thus, given an agent which is shown to relieve suffering, is this effect due to one, two, or a combination of a number of the eight effects of analgesics mentioned above? Clearly, answers to these questions must be obtained if the search for more effective agents is to be fruitful. Among the available data should be the measurements of as many as possible of the dimensions of pain, of the reactions to pain, and of the reactions to noxious stimulation (See p. 304).

The above observations demonstrate that the effectiveness of an agent in reducing pain must ultimately be evaluated by quantitative studies on patients in pain. Thus, animal testing serves as a rough assay of analgesics, tests on normal humans furnish a more accurate assay of potency, and measurements in patients evaluate the effectiveness of the agent under circumstances most relevant to suffering. The final criterion for judging the degree of effectiveness of an analgesic, and of the side reactions it may induce is always based on data obtained on humans.

Denton and Beecher (99) have used a method for the clinical evaluation of analgesics, based on the capacity of an agent to relieve "natural or pathological pain", i.e., pain that is a consequence of disease or trauma. They state that, in distinction to "experimental pain", "natural pain" consists of both the perception of painful stimuli and "the psychic modification of these stimuli". They employed two groups of subjects: a) healthy volunteers, solely for the appraisal of side reactions of the new agent; and b) 429 post-operative patients from the gynecologic, orthopedic and general surgical wards for the evaluation of the effect on pain and the side action liability of analgesic agents. The patients chosen were adults who had recently undergone a major surgical procedure and who were "psychologically oriented" and capable of answering questions referable to their pain. They exhibited no evidence of surgical shock, impaired hepatic function, "active asthma", myxedema, or seriously reduced vital capacity. The identity of all agents was concealed from both the subjects and the observer. Initially, each new agent was given in small amounts. The effects of the analgesics to be tested were compared with those of morphine sulphate. One group of patients received morphine sulphate, 10 mg./150 lb., as the initial medication after operation, and a second group received the test agent. If the latter was ineffective within 90 minutes and produced no serious side effects the amount administered was increased until "pain was adequately controlled". All agents were administered subcutaneously.

In these studies, the analgesic effect of each agent was assayed in groups of 25 or more patients, according to the amount which, in comparison with morphine, gave "relief" of pain in 90 per cent of the subjects. "Relief" was defined as the disappearance of "most" or "more than half" of the pain; an effect less than this was considered to be "no relief". An agent was considered analgesic only when "relief" was reported at both 45 and 90 minutes following administration. Analgesic potency was expressed as a "percentage" of the "relief" obtained from the test agent to that obtained from administration of 15 mg. of morphine. This "relief" was expressed both in terms of the number of patients "relieved" and in terms of the number of doses required for "relief". Observations began with the first post-operative administration of the analgesic, and continued until "relief" was achieved to such an extent that the analgesic being tested was no longer needed. Relief was graded as none, slight, moderate, or complete, on the basis of the patient's estimate. If the patient went to sleep after administration of the agent, "relief" was classified as complete. A technician first interviewed the patient; then, after administering the agent remained with him for at least half an hour to ascertain the time of onset and degree of "relief". Thereafter the patient was interviewed once every hour until ten o'clock in the evening.

The second and third of the four general types of investigation of analgesic potency as mentioned above, have been used on normal subjects and on patients in the laboratory at Cornell University Medical College and the clinics of The New York Hospital. They are measurements of a) the pain threshold-raising action, and b) the pain-reducing action.

STUDIES OF PAIN THRESHOLD-RAISING ACTION

A measurable aspect of analgesic action is a raised threshold to noxious stimulation in any part of the body. This effect of raising the pain threshold has been inferred to arise from the action of analgesic agents upon the central nervous system, since in concentrations used in man, analgesic agents do not affect the function of the pain receptors or the conducting pathways. Thus, analgesic action can be studied by measurement of the pain threshold for any type of pain in any convenient location on the body.

SUGGESTION

Before giving a detailed account of the experiments on pain threshold-raising action, it is necessary to discuss the effects of suggestion upon these measurements. Suggestion is a potent factor modifying discrimination of pain threshold following administration of analgesic agents, or of placebo substitutes. Suggestion is always present in experiments aimed at measurement of analgesic action, although under suitably controlled conditions its effect can be evaluated. For example, a subject who knows he has been given an analgesic will demonstrate more pain threshold-elevating effects of the agent than does the subject who, receiving the same agent, is convinced that he has not received an analgesic. Thus, in seven out of nine tests on three trained subjects, a greater threshold-raising effect was observed after administering an agent when the subjects were assured that it was an analgesic than when told that one or more of the tablets might be placebos. The first situation contained a greater "positive" suggestion than did the second. In the presence of such positive suggestion isotonic saline injections and placebo tablets often have the effects of mild analgesic agents, both in allaying distress in a suffering patient, and in raising the pain threshold. Inversely, skepticism, or an attitude of excessive caution in compensation for a dulled mental state following administration of an analgesic agent, may cause a subject to report no change, or even a lowering of pain threshold. A dramatic example of the effectiveness of positive suggestion is contained in the observations of Beecher (25). He found that 20 to 35 per cent of patients, following extensive operative procedures and battle wounds, obtained "complete relief" after subcutaneous injection of saline.

As an example of negative suggestion, seven medical students, following intramuscular injection of 40 mg. of Meperidine, after having been told that some placebos were included, showed 33 reports of no effect or of *lowered* pain threshold. In only seventeen of the 50 tests were raised pain thresholds reported (177).

Testing of pain threshold-raising action is a procedure requiring a stable, favorable attitude toward the tests, maximum concentration at the level of perceptual discrimination, and a feeling of confidence in the correctness of an estimate when it has been made. A desire to make the report pleasing to the observer is as unacceptable as an unsympathetic attitude toward the procedure.

To evaluate more clearly the effects of subject attitude and of operator-subject influence, three series of experiments were performed under different circumstances with three common analgesic drugs—Meperidine, codeine, and aspirin. Measurements of pain threshold were made prior to receiving any agent to establish a control level. After administration of the drug threshold measurements were made at fifteen-minute intervals for a period of about 90 minutes or until the maximum effect of the agent was obtained.

In the first series of studies the subjects were the three authors. The individuals, one woman and two men, were of approximately the same age and weight (i.e., 65 kg.) and, as might be expected, were conscientious witnesses, interested and willing. During these experiments the subjects were free of all pain other than that induced by the test procedure. Freedom from pain before and during the period of pain threshold measurement is important, as it will be seen that pain, per se, raises the pain threshold, and that pre- or co-existing pain seriously alters the threshold-raising action of analgesics. In these experiments the subjects were given aspirin and were usually aware of the nature and amount of agent given.

In the second series of experiments the above routine was altered by having one person who received no agent operate the pain threshold apparatus and keep the record of all measurements and observations on each subject's behavior. The subjects were the three authors and three trained research workers; they received placebos, aspirin, Meperidine, and codeine. Neither observer nor subject was aware of the nature or amount of the agent administered, and each subject kept his own notes of his feeling state. Most consistent measurements were obtained when a quiet room was set aside for the testing and only the subject and the operator were present during the measurement. This minimized the effects of distraction.

The third series of experiments was performed on 80 medical students by testing the subjects in groups of four to six under the direction of a trained observer. The subjects and observers were not informed as to the nature of the agent given, although they were told that placebos would be included. The subjects were untrained but were intelligent and had been instructed in the recognition of the pain threshold.

OBSERVATION

The three trained subjects were tested in twelve experiments following ingestion of 0.3 to 1.8 gm. amounts of aspirin (acetylsalicylic acid). As the agent was given in the familiar tablet form taken from a labelled bottle there was no question in the minds of the subjects or observers as to whether an active agent was being ingested. The curve of pain threshold raising effects for the 0.3 gm. amount is shown in figure 99. Almost identical curves were noted following ingestion of 0.3, 0.6, 0.9 and 1.8 gm. amounts. indicating a maximal pain threshold-raising effect for aspirin of 30 to 35 per cent (fig. 100).

Five trained subjects were given identical appearing capsules, some containing lactose, and some containing 0.6 gm. of aspirin. It was emphasized that an analgesic agent was being given each time to each subject. In spite of this attempt to induce "positive suggestion" as to the nature of the agent, skepticism existed in the minds of some subjects, resulting in a degree of "negative suggestion". The results of these tests are shown in figure 101.

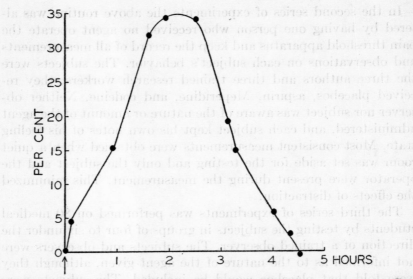

FIG. 99. AVERAGE VALUES OF PAIN THRESHOLD-RAISING ACTION OF 0.3 GM. ASPIRIN IN 3 TRAINED SUBJECTS

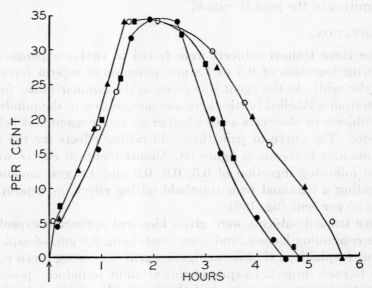

FIG. 100. INFLUENCE OF 0.3 (●), 0.6 (■), 0.9 (▲), and 1.8 (○) GM. AMOUNTS OF ASPIRIN UPON THE PAIN THRESHOLD IN 3 TRAINED SUBJECTS

In the 32 tests on these six subjects, made between 45 and 90 minutes after the ingestion of the capsules (the approximate period of maximal action of aspirin), there were sixteen comparisons possible between reports of subjects who had received aspirin and those who had received lactose. Significant pain threshold-

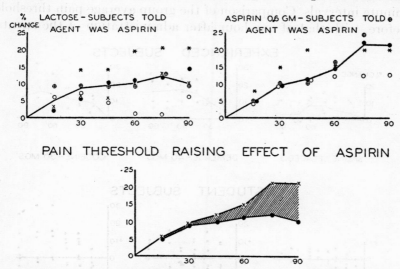

FIG. 101. THE PAIN THRESHOLD-RAISING EFFECT OF ASPIRIN COMPARED WITH THAT OF LACTOSE, SUBJECTS BEING TOLD THAT INGESTED AGENTS WERE ASPIRIN

Abscissa = per cent elevation of threshold above control level. Ordinate = time in minutes. The upper two curves are individual measurements for 5 trained subjects. Lower curve is the averages of the values from the upper curves. The shaded area represents the pain threshold-raising effect of aspirin over and above that of lactose.

raising action (i.e., more than five per cent) of aspirin over and above the effect of the lactose was evident in thirteen of the sixteen comparisons. From this it may be concluded that aspirin has a small but significant pain threshold-raising action of roughly fifteen per cent, which is over and above placebo action operating under the special circumstances of this experiment. This is shown by the shaded area in figure 101.

The 80 medical students were studied following administration of 0.6 gm. of aspirin to 40 of the group and lactose placebos to the

other 40. The agent and the placebo were contained in identical
appearing capsules, administered by a third person so that neither
subject nor observer was aware of the nature or amount of the
contents. Control pain thresholds were established prior to taking
the agent, after which pain thresholds were measured at fifteen-
minute intervals. Comparison of the group average pain threshold
before, with that of one hour after administration of the agents,

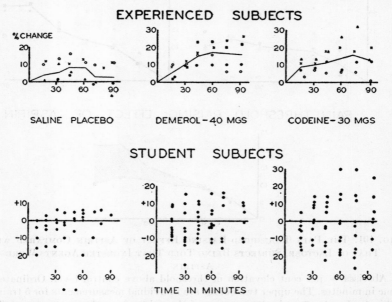

FIG. 102. COMPARISON OF MEASUREMENTS OF 5 TRAINED SUBJECTS AND 80
STUDENT SUBJECTS, FOLLOWING SUBCUTANEOUS INJECTION OF SALINE
PLACEBO, MEPERIDINE 40 MG. AND CODEINE 30 MG.

showed no significant change. Similar findings have been reported
from other laboratories (414, 333). These same 80 students, in
another group of tests, exhibited a group average of *lowered* pain
thresholds after administration of 40 to 100 mg. amounts of
Meperidine and 30 to 60 mg. amounts of codeine by subcutaneous
injection. Thus, it was concluded that such subjects, under the
laboratory conditions prevailing at the time, were not suited to
the study of pain threshold-raising effects of these analgesic agents.
A comparison of the performance of untrained subjects with that

of experienced subjects under identical laboratory conditions, following administration of placebos, 40 mg. of Meperidine (Demerol), and 30 mg. of codeine is shown in figure 102. The wide scatter of the reports of the student subjects is due to the lack of training and to variable attitudes toward the tests. Also, in some especially suggestible individuals it is not possible to obtain predictable reports of threshold during test procedures.

Meperidine and codeine show significant pain threshold-raising effects in the amounts given when the tests are carried out on trained subjects (see fig. 102).

COMMENT

From the data presented above for the three test situations, it is concluded that the degree of pain threshold-raising action which is obtained depends in large measure upon the circumstances surrounding the test procedure. Thus, the procedure in the first series results in values of pain threshold-raising action which include a factor of *positive* suggestion as well as the pharmacodynamic action of the analgesic. The psychological conditions of this series are in many respects similar to those of the patient who receives an agent from a trusted physician. For this reason these procedures are reported in more detail in this chapter.

The data of the second series are more nearly of the type sought by those interested only in the pharmacodynamic effect of the agent in raising the pain threshold. However, due to unavoidable *negative* suggestion under such experimental conditions the pain threshold-raising action may be somewhat suppressed.

The data of the third series indicate the impracticability of making tests of threshold-raising action on groups of untrained subjects.

Measurements of the Pain Threshold-Raising Effects of Analgesic Agents in Three Trained Subjects

The experiments to be described were performed in the manner of the first series above. Two reasons prompted this: a) it was hoped to keep suggestion strongly positive by permitting the subject to know that an analgesic had been given, although occasionally a placebo was introduced; b) with even moderate amounts of such analgesics as the opiates it is not possible to disguise the fact that a particular subject has received a placebo. Accepting this experimental plan, however, has the disadvantage that results obtained under it will not be in agreement with those obtained by the usual pharmacological control techniques such as those described in the second series. This latter method will yield more nearly the minimal pain threshold-raising effects for a given amount of an agent as compared to the higher and perhaps more realistic values obtained by the method of the first series. Results obtained by the two methods can be brought into agreement by subtracting ten to twenty per cent from the values obtained by the first experimental plan. Useful results cannot be obtained by the method of the third series within the range of pharamacologic action of interest.

EXPERIMENTAL METHOD

The average pain threshold was ascertained during a control period, to an accuracy of ± two per cent (see Chapter IV). After establishing the control levels of pain threshold an analgesic agent was administered and subsequent measurements of pain threshold were made at ten to fifteen minute intervals. Measurements were continued until pain threshold-raising action had passed its peak as evidenced by a return of the pain threshold toward the control level. The degree of the pain threshold-raising action is expressed in per cent elevation above the control levels in terms of units of stimulus applied. However, a more generally useful method of expressing the data would be in terms of the number of "dols" elevation above threshold pain. This latter expression gives information as to the analgesic effect measured by any method of noxious stimulation (see Chapter VI). Protocols were distributed so that the threshold of each subject was measured by a colleague who in turn was unfamiliar with the change in his own threshold. Thus, independent protocols were made, no individual knowing how much his own threshold had been altered. The agents were administered either orally or intramuscularly. At intervals lactose or NaCl was introduced into one of the capsules or syringes so that it was known to all that one of the subjects had not received an analgesic drug, although which one had received a placebo was not revealed until the end of the experiment.

With each pain threshold reading the subject made a concise statement of his feeling state. In the ten to fifteen minute intervals between readings the subjects sat comfortably in a quiet room, engaged in reading, writing or conversation, and were free from all interruption. Sleep was not permitted and if drowsiness became difficult to manage the subjects walked about the laboratory. During long experiments a sandwich was eaten but not until sufficient time had elapsed for the development of maximum effects of the analgesic agents.

THE OPIATES

Up to the present by far the greatest investigative effort has been directed toward the study of the analgesic and other effects of the opiates. A large part of this effort has had as its goal the development of new potent analgesics which would not produce the psychological and physiological dependence developed in the patient by repeated administrations of morphine. Eddy and his co-workers in the United States Public Health Service (110, 410, 245, 111, 112) have made the most thorough study in this direction. The results of their many years of effort are contained in several monograph publications which contain the chemical as well as the analgesic investigations of this prolific group. Several new and potent analgesics of the morphine group were discovered during the course of this study. Eddy did most of his work on analgesics with animals, using compression of the tail and the outcry of the animal as the indicator of pain. His monographs contain exhaustive surveys of the literature up to 1935. Much work with various testing techniques has been done in the past fifteen years and a brief listing of some of the principal papers is given in the bibliography. In general, the effects reported were similar to those found by Eddy.

In 1916 Macht, Herman and Levy (300), using faradic stimulation of the skin, made one of the first studies of a quantitative nature of the effects of the opiates upon normal man. Seevers and

Pfeiffer (396), in 1934, made a study using von Frey hairs on the upper lip as a test procedure. This study was of modern design, consisting of, first, establishing control levels of threshold before administration of the agent, and subsequent study of the threshold level for the duration of the effect. Records of sensations were made and the activity of the subjects was controlled. Care was taken in selection of mature, stable subjects, and in their indoctrination in the testing process. The results of the tests agree in a remarkable way with the values of analgesic potency found by Eddy in animal tests.

Since 1932 an additional effort has been made to study the analgesic action of the opiates in man not experiencing pain, and also to some extent in subjects experiencing pain. The pain threshold-raising activity of these agents in man without pain, by whatever method tested, is similar to that observed in the experiments presented below. The pain threshold-raising effects found by different investigators have varied, and, as has been indicated, this is to be expected. The presentation of the effect of the opiates will be in terms of the work done in the Cornell laboratory, with appropriate references to the work of other observers who have contributed to the present state of knowledge (9, 408, 62, 93, 226, 227, 233, 267, 268, 407, 406, 454, 469, 18, 20, 21, 170, 215, 266, 392, 415, 430, 431, 432, 4a).

MORPHINE SULFATE

The average of the results of the experiments with different quantities of morphine from 0.1 to 30 mg. are shown in figure 103. The threshold for pain was observed to rise within ten minutes following injection, except for the smallest dose. The degree and duration of the threshold-raising effect increased with the amount administered. Whether the amount of the agent was large or small the threshold began to rise after the same interval of time but continued to rise at different rates until the peak effect for the particular amount had been reached. When the morphine was given in quantities from 0.5 mg. upward, the peak of action was reached at almost the same time, namely, in approximately 90 minutes. With 30 mg., however, the peak effect was not reached until 150 minutes after administration. The duration of action from control threshold back to control threshold varied from three hours in the case of 0.5 mg. amounts, to somewhat over seven

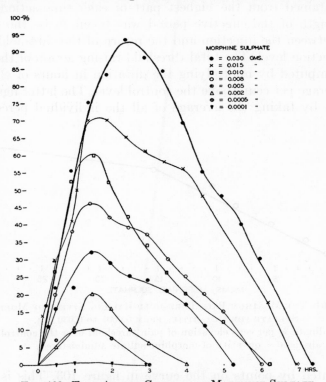

FIG. 103. TIME-ACTION CURVES FOR MORPHINE SULFATE

Pain threshold elevation after morphine sulphate in quantities of 0.0001 to 0.030 gm. The ordinate = per cent elevation of pain threshold over the control level as zero. The abscissa = duration of effect. The zero indicates the time of injection of the morphine sulphate. Each point represents the average of the threshold levels for 3 subjects.

hours in the case of 30 mg. amounts. The 0.1 mg. amount of morphine sulfate was apparently without any threshold-raising action.

COMMENT

The time-action curves of figure 103 can be analyzed in three ways as regards the amount of agent given: 1) the maximum height of the pain threshold-raising effect, 2) the length of the period of effectiveness, and 3) the total threshold-raising action of the agent. The maximum height of the threshold-raising action was obtained from the highest part of each time-action curve. The length of the effective period was taken to be the elapsed time between the injection and the return of the threshold to the pre-injection level. The total threshold-raising action of the agent was computed by multiplying the duration in hours of effect by the average per cent above the control level. The latter figure was derived by taking the average of all the individual percentages

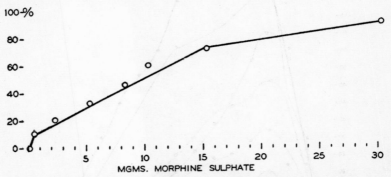

FIG. 104. THE MAXIMUM PAIN THRESHOLD-RAISING EFFECT OF MORPHINE SULFATE FOR QUANTITIES FROM 0.0001 TO 0.030 GM.
The ordinate = per cent elevation of pain threshold over the control level as zero. The abscissa = quantity of morphine sulfate administered.

represented by points on the curve in figure 103. This is represented by the area under each time-action curve.

It will be seen (fig. 104) that the maximum analgesic effect in terms of quantity is a straight line function of the dose from 0.5 to 15 mg. A similar dose-response relationship has been obtained by Beecher from an analysis of reports of "relief" following injections of morphine. Doubling the amount of the agent, i.e., from 15 to 30 mg., increases the threshold-raising effect less than 20 per cent.

The pain threshold-raising effects of morphine sulfate in amounts of 2 mg. or less come within the range of "placebo action" (see below) when it has been suggested to the subject that the agent he received has a threshold-raising effect. Placebo action in these experiments is further evident from the fact that the extrapolation of the dose-response curve through zero amounts

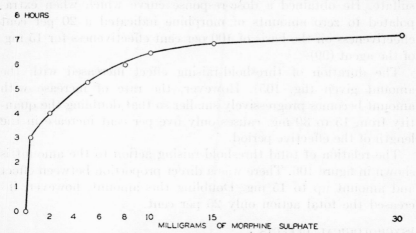

FIG. 105. THE RELATION BETWEEN DURATION OF THRESHOLD-RAISING EFFECT (ORDINATE) AND THE QUANTITY OF MORPHINE SULPHATE ADMINISTERED (ABSCISSA)

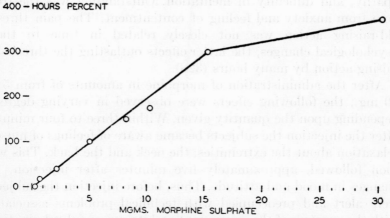

FIG. 106. THE RELATION BETWEEN THE TOTAL THRESHOLD-RAISING EFFECT AND THE QUANTITY OF MORPHINE SULFATE ADMINISTERED

The ordinate was computed by multiplying the average per cent rise in pain threshold by the hours of duration of effect resulting from a given quantity of morphine sulphate. The abscissa represents quantity of morphine administered.

of morphine indicates a threshold-raising effect of ten per cent due to suggestion. A similar effect was found by Beecher in assaying the pain-reducing effects of various amounts of morphine sulfate. He obtained a dose-response curve which when extrapolated to zero amounts of morphine indicated a 20 per cent effectiveness on the basis of 100 per cent effectiveness for 15 mg. of the agent (99).

The duration of threshold-raising effect increased with the amount given (fig. 105). However, the rate of increase with amount becomes progressively smaller so that doubling the quantity from 15 to 30 mg. causes only five per cent increase in the length of the effective period.

The relation of total threshold-raising action to the amount is shown in figure 106. There was a direct proportion between effect and amount up to 15 mg. Doubling this amount, however, increased the total action only 25 per cent.

PSYCHOLOGICAL EFFECTS

In addition to the rise in pain threshold, the administration of morphine resulted in relaxation, freedom from anxiety, lethargy, apathy, and difficulty in mentation. Outstanding was the freedom from anxiety and feeling of contentment. The pain threshold-raising action was not closely related in time to these psychological changes, the latter effects outlasting the threshold-raising action by many hours (328).

After the administration of morphine in amounts of from 5 to 30 mg., the following effects were observed in varying degrees, depending upon the quantity given. Within three to four minutes after the injection the subjects became aware of feelings of muscle relaxation about the extremities, the neck and the back. This was soon followed, approximately five minutes after injection, by changes in mood and attitude. Thus, before injection the subjects were alert and preoccupied with technical problems associated with the progress of the experiment and its successful culmination. After injection "all seemed to be going well". Time between readings, which formerly seemed long and tiresome, became short and pleasurable. Loquacity was evident within a half hour after the injection. Conversation was agreeable and steady without push. Anxieties or dilemmas not concerned with the experiment also seemed less weighty, and anticipation of events immediately to follow the experiment was free from conflict. This change in attitude was maintained for the next two to three hours.

After about 30 minutes, attention, retention, and concentration became more difficult, as did clear, logical, or continuous thinking. Such difficulties in mentation continued for three to four hours.

Commonly, freedom from anxiety was associated with and followed by apathy. There was an increasing indifference to situations and decisions, with little concern about either difficulties or opportunities. As a manifestation of apathy, the attitude toward vomiting experienced with the 30 mg. amounts was instructive. While the vomiting was repeated and violent it was associated with no more emotional reaction than would ordinarily accompany rinsing the mouth or swallowing.

Lethargy outlasted the above effects and was present often for as long as 24 hours. Toward the end of this time it ceased to be accompanied by a mood which made acceptance or indifference possible. Apparently, in reaction to decreased effectiveness, the subjects experienced annoyance, impatience, and resentment. Such states became manifest sometimes as soon as four hours after injection and persisted for 24 to 72 hours.

The administration of 30 mg. of morphine sulfate produced, in addition to the changes described above, a state akin to prostration. Pallor, loss of initiative, nausea, vomiting, sweating, weakness, and unsteadiness of gait were the dominant features.

MORPHINE WITH SCOPOLAMINE

The combination of morphine sulfate and scopolamine hydrochloride (in amounts of 8 and 0.4 mg., respectively) was injected intramuscularly. The pain threshold-raising effect of morphine was not increased, nor was the duration of action prolonged as a result of the addition of scopolamine. All the usual physiological and psychological effects of morphine were present and the following appeared in marked degree: dry mouth, unsteady gait, difficulty in accomodation, dry smarting eyes, difficulty in mentation, and lethargy. The combination may have assets as regards the induction of sleep or relaxation, but its threshold-raising action is not superior to that of morphine alone.

CODEINE PHOSPHATE

Codeine phosphate was injected intramuscularly in amounts of from 15 to 120 mg. The time-action curves for 60 and 120 mg. amounts of this agent are shown in figure 107. As in the case of morphine, the maximum threshold-raising effect was reached at approximately the same time for all the aforementioned quantities, i.e., in about 90 minutes. The duration of action varied from three hours with doses of 15 mg. to somewhat more than five hours after 120 mg.

COMMENT

The maximum pain threshold-raising effect of this agent was proportional to the amount administered, from 15 to 60 mg. (fig. 108), resulting in a rise of 45 to 50 per cent above the normal threshold. Administration of double this amount, or 120 mg., caused no further rise in threshold. Therefore, 60 mg. may be considered the saturation quantity for codeine, and a 50 per cent rise in threshold above the control may be considered its saturation level.

To test the concept of "saturation" level and quantity, a second dose of 60 mg. was given when the pain threshold had been raised to the established maximum effect of approximately 50 per cent above the control level by an initial 60 mg. dose.

Figure 109 shows that despite three attempts to raise the threshold above the previously attained maximum through the addition of 60 mg. of codeine at 80-minute intervals, no further elevation was observed. The threshold-raising effect was not increased beyond that produced by the first 60 mg. injection. The threshold returned to the control level four hours after the last injection.

The above experiment demonstrated the validity of the concept of a "saturation" quantity and level, and showed that the only effect of additional amounts as regards threshold-raising is

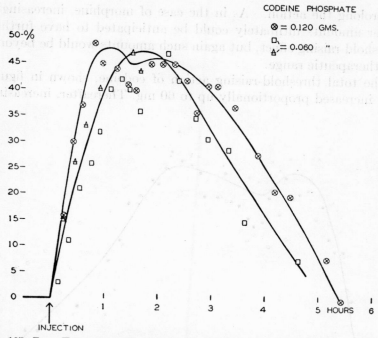

FIG. 107. PAIN THRESHOLD ELEVATION AFTER QUANTITIES OF 0.60 AND 0.120 GM.
OF CODEINE PHOSPHATE

The ordinate = per cent of pain threshold elevation over the control level as zero. The abscissa = duration of effect. Each point represents the average of the threshold in 3 subjects.

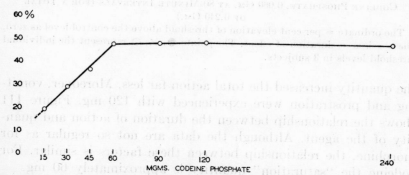

FIG. 108. THE MAXIMUM THRESHOLD-RAISING EFFECT OF CODEINE PHOSPHATE
FOR QUANTITIES FROM 0.015 TO 0.240 GM.

The ordinate = per cent elevation of pain threshold over the control level as zero. The abscissa = quantity of codeine phosphate administered.

to prolong the action. As in the case of morphine, increasingly larger amounts ultimately could be anticipated to have further threshold-raising effect, but again such amounts would be beyond the therapeutic range.

The total threshold-raising action of codeine, shown in figure 110, increased proportionally up to 60 mg. Thereafter, increasing

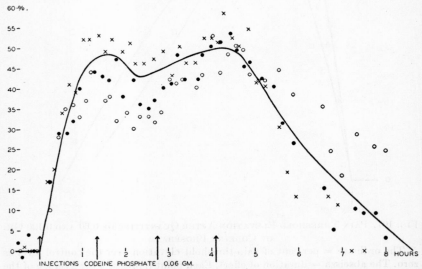

FIG. 109. THE EFFECT ON THE PAIN THRESHOLD OF REPEATED INJECTIONS OF CODEINE PHOSPHATE, 0.060 GM. AT 80-MINUTE INTERVALS (FOR A TOTAL OF 0.240 GM.)

The ordinate = per cent elevation of threshold above the control level as zero. The abscissa = duration of effect. The points ●, ×, ○ represent the individual threshold levels in 3 subjects.

the quantity increased the total action far less. Moreover, vomiting and prostration were experienced with 120 mg. Figure 111 shows the relationship between the duration of action and quantity of the agent. Although the data are not so regular as for morphine, the relationship between these factors is similar. For codeine the "saturation" quantity is approximately 60 mg.

Several other well known related compounds were tested to ascertain whether they possessed more effective pain threshold-raising qualities than morphine or codeine.

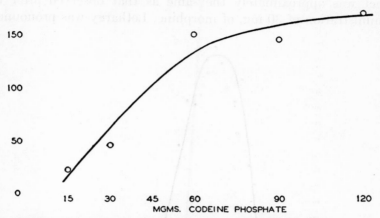

FIG. 110. THE RELATION BETWEEN THE TOTAL THRESHOLD-RAISING EFFECT
AND THE QUANTITY OF CODEINE PHOSPHATE ADMINISTERED

The ordinate was computed by multiplying the average per cent rise in pain threshold by the hours of duration of effect resulting from a given quantity of codeine phosphate. The abscissa represents the quantity of codeine administered.

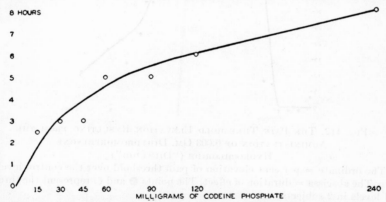

FIG. 111. THE RELATION BETWEEN DURATION OF THRESHOLD-RAISING EFFECT
(ORDINATE) AND THE QUANTITY OF CODEINE PHOSPHATE ADMINISTERED
(ABSCISSA)

DIHYDROMORPHINONE HYDROCHLORIDE ("DILAUDID")

Three mg. of this agent were given intramuscularly to two subjects. The psychological effects were pronounced and the pain threshold-raising action dramatic. At the peak of its action the threshold was raised somewhat over 100 per cent (fig. 112). This effect was approximately the same as that observed after the administration of 30 mg. of morphine. Lethargy was pronounced

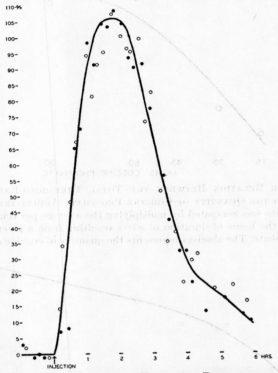

FIG. 112. THE PAIN THRESHOLD ELEVATION RESULTING FROM THE ADMINISTRATION OF 0.003 GM. DIHYDROMORPHINONE HYDROCHLORIDE ("DILAUDID")

The ordinate = per cent elevation of pain threshold over the control level as zero. The abscissa = duration of effect. The points ● and ○ represent the threshold levels in 2 subjects.

and there was repeated vomiting. The psychological effects were little different from those experienced after 30 mg. of morphine sulphate.

PANTOPIUM HYDROCHLORIDE ("PANTOPON")

Twenty mg. of "Pantopon", given intramuscularly, raised the pain threshold about 35 per cent and the duration of the effect was five hours (fig. 113). Many of the psychological and physiological effects common to morphine were encountered. The threshold-raising action of 20 mg. of pantopium was equivalent to that of about 8 mg. of morphine sulfate.

METHYLDIHYDROMORPHINONE ("METOPON")

The injection of 6.6 mg. of methyldihydromorphinone had a threshold-raising action which was comparable to that of approxi-

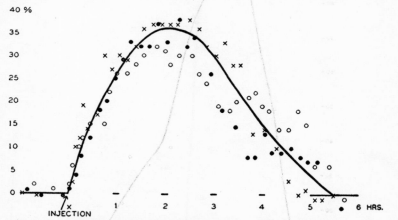

FIG. 113. THE PAIN THRESHOLD ELEVATION RESULTING FROM THE ADMINISTRATION OF 0.020 GM. PANTOPIUM HYDROCHLORIDE ("PANTOPON")

The ordinate = per cent elevation of threshold above the control level as zero. The abscissa = duration of effect. The points ●, ×, ○ represent the individual threshold levels in 3 subjects.

mately 30 mg. of morphine sulphate. The peak effect was attained in about 90 minutes and remained at a level of approximately 90 per cent above control threshold for one and one-half hours, after which the threshold gradually lowered, reaching the control level about seven hours after administration (fig. 114). Vomiting began two hours after injection and occurred intermittently for the next two hours. The symptoms of prostration, as described with 30 mg. of morphine, were present.

Psychological effects were first manifested within ten minutes of the time of injection of the above compound. They began with feelings of "light-headedness," relaxation, and fullness in the head.

The freedom from anxiety and feelings of contentment bordering on euphoria, characteristic of morphine, soon followed. Time sense was shortened. The mood alteration persisted for about two

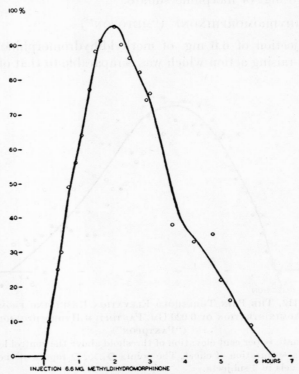

FIG. 114. THE PAIN THRESHOLD ELEVATION RESULTING FROM THE ADMINISTRATION OF 6.6 MG. METHYLDIHYDROMORPHINONE ("METOPON")

The ordinate = per cent elevation of pain threshold over the control level as zero. The abscissa = duration of effect. Each point represents the average of the threshold levels in 3 subjects.

hours, after which followed lethargy and a state bordering on prostration. As demonstrated by the ability to retain numerals, concentration and retention were disturbed. Four hours after the injection there was still lethargy and indifference to intermittent vomiting. The subjects were unable to differentiate these effects from those which were experienced with 30 mg. of morphine sulfate or with 3 mg. of dihydromorphinone hydrochloride ("Di-laudid"). However, the sequelae of the methyldihydromorphinone were of shorter duration, and 24 hours after the injection no after-effects were noted.

COMMENT

Aside from the fact that different amounts of the various mor-phine-like compounds were required to produce the same thresh-old-raising effect, no other marked differences in the effects of these agents were noted. Thus, as regards the eight prominent effects of analgesics previously mentioned, it may be concluded that all of the compounds studied have actions in rough proportion to their pain threshold-raising ability.

The inferences from these experiments concerning the assay of threshold-raising effects of opium derivatives might be criticized on the basis that they represent the action upon only one quality of pain and that they may not be valid for deep pain of aching quality. However, there is evidence which indicates that these analgesics also have similar threshold-raising effects as regards deep, aching pain sensation.

The deep pain threshold-raising effects of codeine phosphate was tested in three subjects who received 30 mg. of the agent, subcutaneously. The maximal effect of the agent for deep pain was comparable to that obtained for cutaneous pain by expressing the threshold-raising effect in terms of capacity to reduce pain of measured intensity to zero. Another commonly used analgesic agent, Meperidine ("Demerol"), was assayed both as regards cutaneous pain threshold-raising effect, and deep pain threshold-raising effect. Results indicated that by both methods, the thresh-old-raising effect of 40 mg. of Meperidine, intramuscularly, was equivalent to the action of 30 mg. of codeine. In terms of ability to reduce pain intensity to zero, the above amounts of each of these agents should be effective in abolishing a two- to three-"dol" pain.

OTHER ANALGESIC AGENTS

Among the most commonly used analgesics are those of the group of coal-tar derivatives, acetylsalicylic acid (aspirin), acetanilid, and acetophenetidin. These agents have so mild an effect, compared with that produced by the opiates, that some question has been raised as to whether their pain threshold-raising action is the principal factor in reducing pains from headache, myalgia, neuritis, and other bodily disorders. To test the pain threshold-raising effects of these agents, especially carefully conducted experiments were necessary as it was evident that such pain threshold-raising effects as were present were of the magnitude of those usually obtained by "positive suggestion" and placebo action.

ASPIRIN

Being the most important of this group, experiments were made with aspirin according to both the plans of the first and second series described at the beginning of this chapter. The curves of pain threshold-raising effect in the three trained subjects for 0.3 to 1.8 gm. amounts of the agent are shown in figure 100. Amounts of the agent greater than 0.3 gm. prolonged the threshold-raising effects but did not increase it beyond the 30 to 35 per cent level.

The only noticeable reaction of this agent upon the subjects, even in the largest amounts given, was that of mild relaxation. No change could be detected in attention, retention, or in appreciation of the passage of time.

ASPIRIN AS A THERAPEUTIC AGENT

The ability to raise the pain threshold, coupled with relatively minor effects on mood or mentation gives this agent, and presumably other salicylates, a unique position in therapy. It may be administered in relatively large amounts over long periods with slight danger of dependence.

Aspirin has been found to be especially useful in pains of low intensity, not only when circumscribed but also when widespread in origin. If the pain is of an intensity that cannot be abolished or greatly reduced by the threshold-raising effect of the agent, then no matter how limited the area of distribution is, no amount of this substance will stop the pain. For example, the intense pain associated with coronary occlusion, though it emanates from a very limited area, is not eliminated by aspirin. On the other hand, the relatively low grade pain of rheumatic fever, although very widespread in origin, is dramatically abolished.

These facts are compatible with the evidence that there is no spatial-summation for pain, formulated elsewhere. Thus, the total intensity of several areas of different intensities of pain is equal not to their sum, but merely to the intensity of the severest pain. It requires no more of an analgesic to abolish a widespread area of low-grade pain than it does to abolish a very small area of pain of the same intensity.

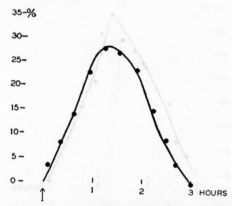

FIG. 115. THE AVERAGE PAIN THRESHOLD ELEVATION FOR 3 SUBJECTS
RESULTING FROM THE ADMINISTRATION OF 0.3 GM. ACETANILID
The arrow indicates the time of administration of the acetanilid

There is the possibility that quantities of aspirin greater than those necessary to raise the pain threshold the maximal amount may be required to attain other useful actions of this agent.

ACETANILID

Four experiments on three subjects were done with 0.3 gm. of acetanilid (see fig. 115). The height and duration of the pain threshold-raising effect were of the same order as that of acetyl-salicylic acid. Relaxation, drowsiness and difficulty in mentation were noted, and concentration, retention, and attention were all slightly impaired. Restlessness was allayed and even anxiety was diminished but there was no euphoria.

ACETOPHENETIDIN

Two experiments were made on three subjects to ascertain pain threshold-raising effects of 0.3 gm. of acetophenetidin (see fig. 116). Psychological effects from this agent were more pronounced than from acetylsalicylic acid and similar to those produced by acetanilid.

It is possible that these psychological effects of acetanilid and acetophenetidin, coupled with their threshold-raising action, are

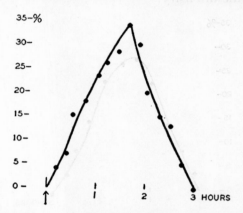

FIG. 116. THE AVERAGE PAIN THRESHOLD ELEVATION FOR 3 SUBJECTS RESULTING FROM THE ADMINISTRATION OF 0.3 GM. ACETOPHENETIDIN
The arrow indicates the time of oral administration

responsible for the popularity of these agents as headache remedies, especially where tension or anxiety is dominant.

ETHYL ALCOHOL

Twenty-five experiments were done to ascertain the pain threshold-raising effects of ethyl alcohol in amounts of from 15 to 90 cc. of 95 per cent alcohol. The alcohol was ingested about three to five hours after the last meal and all of it was swallowed within two minutes. The alcohol was diluted with charged water containing sugar for sweetening so that the total volume of fluid was 250 cc. The pain threshold-raising effects of 30 and 60 cc. amounts of ethyl alcohol are shown in figure 117.

In these subjects alcohol produced important changes in mood, namely, feelings of relaxation, contentment, detachment, and euphoria. Also, time appreciation was altered so that standard intervals seemed shorter. Concentration, attention, and retention were defective, memory for events that occurred during this phase was blurred, and restraint and judgment were impaired. The

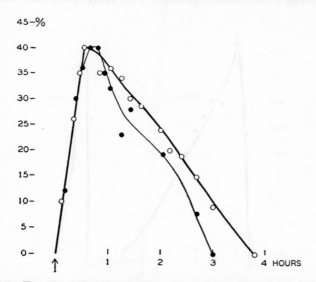

FIG. 117. THE PAIN THRESHOLD ELEVATION RESULTING FROM THE ORAL ADMINISTRATION OF 30 CC. AND 60 CC. OF ETHYL ALCOHOL, 95 PER CENT
●, the average of the threshold levels in 3 subjects after 30 cc. alcohol; ○, the same, after 60 cc. alcohol. The arrow indicates the time of administration of the alcohol.

period of euphoria lasted about an hour and was followed by one of depression and lethargy. Although the mood had changed, the deficiency in concentration, attention, and retention persisted for another two hours.

The peak of the threshold-raising effect and the peak of the excitement and euphoria occurred at about the same time, i.e., within 30 to 40 minutes following ingestion. The period of increasing depression and lethargy was associated with fall of the pain threshold to the normal control level.

TRICHLORETHYLENE

The most swiftly acting of the analgesic agents investigated was trichlorethylene which, when inhaled, had its maximum effect even sooner than alcohol. Two experiments were done. One cc. of trichlorethylene was inhaled under as uniform conditions as inhalation experiments permit. The pain threshold was meas-

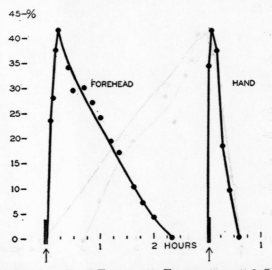

FIG. 118. THE AVERAGE PAIN THRESHOLD ELEVATION FOR 3 SUBJECTS, RESULTING FROM THE ADMINISTRATION (INHALATION) OF TRICHLORETHYLENE
Readings made on the forehead in the first experiment and on the back of the hand in the second experiment. The arrows indicate the periods (four minutes) of inhalation of the contents of 1 cc. trichlorethylene "pearls".

ured on the forehead in the usual manner and on the back of the hand. The time required to reach the maximum elevation was approximately fifteen minutes (see fig. 118). During inhalation the subjects experienced sensations of "lightheadedness" and impending syncope.

BARBITURATES

Nine series of observations were made with 0.5 gm. of the sodium salt of N-methylcyclohexenylmethyl barbituric acid ("Evipal"). This particular barbiturate was selected because of its prompt action which is of short duration. By keeping the subjects awake, the threshold-raising effects due to sleep, per se, were avoided. As seen in figure 119, an amount of the barbiturate barely compatible with a waking state produced a threshold-raising effect of about 21 per cent. Out of all proportion to the threshold-raising effect were the sedative and hypnotic effects. Within 20 minutes of ingestion the subjects became profoundly

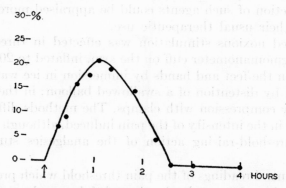

Fig. 119. The Average Pain Threshold Elevation for 3 Subjects, Resulting from the Oral Administration of 0.5 Gm. N-Methylcyclohexenylmethyl Barbituric Acid—Sodium Salt
The arrow indicates the time of administration of the agent

relaxed, lethargic, and unsteady on their feet. They were slightly loquacious. Concentration, attention, and retention were seriously disturbed and manipulative skill was much impaired.

Under these experimental circumstances this barbiturate had relatively slight analgesic action and, since it may be considered as representative, other barbiturates probably behave somewhat similarly. However, if sleep is permitted, a new analgesic factor may be introduced. Sleep as a threshold-raising factor has not been fully studied, but initial experiments indicate considerable threshold elevation during sleep. When consciousness is maintained, barbiturates have little pain threshold-raising action. Eddy previously came to similar conclusions (110, 111).

The Effects of Prolonged Noxious Stimulation and Pain on the
Pain Threshold-Raising Action of Opiates and Other Analgesic
Agents

The aim of the experiments just described was to measure the threshold-raising action of analgesics with as few complications as the situation permitted, and with especial precaution to avoid pain and sleep. In the following experiments prolonged noxious stimulation and pain were introduced as variables since in this way the action of such agents could be appraised more nearly in terms of their usual therapeutic use.

Prolonged noxious stimulation was effected in three subjects by a sphygmomanometer cuff on the arm, inflated to 200 mm. Hg pressure; in the feet and hands by immersion in ice water; in the duodenum by distention of a swallowed balloon; in the trapezius muscles by compression with clamps. The methods differed from each other in the intensity of the pain induced, although the effects on the threshold-raising action of the analgesics studied were similar.

After control readings of the pain threshold which preceded the administration of an analgesic, the painful procedure was begun: 1) 45 minutes before, 2) one minute after, 3) 50 minutes after, and 4) 120 minutes after administration. Pain threshold readings were made every ten minutes for three to seven hours following the administration.

Noxious stimulation and pain induced early during the threshold-raising action of morphine altered the degree and duration of this action. The longer the interval between the injection of morphine and the introduction of the induced pain, the less effect there was upon the threshold-raising action of the agent. On the other hand, if the pain was induced just before or after the injection of morphine the subsequent threshold-raising action was dramatically reduced, as shown in figure 120.

Noxious stimulation and pain were found to have a similar impeding effect upon the pain threshold-raising action of the other agents studied. Thus, when pain was introduced either immediately before or after the administration of an agent the pain threshold was raised to a smaller degree, and the duration of effectiveness was shortened.

MEASUREMENT OF THE EFFECTS OF ANALGESICS IN REDUCING THE INTENSITY OF PAIN

Measurement of pain threshold-raising action of analgesics cannot be said a priori to provide specific information about the influence of such agents upon the intensity of pains above the thresh-

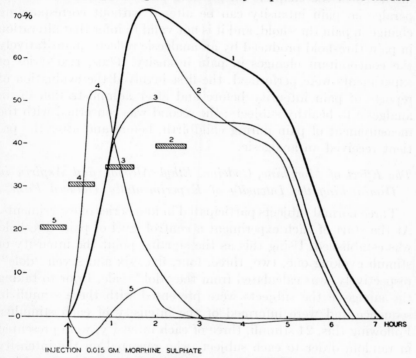

INJECTION 0.015 GM. MORPHINE SULPHATE

FIG. 120. THE EFFECT OF SUSTAINED PAIN (40 MINUTES) ON THE PAIN THRESHOLD-RAISING PROPERTIES OF MORPHINE SULFATE (0.015 GM.)

The heavy black line, 1, represents the pain threshold-raising effect of 0.015 gm. of morphine sulfate in 3 subjects without pain. The lighter lines and blocks represent the following: 2: Pain 120 minutes after the injection. 3: Pain 50 minutes after the morphine injection. 4: Pain immediately following morphine injection (after one minute). 5: Pain preceding and ending 6 minutes before the morphine sulfate injection. The ordinate = per cent elevation of pain threshold over the control level as zero. The abscissa = duration of effect. Each curve represents the average of the threshold levels in 3 subjects.

old. This information can be obtained, however, by measurement of pain intensity according to the "dol" scale which makes possible quantitative estimates of the reduction of pain intensity following administration of an analgesic. Measurements of this second aspect of analgesic action are of practical importance because analgesics are usually administered for the relief of pain which already exists, and such relief may be partial rather than complete. As discussed in the chapters on pricking pain threshold and on hyperalgesia, pain intensity can be altered without corresponding change in pain threshold, and it is not valid to infer that alteration in pain threshold produced by an analgesic reflects quantitatively the concomitant changes in pain intensity. Thus, two series of experiments were performed: the first involved the evaluation of reports of pain intensity before and after administration of an analgesic to healthy subjects; the second was concerned with the measurement of pain during childbirth, before and after the patient received an analgesic.

The Effect of Morphine, Codeine, Ethyl Alcohol, and Aspirin in Diminishing the Intensity of Experimentally Induced Pain

Three normal subjects participated in four series of experiments. At the start of each experiment a control level of pain threshold was established. Using this as the starting point the intensity of stimuli evoking one, two, three, four, five, six and seven "dols", respectively, was calculated from the "dol" scale. Prior to taking the analgesic the subjects were presented with these stimuli in sequence and were informed of the intensity of each stimulus. Following this, 24 stimuli, three of each intensity, were presented in random order to each subject, who reported on the intensity of the pain evoked. The average of the reports of each subject gave a control scale of pain intensity perception prior to the injection of the analgesic. Immediately following the presentation of the 24 stimuli, and the recording of the pain intensity estimates by the observer, the analgesic was administered. Ninety minutes were allowed to elapse so as to permit the development of maximal effects of the agents. The test procedure was then repeated with the subject reporting the intensities of the same 24 stimuli. The reports were again averaged and by comparison with the first reports the effect of the analgesic on the pain threshold and upon pains above the threshold could be evaluated.

The results are shown in figures 121, 122, 123, and 124. The average curve for pain perception prior to receiving the analgesic is shown as a dashed line. The averages of the subject's reports 90

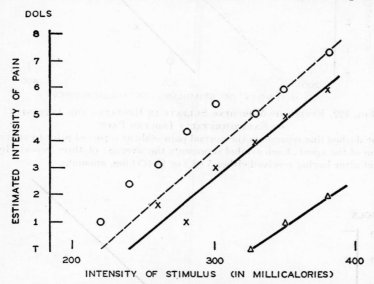

FIG. 121. EFFECT OF CODEINE PHOSPHATE IN REDUCING INTENSITY OF EXPERIMENTALLY INDUCED PAIN

The dashed line represents the normal pain scale as reported prior to administration of the agent. Each symbol represents the average of three reports of one subject after having received either 15 (O), 30 (X) or 60 (△) mg. amounts.

minutes after the administration of the analgesic are shown as plotted points. In figure 121 it is seen that 13 and 30 mg. amounts of codeine had little effect upon pain perception as the variation in reporting of the stimuli by the subject was ±1 "dol". Sixty mg. of codeine, however, raised the pain threshold to 320 mc./sec./cm.², or, reduced a five-"dol" pain to threshold. Similarly, a six-"dol" pain was reduced to one "dol" and a seven-"dol" pain to two "dols". The results for morphine (fig. 122) were like those for codeine in that the pain threshold was raised and the intensity of

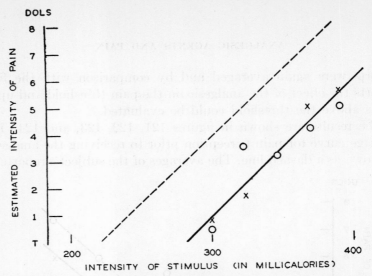

FIG. 122. EFFECT OF MORPHINE SULFATE IN REDUCING THE INTENSITY
OF EXPERIMENTALLY INDUCED PAIN

The dashed line represents the normal pain scale as reported prior to administration of the agent. Each symbol represents the average of three reports by 1
subject after having received either 5 (×) or 10 (○) mg. amounts.

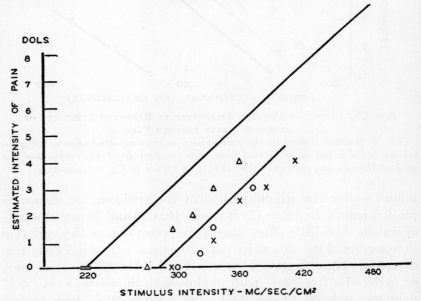

FIG. 123. EFFECT OF ETHYL ALCOHOL IN REDUCING THE INTENSITY OF
EXPERIMENTALLY INDUCED PAIN

The upper line represents the normal pain scale as reported prior to administration of the agent. Each symbol represents the average of three reports by 1
subject after having received either 30 (△) or 60 (○, ×) cc. amounts.

364

the pains above threshold was reduced correspondingly. In figures 123 and 124 are shown the results obtained on two other common analgesics. Their effects upon the perception of pain above the pain threshold were similar to those observed with morphine and codeine.

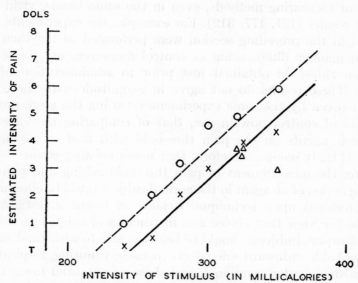

FIG. 124. EFFECT OF ACETYLSALICYLIC ACID IN REDUCING THE INTENSITY OF EXPERIMENTALLY INDUCED PAIN

The dashed line represents the normal pain scale as reported prior to administration of the agent. Each symbol represents the average of three reports by one subject after having received 0.3 gm. amount (×, △). Note also administration of placebo to another subject (O).

The implication from this series of experiments is that under these conditions perception of pain above the threshold pain is modified by the analgesic to the same extent that the agent raises the pain threshold. The effect is one of lowering the scale of pain intensity parallel to itself.

General Comment

In the opening paragraph of this chapter it was mentioned that disagreement exists among investigators as regards the facts of analgesic action and their interpretation. This has come about partly as the result of the difficulty experienced by observers in repeating measurements of pain threshold-raising action obtained by others. At the heart of this difficulty is the fact that no two observers have used exactly the same measuring techniques, and different measuring methods, even in the same hands, yield different results (491, 177, 312). For example, the experiments discussed in the preceding section were performed in the then accepted manner (396), using as control measurements the levels of pain threshold obtained just prior to administration of an agent. These results do not agree in magnitude with those obtained (even by the same experimenters) using the more precise method of control now in use, that of comparing the effect of analgesic agents on the pain threshold with that of a placebo (177, 414). It seems, therefore, that much existing confusion regarding the measurement of pain threshold-raising and pain-reducing action of an agent in the normal subject could be eliminated by agreement upon technique. Reports of recent investigations lead to the view that choice and instruction of subjects is a first consideration. Subjects should be healthy, able to withstand safely any probable untoward side effects (nausea, vomiting, respiratory and cardiovascular reactions), and show no potential toward addiction; they should be interested and willing witnesses but they need not be experimenters themselves. The subjects should be trained to recognize the pain endpoint (threshold, if that be used) but the extent of such training should be clearly outlined.

A second factor is the laboratory, which should be a quiet place held at a comfortable temperature and containing only the observer and a single subject at one time. If several subjects are studied together adjoining rooms are desirable, one for measurement and the second for a waiting room. A careful watch by a medical staff alert for signs of any dangerous reactions in the subjects is essential, especially during the first two hours after the administration of an agent.

The agent should be administered to each subject while alone and placebos should be included so that the probability of a subject's receiving a placebo is about 50%. Neither the subject nor the test operator should know either the nature or amount of agent given. If information is required as regards such side effects as relaxation, lethargy, lightheadedness, etc., each subject should be questioned while alone.

A last consideration is the data. The taking of pain threshold readings periodically after administration is satisfactory, but if the thermal radiation method be used these should always be accompanied by skin temperature measurements taken just prior to exposure to the radiant heat (189). Other precautions against sweating, loss of ink from the test surface, too rapid exposure of the same area, etc., should be taken. A sufficient number of measurements should be made to permit statistical analysis by the method of variance to distinguish placebo from analgesic action. Expression of analgesic action in terms of pain-relieving power is desirable (see Chapter VI). As these criteria for acceptable technique can be met in the ordinary laboratory future differences in experimental results will perhaps have interesting meaning in terms of possible differential action of analgesics upon structures subserving aching, burning or pricking pain (340).

The Effect of Analgesics on the Pain of Labor in Childbirth

It was demonstrated that the pain threshold-raising action of the opiates was greatly reduced when these agents were administered to subjects already experiencing pain. From this one might suspect that the usefulness of such analgesics would be questionable as regards the relief of pain through raising the pain threshold alone. However, the action of an analgesic upon the central nervous system may, without altering the threshold but through some indirect effect upon the painful peripheral organ, cause a marked reduction in pain. In patients in labor it was observed that the opiates reduced or eliminated the labor pains without appreciably affecting the perception of pain as measured by the thermal radiation method (230, 229). Although the action of analgesics in relieving the pain of labor has in the past been attributed solely to elevation of the pain threshold, the major action is probably that of reducing noxious stimulation. To evaluate this effect, measurements of both pain threshold and pain intensity were required.

Twenty-eight healthy young women without obstetrical complications volunteered as subjects for these studies. In eleven primiparas and four multiparas, primiparas being desirable as their labor is generally of longer duration, effects of analgesics were observed. In addition thirteen women, ten primiparas and three multiparas, were studied in the first, second and fourth stages of labor without analgesia, as a control group. As a further control of the effects of the analgesic agents studied, an occasional subject in this group was given 1 cc. of normal saline subcutaneously. Knowledge of the amount and nature of the agent given was kept from the patient and the testing observer so as to minimize the effects of suggestion, although it was always inferred by the patient that the agent would be of benefit. That is, the suggestion was always positive in nature. All subjects had a normal antepartum course, during which they were instructed in the procedure for measurement of pain threshold and for making comparisons of intensity between pains of different qualities. In nearly all cases the measurements were made during the first stage of labor.

The method of testing was uniform throughout the series of experiments and consisted of a pain threshold measurement and pain intensity measurement every twenty minutes. Pain threshold measurements were carried out in the usual way by the thermal radiation method, using the dorsum of the hand as the test surface. Tests for the pain threshold were made during the pain free intervals between uterine contractions. Pain intensity measurements were made in the next pain free interval, following the determination of pain threshold. The experimental routine was briefly as follows: Following a contraction the patient was presented with a stimulus 40 to 50 mc./sec./cm.^{2} above the previously determined pain threshold. She was then asked to state whether the test pain was as intense as her labor pains. If it was not, the stimulus was increased 20 to 30 mc./sec./cm.^{2} and again presented. The patient's attention was continually directed to the *intensity* aspect of the sensation produced by the test stimulus, as distinct from its quality and duration. Tests made within a short period of time showed variation generally not greater than ±1 "dol". As the limit of discrimination for pains of identical quality and duration is usually of the same order, the inference can be drawn that the patients under these circumstances were making satisfactory appraisals.

Usually three or four stimuli were sufficient to "bracket" the intensity level of the uterine pain. Special care was taken not to repeat tests in areas of skin made hyperalgesic by stimulation of the skin with the high intensity stimuli necessary to evoke pain of intensity comparable with that of the labor pains.

The usual observations were made of duration of uterine contraction, contraction interval, fetal heart rate and cervical dilatation. In addition, notes were kept as to the patient's reactions such as sleeping, smiling, crying, complaining, sweating, degree of alertness, and fatigue. The average pain threshold values for the several subjects were all within the normal range (±15%) and thus it is indicated that there was no significant variation in sensitivity to pain in this group of women. However, as labor progressed, the distracting effect of the increasing vigor of the labor resulted in a widening spread of individual pain threshold values.

MORPHINE AND SCOPOLAMINE

These agents were administered together subcutaneously in amounts of 15 and 0.4 mg., respectively, in four tests on two subjects. The chart of subject H (fig. 125) demonstrates the action of these agents in repeated doses. Three curves are plotted: the pain threshold as shown by solid dots was in the normal range prior to administering the drugs and is indicated as "zero dols". The first administration caused a rise in pain threshold to a degree which would cause a pain of one-"dol" intensity to be eliminated. The second injection had no immediate effect upon the pain threshold but the third injection caused a rise in pain threshold to a degree which would eliminate a pain of eight-"dol" intensity.

The second curve, indicated by circles, represents the intensity of noxious stimulation which was required to elicit a pain equivalent to the subject's labor pain (anadols). It has been demonstrated above that the perceived intensity of pain can be calculated from the difference between the level of pain threshold and this level of intensity of noxious stimulation. Thus, the difference is charted as a dashed line and is labelled "true dols".

A summary of the effects of morphine and scopolamine upon

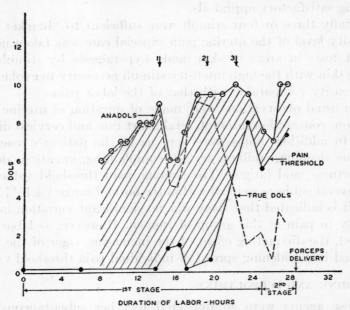

FIG. 125. THE EFFECT OF 3 DOSES OF 15 MG. MORPHINE AND 0.4 MG. SCOPOLAMINE UPON PAIN INTENSITY DURING LABOR

O, anadols, intensity of stimuli required to match intensity of labor pain. ●, pain threshold. ----, difference between anadol and pain threshold, net intensity of pain experienced. Shaded area indicates range of pain intensity experienced by the patient.

the pain experienced is shown in figure 126. The diagonal line is the average of the pain levels observed in patients who received no analgesics.

In the amounts given, a single injection of morphine and scopolamine had little or no effect upon the pain threshold as measured by the thermal radiation method. This is to be expected as it has been shown that pain existing at the time of administration of morphine reduces the threshold-raising effects of this agent. In addition to the pain relieving action these agents reduced rest-lessness and promoted sleep. Such effects paralleled the pain-reducing action and disappeared as the pain increased. Alleviation of anxiety and reduction of profuse sweating were also observed.

MORPHINE SULFATE

One injection of 15 mg. of morphine sulfate was given to each of three patients during the latter part of the first stage of labor.

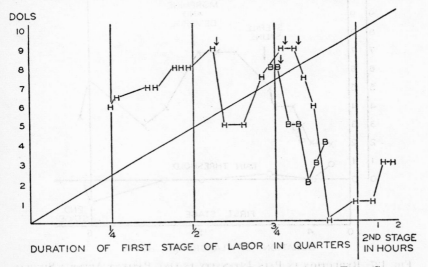

FIG. 126. REDUCTION IN PAIN INTENSITY OF 2 PATIENTS IN THE FIRST STAGE OF LABOR, AFTER ADMINISTRATIONS OF 15 MG. MORPHINE AND 0.4 MG. SCOPOLAMINE
Each arrow indicates an injection of both these agents

The results were essentially the same but of lesser degree than those observed with a comparable amount of morphine plus sco-polamine.

MORPHINE AND MEPERIDINE

These agents were given together in amounts of 6 mg. and 100 mg., respectively, to seven patients. In a typical experiment (fig. 127) the patient received a placebo when the labor pain had reached a five-"dol" intensity. This had no effect in reducing pain and no effect upon the pain threshold. When the pain reached

seven "dols", the analgesic combination was administered subcutaneously. There followed a drop in pain intensity over a period
of half an hour, to a three- "dol" level. Half an hour later the
intensity of pain was again five "dols". There was no significant
change in the pain threshold throughout. The results of the

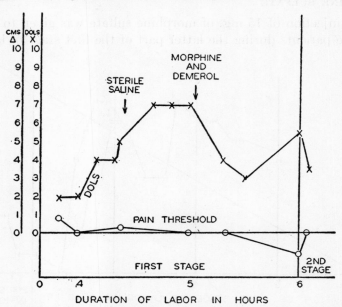

FIG. 127. REDUCTION IN PAIN INTENSITY IN ONE PATIENT AFTER A SINGLE
INJECTION OF 15 MG. OF MORPHINE AND 50 MG. OF DEMEROL
Injection of sterile saline as control

measurements on all patients who received this combination of
analgesics may be summarized as follows:

No change in pain threshold was noted.

Pain intensity was reduced an average of four "dols", ±1 "dol".
Figure 128 summarizes the observations in five patients who
received morphine and Meperidine. Prime letters show pain levels
after administration.

APOMORPHINE AND SCOPOLAMINE

This combination of agents was chosen because it has no known
pain threshold-raising action and because it has had a thorough

clinical test as an obstetrical analgesic by Hershenson and Brubaker (213). These authors concluded that these two agents in
combination serve satisfactorily as analgesics in labor. In the
present study three injections in amounts of 0.65 mg. apomorphine
and 0.4 mg. scopolamine were given to a single patient. A summary

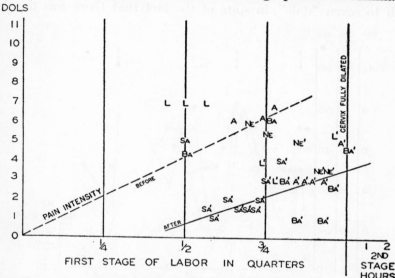

FIG. 128. PAIN INTENSITY BEFORE AND AFTER ADMINISTRATION OF MORPHINE
AND DEMEROL TO 5 PATIENTS

Each letter represents measurements on a single patient. Plain letters indicate
pain intensity before, and prime letters pain intensity after, administration of
the agents.

of the data on this patient is shown in figure 129. Following administration of these agents there was:

No change in cutaneous pain threshold;

An average reduction in pain intensity by five dols, ±1 dol;

Lengthening of the contraction interval and shortening of the
    period of contraction of the uterus;

Mild nausea, drowsiness.

DIACETYLMORPHINE (HEROIN)

Three tests were made with this agent on two patients who received injections in amounts of 6 mg. Levels of pain intensity and

pain threshold are plotted in figure 130, for a patient who received a placebo followed by two injections of heroin. It will be seen that some reduction in pain intensity followed the injection of the saline placebo. After administration of the heroin in each instance there was observed a reduction in pain intensity of three and one-half to seven "dols", in spite of the fact that there was no ob-

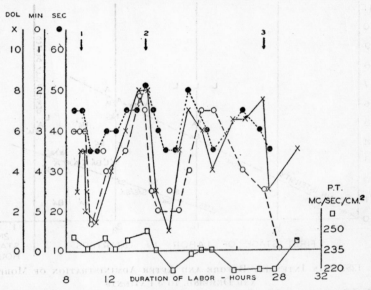

FIG. 129. THE INFLUENCE OF 3 INJECTIONS (↓) OF 0.65 MG. APOMORPHINE AND 0.4 MG. SCOPOLAMINE UPON PAIN INTENSITY, PAIN THRESHOLD, DURATION OF UTERINE CONTRACTION, AND INTERVAL BETWEEN CONTRACTIONS

served elevation of pain threshold. Marked effects of this agent are euphoria, drowsiness, and muscular relaxation.

From the data presented above it is inferred that the pain reducing action of analgesics and analgesic combinations in labor is attributable to two effects, namely, that of suppression of pain sensation by raising the pain threshold, and that of lessening the degree of noxious stimulation of the uterus. The mechanism by which the pain from the pelvic viscera and perineal tissues is reduced without affecting perception of noxious stimulation elsewhere is postulated to be due to repression of visceral and somatic reflexes resulting in reduction of uterine activity, and thereby of noxious stimulation of the uterus (361, 53, 412, 428, 100, 210, 16, 323, 376, 294, 293, 205, 452).

This concept is particularly well supported by the observations following administration of apomorphine and scopolamine in which the parallelism between pain intensity reduction and decreased frequency and duration of uterine contraction is strik-

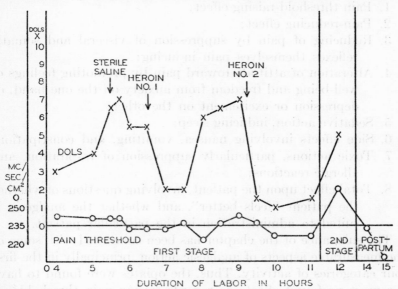

Fig. 130. Reduction in Pain Intensity after Two Injections of Heroin
Injection of sterile saline as control

ingly demonstrated. Similar observations were made in each of the patients studied following administration of morphine and scopolamine, morphine and Meperidine, and diacetylmorphine. However, in spite of this reduced activity the duration of labor was not prolonged, presumably because the effectiveness of each uterine contraction was relatively increased by concomitant relaxation of the muscles of the lower uterine segment and perineum.

The results reported above confirm the view that in the action of analgesics in relieving the patient in pain, important factors are present that have not been taken into account previously.

Measurement of pain threshold is one important tool in the analysis of analgesic action but a far more effective approach is afforded when pain intensity measurements are also made.

SUMMARY

Listed at the beginning of the chapter are eight modes of action of analgesics in the human subject, which are:

1. Pain threshold-raising effect;
2. Pain-reducing effect;
3. Reducing of pain by suppression of visceral and somatic reflexes themselves pain inducing;
4. Alteration of attitude toward pain by promoting feelings of well-being and freedom from anxiety on the one hand, or depression or excitement on the other;
5. Sedative action, inducing sleep;
6. Side effects involving nausea, vomiting, and constipation;
7. Toxic actions, particularly suppression of respiration, and allergic reactions;
8. Total effect upon the patient, involving questions of whether the patient "feels better", and whether the analgesic is suited to administration in the particular patient.

The substance of the chapter has been concerned with some of the measurable aspects of analgesic action, principally in the first four categories of activity. Thus, the opiates were found to have the most profound effects as regards raising pain threshold, reducing pain, suppression of reflexes, and alteration in attitude. Alcohol was similarly effective but to a lesser degree than the opiates. The coal tar derivatives had a lesser though measurable activity. The presence of pain before or at the time of administration of the analgesic had an important action in preventing elevation of pain threshold.

Many of the most useful and desirable effects of analgesics for controlling an acute episode of pain are such as to make many of the agents unsuited and even dangerous for general, prolonged use. Among such effects are suppression of reflexes, alteration in attitude, and reduction of sensation.

Pain arises from noxious stimulation which itself is a product of tissue injury. Thus, procedures which can limit or reverse the underlying processes of noxious stimulation are obviously the most desirable from the point of view of pain relief. However, agents which act in this way are not usually classed as analgesics (ergot for headaches, milk and alkalizing agents for gastric pain) and thus do not come under the present discussion. The problem, then, is how, in the presence of continued noxious stimulation, can pain best be reduced or abolished? It is likely that the problem will continue to be a perplexing one, but on the basis of existing information some partial answers can be made.

Pain of long duration is of necessity always one of low intensity, since the rate of tissue injury required to produce noxious stimulation intense enough to evoke a severe pain, five to eight "dols", will probably destroy the pain fibers and surrounding tissues so rapidly as to cause a reduction in pain. It is for this reason, perhaps, that in chronic diseases associated with pain, painful episodes alternate with painfree periods of relatively long duration and even low intensity pains are variably present. Constant noxious stimulation of the skin at the pain threshold level will in the course of about five hours cause hyperemia and in roughly six hours complete epidermal necrosis (316). On the other hand, continued noxious stimulation evoking a five-"dol" pain will produce necrosis in fifteen to twenty minutes. Thus, it is clear that high intensity pains must be of short duration, a matter of minutes at most, whereas pain of low intensity can be supported by the tissues for hours or, with nonpainful periods interspersed, indefinitely.

Pain of low intensity, for which the rates of tissue injury and repair are compatible with tissue integrity (threshold to two "dols") can fortunately be controlled by the analgesics of mildest action, such as the coal tar derivatives, by placebos, or by distraction, especially during daylight hours. Only ten to twenty per cent pain threshold-raising action is required to reduce such low intensity pain below threshold.

Pain of moderate intensity (three to five "dols"), and short duration, can be eliminated by the opiates. It is important that such pain be quickly abolished in order that the powerful reaction patterns to pain do not become established and in themselves become effective sources of further noxious stimulation and pain.

Pain of high intensity necessitates for its control the elimination of the noxious stimulation or complete unconsciousness. For example, in childbirth, certain analgesics effectively reduce the noxious stimulation of labor but for the pain accompanying major operative procedures an anesthetic either general or local is required. Again, the necessity of abolishing such pain is of paramount importance to avoid the reactions to noxious stimulation and pain.

In short, the analgesics are optimally useful in the management of painful episodes of relatively short duration, in promoting "rest", a state in which the reparative and restorative forces are fostered and exceed those of destruction. To the extent that an analgesic through any or all of the aspects listed above succeeds in inducing rest, its use is appropriate. Inversely, when used in any other manner, it jeopardizes the patient's well being.

Chapter XIV

THE PAIN EXPERIENCE: A FORMULATION

Sensation constitutes an awareness of stimulation and bears a highly predictable relation to the intensity of the stimulus. Pain is no different from other sensations in this regard. It does differ, aside from its qualitative features, in that the adequate stimulus for pain sensation is the damaging of tissue. Perception may be viewed as an awareness of stimulation and considered as sensation with concomitant associations and reactions. The average level of stimulus at which pain sensation is first recognized is predictable and can be appraised quite apart from its associated meaning to the individual. Throughout this presentation, emphasis has been placed upon the need to deal separately with the effects of noxious stimulation leading a) to adjustments without giving rise to sensation, b) to the sensation of pain, and c) to adaptations to pain per se. Taken together they include perception, feeling states, moods and a variety of bodily reactions and behavior patterns.

THE ADEQUATE STIMULUS

The initiating event for neural impulses involved in pain is the damaging of tissue, and is termed "noxious stimulation". Tissue damage, then, often extremely slight and completely reversible, becomes the keystone of the type of adjustments, sensations, feeling states, and behavior that constitute the pain experience.

The degree of stress which a particular human tissue can withstand without being damaged is, under given conditions, uniform. The means of damaging tissue as a factor in such a generalization is a fundamental consideration since there must be a demonstrably close relationship between the energy applied and the rate at which damage is done.

THE DIMENSIONS OF PAIN

Pain sensation is readily recognized and appreciated as different from other sensations on the basis of its qualitative features, its functional importance, and the anatomy of its nervous system. There are several measurable dimensions of pain sensation considered under the following headings: quality—pricking, burning, aching; intensity—threshold to ten and one-half "dols"; extension—having to do with site, localization (circumscribed or diffuse), area, and volume; and temporal aspects—duration, intermittent, rhythmic, pulsatile, seasonal, diurnal. Anatomically, pain is considered in two categories: superficial—with identifiable qualities as pricking, burning, and aching, and itching as a variation and combination of the first two qualities; and deep pain—with aching as the most prominent quality. Burning pain sensations may also arise from deep tissues, as, for instance, from the esophagus, stomach, or bone marrow.

When pain is analyzed for the purpose of identifying the organ or part involved, valuable information is gained by considering its modifiability, i.e., what causes the pain to increase or to decrease. To the precise identification of the structures responsible for pain, observations of concurrent motor and vasomotor effects are pertinent.

The sensation of pain has a lowest intensity, the threshold pain, and a maximum intensity beyond which no further discriminations of intensity can be made. There are a limited number of just noticeable differences in pain intensity, approximately 21 from threshold to maximum. An intensity of pain has been elaborated, using the word "dol" to indicate two steps in discrimination of intensity. Pain intensity is determined by the intensity of noxious stimulation, although modification of pain intensity can occur in areas of hyperalgesia. Furthermore, zones in which painful stimuli are perceived as more than usually intense do not necessarily have lowered pain thresholds. Indeed, two categories of hyperalgesia can be defined: one ("primary") in which the pain threshold is appreciably lowered, occurs with tissue damage; and the second ("secondary") in which the pain threshold is unaltered but due to alterations in the excitatory state in the central nervous system, those impulses which enter the neuraxis result in an increase in intensity of pain sensation.

For these adjustments, feelings, and sensations from noxious stimulation to ensue neural endings must be viable. It is not established, however, whether these endings per se have to be injured by the noxious stimulation, nor, indeed, that they need be stimulated directly. It may be that nerve endings are stimulated as a sequel of liberated products of injury, since it has been shown that the latter can exert such an effect.

THE RESPONSE

Although not all noxious stimulation and tissue damage give rise to pain sensation, they give rise to a host of other reactions essential to adjustment. Further, these reactions to noxious stimuli, although conditioned for the body's protection, may be so costly to the body economy as themselves to damage tissue, giving rise to further adjustments and secondarily to pain. It is ironic that the protective and adaptive reactions to noxious stimulation may be so vigorous as to cause more damage and pain than the initial assault. Indeed, these phenomena of adjustment may become a greater threat to the integrity of the organism than the original damage. The fact that adaptive reactions per se may become a major threat to the organism is especially impressive when the individual reacts to the symbols of danger as he would to tissue damage.

Predictability is a feature of reactions to noxious stimuli when segmental levels are freed of the modifying influence of the suprasegmental apparatus, as in so-called "spinal" animals. But such unconditioned reflexes are less predictable in the individual with intact nervous system. Patterns of reaction to noxious stimuli, involving the highest integrative functions, dependent as they are upon many circumstances, influence lower or segmental reflexes, and reaction thresholds when measured in the intact individual are a feature of individual experience rather than being inborn.

Hence, "reaction thresholds" to noxious stimuli fall into two general categories: the one is stable, fixed, and highly predictable, (i.e., the flexor reflex to noxious stimuli in a spinal man); the other is labile, dependent on many circumstances, and only to a limited degree predictable, (i.e., the conditioned reflex). When "reaction threshold" to noxious stimuli in the intact individual is defined in terms of skin resistance, blood pressure, "wincing", pulse rate, etc., it must be appreciated what a labile entity is being appraised.

The impulses arising from noxious stimulation have a strikingly varied summative effect as regards the number of nerve fibers involved in the noxious stimulation. However, these spatial summative effects are conspicuous only in the realm of simple and local reflex adjustments. There is no spatial summation as regards the intensity of pain sensation. Were this not so, intense pain would be omnipresent.

The pain threshold may be raised by a variety of alterations within and outside the nervous system, i.e., interference with function of the conduction pathways and central integrative apparatus, either reversible or irreversible; co-existence of other vivid sensations, particularly pain; distractions, suggestion, hypnosis, and the action of chemical agents known as analgesics and anesthetics.

Pain of high intensity, resulting from noxious stimulation at the periphery, is seldom of more than brief duration because such intense stimulation either 1) destroys the neural equipment implicated, or 2) so damages the tissue between the stimulus and the nerve endings as to prevent the stimuli from reaching nerve endings. On the other hand, mild pain may persist for months or years. Moderately severe pain may last for hours or days, but again is usually self-limiting because of local tissue alterations which reduce the number of neural impulses resulting from noxious stimulation.

STRUCTURES INVOLVED

All neural impulses having to do with noxious stimulation and pain are funnelled through the dorsal roots, the bulk ascending in the cord and brain stem through the ventral lateral tracts to the thalamus. There appears to be no cortical representation of pain. Although the cerebral cortex is necessary to pain discrimination, it is doubtful whether any one part of the cerebrum is specifically involved.

It seems likely, however, that major brain damage, particularly in the frontal lobes, interferes with the appreciation of pain from prolonged noxious stimulation. Neural impulses from noxious stimulation may be conveyed by fibers of many sizes following various routes to the dorsal ganglia and up the cord. It is, however, likely that the fibers involved in aching and burning sensations are anatomically and physiologically different from those involved in pricking pain. The latter apparently are phylogenetically more recent, are myelinated, larger, and conduct impulses more rapidly.

Short intercalated neurons within the segments of the cord, brain stem, and probably in the cerebral cortex are essential to the phenomenology of pain sensation since they are responsible for the maintenance of augmented central excitatory states such as produce itching, hyperalgesia, altered discrimination of intensity, emotional excitement, and complicated behavior patterns.

CENTRAL EXCITATORY STATES

The damaging of tissue may set in motion hyperexcitatory states which require very little additional peripheral stimulation for their maintenance. Such hyperexcitatory states may become self-perpetuating, but once interrupted may not be re-initiated. Central excitatory states are furthered or hindered by a variety of factors in the internal and external environment and only in part are they dependent upon impulses from the area initially damaged (81). However, heightened excitation in the suprasegmental apparatus may be built up by prolonged mild noxious stimulation, either from the periphery or from lesions within the brain itself.

Central excitatory events at segmental or suprasegmental levels are of importance to an understanding of referred pain. "Referred pain", or pain experienced at a site other than that of noxious stimulation, is to be distinguished from pain which arises as a sequel of motor or vasomotor reflex effects. Such pain results from noxious stimuli of intensity below the level necessary for the production of pain sensation. Both types of pain are, in a sense, subsidiary effects: referred pain results from a spread within the neuraxis, producing sensations at a remote site; the second type of pain results from "spread" within a segment ending in reflex contraction and tissue damage. These effects are easily confused and are often spoken of interchangeably, but actually represent different processes having a common denominator in a heightened level of central excitation. Thus, although noxious stimulation of tissue must be of a given intensity to evoke pain sensation directly, nonetheless, even those stimuli insufficiently intense to evoke pain may, by altering central excitatory states, become involved in pain sensation. However, far more frequently noxious stimulation of such low intensity induces local adjustments essential to homeostasis, without evoking the sensation of pain.

Most relevant to the intensity of central excitation and pain is so-called "rest"—a state variously defined by different cultures. Consequently there is no general unanimity of opinion concerning its operation. Perhaps basically, however, it is that state in which reparative or restorative forces are fostered and exceed destructive forces. Such a view circumvents the question whether mobilization vs. immobilization, or one type of inactivity vs. another, or one bodily posture vs. others is operatively more effective. It defines merely the fact that under a given set of circumstances reparation prevails. At the simplest physiological level, this is accomplished by means that reduce noxious stimuli and local vasomotor and skeletal muscle effects which in themselves produce pain or maintain a state of central excitation of a costly and destructive nature. The diminishing of excitation within the neuraxis can be accomplished by the use of agents that have very little pain threshold-raising effect (e.g., barbiturates, administered intravenously, may reduce strikingly the amount of pain experienced by those exhibiting secondary reflex skeletal muscle contraction). But relevant also in a consideration of effects of "rest" is the removal of individuals from stressful life situations created by personal and social pressures. Again by lowering the general level of excitation within the neuraxis, pain is reduced or eliminated. This may be attained by "invalidism". Also, "complete bed rest" in a society that views the "sick bed" as sanctuary, may have such an effect, assuming that the individual's frustration of his own drives and goals is outweighed by the immunity and even prestige afforded by being "sick in bed". Further factors that reduce excitation within the nervous system are sleep, the elimination of prolonged or excessive effort, relative freedom from harassing anxieties and conflicts, and the delegation of responsibilities and guilt to the group at large and to other individuals. Moreover, the passage of time with its opportunities for alterations and adaptations may be a most important factor in the waning of central excitation.

The phenomena of itch and secondary hyperalgesia are closely linked, both representing local augmentation in the central excitatory state. Itch does, however, depend as well upon the periodic discharge and re-establishment of the state of hyperexcitability by noxious stimulation of low intensity. Yet these discharges must occur sufficiently frequently to evoke a sensation with the peculiar features which give itch its name. Itching is augmented during periods of skin vasodilatation. During the actual itching, which is phasic and seldom of long duration in any one area, the pain threshold is lowered. With the introduction of additional noxious stimuli such as result from pin prick or "scratching", the itch sensation is promptly dispelled. Similarly, the application of cold reduces itching in contrast to heat which augments it. States of emotional tension, fatigue, frustration, and depression augment itching. Mild analgesics reduce or eliminate itch sensation.

From such studies on secondary hyperalgesia, interest has focused upon the degree of central activity which may occur at a number of levels within the neuraxis. The intensity of excitation at the highest levels, stemming from the individual's adjustments to a variety of environmental and social circumstances, may be as significant as that at the segmental level to which impulses arrive from damaged tissue.

On the other hand, an understanding of the nature of secondary hyperalgesia and an appreciation of the fact that relatively few impulses from the periphery may maintain a state of hyperexcitability exhibiting itself in part as pain, has once again focused interest on the expediency of blocking impulses at their source. Interruption of the inflow of impulses from noxious stimulation even temporarily may lower the level of central excitation so as to interrupt a cycle of events which has become almost self-sustaining. Hence, as indicated above, painful states in areas exhibiting either secondary hyperalgesia or painful reflex vasomotor and skeletal muscle effects from such heightening of excitation within the neuraxis, when interrupted, sometimes do not recur.

Procainization terminates the pain from contracted skeletal muscle either by blocking afferent impulses from the contracting tissue or by altering the contractile state of the muscle. Secondary hyperalgesia, either superficial or deep, may be dispelled by blocking afferent impulses through the use of local anesthetic agents, or by means of counterirritants.

A dramatic instance of the interplay of the effects of low intensity peripheral noxious stimulation and the effect of social and personal pressures in a maladjusted individual is witnessed in the intractable pain exhibited by some amputees. Such persons experience prolonged intractable pain associated with kinesthetic experiences of the amputated part. Sometimes the elimination by local nerve block or by operative removal of a scar about the terminal portion of the severed nerve abolishes this phenomenon. At other times, however, a self-maintaining system of excitation has apparently become so well established that neither operative removal of scars, nerve pathways or even serious brain damage can completely eliminate it.

FACTORS THAT MODIFY PERCEPTION OF AND REACTION TO PAIN

This consideration of the general level of excitement within the neuraxis, as indicated earlier, leads directly to a consideration of the individual's reactions to the sensation of pain per se. Impulses reaching the neuraxis, regardless of whether they evoke pain, modify neural activity in such a way as to effect moods, feeling states, and behavior patterns. Pain sensation can evoke responses beyond those appropriate, and out of all proportion to the danger of the situation. Inversely, pain sensation can be a factor in suppressing reactions because of an appreciation that no genuine threat is involved or that the assault can be readily withstood. In other words, the response to pain sensation depends to a greater or lesser degree on an individual's past experience and the meaning of pain sensation in terms of threat. The attitude of the society in which the individual finds himself and the latter's own point of view about pain sensation, although they do not modify the pain threshold and the ability to discriminate the intensity of pain sensation, become factors which augment the protective-adaptive patterns or repress them.

Remarkable tolerance for mild pain can be developed and maintained through such unrelated agencies as chemical substances, brain damage, group pressures, and reassurance by other individuals (13, 14). Also, reactions of maximal strength can be elicited by pain of threshold intensity, and in properly conditioned individuals by stimulation below threshold intensity. Inversely, placebo agents become remarkably effective in the relief of "suffering" even when pain is of moderate intensity and when reactions to pain are prominent.

All agents known as analgesics raise the pain threshold and alter pain perception. However, the suppression of sensation is usually not as important an action as regards pain relief as are the effects upon reactions to noxious stimulation and to pain itself. Thus, the pain of a patient in labor is greatly reduced following administration of an opiate, without alteration in pain threshold or in ability to discriminate differences in pain intensity. Analgesics alter reaction patterns to pain by inducing relaxation, feelings of well being, and sleep. The untoward aspect of these effects is that only those agents which have conspicuous and perhaps, from a social point of view, dangerous "side effects", best relieve suffering. Clearly exhibiting the "defects of their qualities", they present a dilemma, since the very effects which make for usefulness as analgesics, make for danger of addiction for those who suffer, regardless of whether the suffering is induced by noxious stimulation of bodily tissue or by threatening circumstances resulting from interpersonal or social stresses. The search for agents that raise the pain threshold alone continues, though to date there is nothing to indicate that the possibility of finding one exists.

Appreciable differences concerning pain threshold-raising properties are exhibited by such varying classes of agents as are represented by morphine, codeine, Meperidine, and the antipyretics. In general, the coal tar products in maximal amounts raise the threshold so as to eliminate two-"dol" pain. Codeine and Meperidine raise the threshold so as to eliminate pain of two- to four-"dol" intensity. Morphine may eliminate pains of four- to six-"dol" intensity, but pains of six- to ten-"dol" intensity cannot be eliminated without anesthesia, although they may be reduced to three- to four-"dol" intensity.

Whether primary hyperalgesia be due to peripheral tissue damage or to damage in the conducting peripheral pathways, the pain threshold is lowered. Indeed, it may be so lowered that even those centrally acting analgesics capable of eliminating four- to six-"dol" pain are incapable of bringing the threshold up to the usual level. Effective procedures are those that prevent further stimulation of the damaged parts. After extensive skin burns, for example, the collection and drying of the surface serum usually gives the organism precisely this kind of protection. In those with peripheral neuropathy, relief from weight bearing, even that of the slightest covering, and the lessening, by exposure, of the heat produced by the individual's own body serves such an end.

The Significance of Pain in Human Adjustments

Man's ability to experience pain is possibly not essential to suitable biological adjustment. Children congenitally without the capacity to experience pain, at least when surrounded by pain sensitive adults, adequately adjust themselves to their environment, as do persons who have had pain pathways surgically interrupted (249, 299). Since, with exposure to noxious forces, the rate of tissue damage rather than the amount or seriousness of such damage determines intensity of pain, the latter is a poor indicator of the gravity of the subject's plight. Moreover, when injury is slow or not progressive, even though extensive and ominous, little or no pain may be experienced. Persons critically ill, as with terminal neoplastic disease, and those gravely injured do not inevitably experience intense pain. Hence, man has been obliged to develop other means of protecting himself and pain experienced by a patient may be of secondary importance to diagnosis. Alarm or defense reactions, identical in pattern to reactions to intense pain, may be initiated by any stimulus if that stimulus has been previously associated with injuries, dangerously threatening situations, or frustration. As a matter of fact, the bulk of such reactions involved in common experience are initiated by non-painful stimuli.

In a variety of cultures, the recognition that a certain amount of pain is an inevitable consequence of living, coupled with the appreciation that a pattern of complete avoidance of pain endangers the attainment of full maturity, has been the basis for the development of the thesis that some pain is a "good thing" (273b). A feature of rapidly changing mores and one which is conspicuous in our culture is epitomized in the question, "how much should I put up with?" This query is especially conspicious in cultures where the importance of the individual is stressed. This uncertainty arises from failure to distinguish between those aspects of man's relation to his universe that may change rapidly and those that must change slowly.

Certainly pain sensation is a prime provocator of adjustment to environmental stimuli and, as such is a highly important biologic function for man. It grossly defines the nature of man's life, but symbols and threats of pain soon become substitutes for noxious stimulation. Moreover, danger, threats to security, or disapproval by group or individual evoke the same protective and adaptive reactions and almost the same feeling states, emotions and behavior patterns as does noxious stimulation. This illuminates the nature of human protective reactions; and yet, on the other hand, the similarity of responses has blurred the distinction between the sensation of pain and the reaction to noxious stimulation and to pain.

The magnitude of protective responses induced by pain is based in large part on the way the affected subject perceives it. Perception depends upon a multiplicity of factors including the genetic equipment, basic individual needs and longings, earlier conditioning influences, the host of later life experiences and the nature of cultural pressures. Indeed, the common denominator, as regards magnitude of reaction to pain, is the interpretation of an event as more or less threatening. This follows because the response may be in terms of a conditioned pain stimulus, which, though slight as regards its destructive effects on the organism, nevertheless has taken on, because of earlier experience, implications of grave danger. Hence, in man it is the response to pain per se that becomes of major importance, and, indeed, is capable of becoming a greater threat to survival than the assault.

Moreover, the response, regardless of the personal significance of the noxious stimulus, may be a function of the pre-existing level of central excitation. The latter, in turn, is a reflection of the cumulative effects of the various noxious stimuli of life stress, and in defining the magnitude of central excitation, shapes the magnitude of the response.

In brief, pain sensation has a basic significance in earlier life adjustments of man, though it becomes less and less essential with growing individual experience. Indeed, noxious stimulation and pain may evoke reactions that are more dangerous than the assault, and may even threaten survival. Those who would deal with pain as therapists must concern themselves especially with reactions to pain. The magnitude of protective reactions are dependent in part on concurrence of noxious stimuli, perhaps of low intensity, arising from parts remote from the main noxious source, as well as upon other non-noxious, but disagreeable stimuli.

Moreover, in the total pain experience not only the immediate setting of the pain, but the meaning of such pain for the individual in terms of his past must be appreciated. Hence, man, with the capacity to react defensively to symbols of danger, is espcially vulnerable, since he reacts not only to noxious stimuli but to a host of threats, and, indeed, may dangerously overreact to both, using both appropriate and inappropriate protective patterns. It thus becomes clearer why a physician who deals with the broader aspects of the sufferer's life experience and so makes efforts to support him in every way during a period of stress, is often more effective in a crisis than one who deals merely with the source of noxious stimulation. A transient painful incident for man is only one of a series of threatening circumstances to which he is exposed, his recent and remote past being perhaps the major factor in defining what the pain means to him and how he will meet it.

The Nature of the Pain Experience

It is appropriate to return again to the concepts which have been held of the nature of pain and to suggest a thesis which is compatible with present knowledge. Widely held in the nineteenth century, the intensive theory proposed to account for pain as the end result of strong stimulation of any sensory equipment, for example, visual, auditory, thermal or tactile. Such a view is not supported by data now available.

The ancient concept of pain as an emotion is supported by the newer information, at least to the extent that emotions and attitudes are among the identifiable reactions to pain. However, pain is a sensation, and, like other sensations, is mediated by specialized neural equipment. The adequate stimulus for pain sensation is the alteration in the pain fiber endings from a force of whatever nature, at a rate sufficiently rapid as to result eventually in tissue damage, and, within limits, the rate of tissue alteration determines the intensity of pain.

Better to understand the phenomenology of pain, it was found desirable to separate the responses to noxious stimulation into a) those not dependent upon consciousness, and b) those involving consciousness. The former includes the automatic reflex responses; the latter includes on the one hand the pain sensation, and on the other hand the feeling, mood and attitude reactions largely determined by the past experience of the individual to the automatic responses and to the sensation of pain. It is the interplay of these fundamental components within the individual which comprises the pain experience. Such a broad specification was found necessary if the pain experience is to include the reportable feeling states and other sensations correlated with the report of pain. The reactions to noxious stimulation not dependent upon consciousness and those represented by the pain experience have been shown to be intimately interwoven.

Despite the obvious personal nature of the pain experience, bearing as it does the stamp of individual and differentiated cultural conditioning, there are within this experience predictable aspects which lend themselves to investigation with quantitative techniques. Separation of the pain experience into one or more of its components for study and analysis is done with the full recognition that the total experience is more (or less) than the sum of its parts. This comprehension of the pain experience may serve as a point of departure for further exploration both of its parts and of their integration.

BIBLIOGRAPHY

1. ADRIAN, E. D.: The Mechanism of Nervous Action. Philadelphia, University of Pennsylvania, 1932.
2. ADRIAN, E. D.: Sensory areas of the brain. Lancet **2**: 33, 1943.
3. ADRIAN, E. D., CATTELL, McK. AND HOAGLAND, H.: Sensory discharges in single cutaneous nerve fibres. J. Physiol. **72**: 377, 1931.
4. ADRIAN, E. D. AND ZOTTERMAN, Y.: The impulses produced by sensory nerve endings III. J. Physiol. **61**: 465, 1926.
4a. ALBERT, E. AND LAURIAT, E.: Analgesic properties of derivatives of diphenylethylamine. Nature **158**: 202, 1946.
5. ALRUTZ, S.: Studien auf dem Gebiete der Temperatursinne. I. Zu den Kälte und Wärmepunkten. Skandina. Arch. f. Physiol. **7**: 321, 1897.
6. ALVAREZ, W. C.: Nervous Indigestion and Pain. New York, Paul B. Hoeber, Inc., 1943.
7. ANDREWS, H. L.: Skin resistance changes and measurements of pain threshold. J. Clin. Invest. **22**: 517, 1943.
8. ANDREWS, H. L.: The effect of morphine and prostigmine methylsulfate on measurements of pain threshold. J. A. M. A. **120**: 525, 1942.
9. ANDREWS, H. L.: The effect of opiates on the pain threshold in post-addicts. J. Clin. Invest. **22**: 511, 1943.
10. ANDREWS, H. L. AND WORKMAN, W.: Pain threshold measurements in the dog. J. Pharm. & Exper. Therap. **73**: 99, 1941.
11. ARISTOTLE: Treatise on the Principles of Life, Eng. Trans. W. A. Hammond, bk. ii, chap. 6; bk. iii, chap. 1. 1902.
12. ARISTOTLE: Nicomachean Ethics. Bk. II. Man and Man: The Social Philosophers. New York, Random House, 1947.
12a. ARMSTRONG, D., DRY, R. M. L., KEELE, C. A. AND MARKHAM J. W.: Method for studying chemical excitants of cutaneous pain in man. J. Physiol. **115**: 1, 1951.
13. AUSTREGESILO, A.: Psychology and psychotherapy of pain; the concept of pain. J. Neuropsiquiat. panamer. **1**: 27, 1939.
14. AUSTREGESILO, A.: Psicologia y psicoterapia del dolor y conceptos del mismo. Rev. Psiquiat. Crim. Buenos Aires **4**: 431, 1939.
15. BALLANTINE, H. T. JR., HUETER, T. F. AND LUDWIG, G. H.: Establishment of thresholds of pain and damage by ultrasonic irradiation. Quarterly Progress Report, Acoustics Lab. MIT, Jan.–Mar. 1950, p. 33.
16. BARKER, P. C.: Concerning action of opium upon uterus and particularly as parturient agent. New York Med. J. **9**: 261, 1869.
17. BARMACK, J. E.: Personal communication.
18. BATTERMAN, R. C.: Clinical effectiveness and safety of a new synthetic analgesic drug, demerol. Arch. Int. Med. **71**: 345, 1943.
19. BATTERMAN, R. C.: Evaluating analgesic agents. Yale J. Biol. & Med. **18**: 595, 1946.
20. BATTERMAN, R. C. AND HIMMELSBACH, C. K.: Demerol—a new synthetic analgesic. J. A. M. A. **122**: 222, 1943.
21. BATTERMAN, R. C. AND MULHOLLAND, J. H.: Demerol. Arch. Surg. **46**: 404, 1943.

22. BAZETT, H. C. AND MCGLONE, B.: Temperature gradients in the tissues in man. Am. J. Physiol. **82:** 415, 1927.

23. BEEBE-CENTER, J. G.: The Psychology of Pleasantness and Unpleasantness. New York, D. Van Nostrand Co., 1932.

24. BEEBE-CENTER, J. G. AND WADDELL, D.: A general psychological scale of taste. J. Physiol. **26:** 517, 1948.

25. BEECHER, H. K.: Pain in men wounded in battle. Bull. U. S. Army Med. Dep. **5:** 445, 1946.

26. BELL, C.: Anatomy of the Human Body. **3:** 224, 1803. *Also:* J. AND C. BELL: The Anatomy and Physiology of the Human Body. 5th Amer. ed., revised by C. Bell, **2:** 154, 1827.

27. BENDER, M. B.: Extinction and precipitation of cutaneous sensations. Arch. Neur. & Psychiat. **54:** 1, 1945.

28. BENDER, M. B., FINK, M. AND GREEN, M.: Patterns in perception on simultaneous tests of face and hand. Arch. Neurol. & Psychiat. **66:** 355, 1951.

29. BENDER, M. B.:, TEUBER, H.-L. AND BATTERSBY, W. S.: Visual field defects after gunshot wounds of higher visual pathways. Program Abstract, Am. Neurol. Assn. 76th Annual meeting, 1951.

29a. BERLIN, L., GUTHRIE, T., GOODELL, H., AND WOLFF, H. G.: Analysis of "Central Excitatory State" in man by means of the flexor reflex and stimulation of measured intensity. Ibid., 77th An. Meeting, 1952.

30. BICKFORD, R. G.: The fibre dissociation produced by cooling human nerves. Clin. Sc. **4:** 159, 1939.

31. BICKFORD, R. G.: Experiments relating to the itch sensation, its peripheral mechanism and central pathways. Clin. Sc. **3:** 377, 1937–38.

32. BIGELOW, N., HARRISON, I., GOODELL, H. AND WOLFF, H. G.: Studies on pain: Quantitative measurements of two pain sensations of the skin, with reference to the nature of the "hyperalgesia of peripheral neuritis". J. Clin. Invest. **24:** 503, 1945.

33. BISHOP, G. H.: Nerve and synaptic conduction. Ann. Rev. Physiol. **8:** 355, 1946.

34. BISHOP, G. H.: The structural identity of the pain spot in human skin. J. Neurophysiol. **7:** 185, 1944.

35. BISHOP, G. H.: The peripheral unit for pain. J. Neurophysiol. **7:** 71, 1944.

36. BISHOP, G. H. Responses to electrical stimulation of single sensory units of skin. J. Neurophysiol. **6:** 361, 1943.

37. BISHOP, G. H.: The skin as an organ of senses with special reference to the itching sensation. J. Invest. Dermat. **11:** 143, 1948.

38. BISHOP, G. H.: Relation of pain sensory threshold to form of mechanical stimulator. J. Neurophysiol. **12:** 51, 1949.

39. BISHOP, G. H.: Neural mechanisms of cutaneous sense. Physiol. Rev. **26:** 77, 1946.

40. Blank, I. H. AND FINESINGER, J. F.: Electrical resistance of the skin. Effect of size of electrodes, exercise and cutaneous hydration. Arch. Neurol. & Psychiat. **56:** 544, 1946.

41. BLANKENHORN, M. A. AND FERRIS, E. B. JR.: On the nature of aviators' bends. Trans. Assn. Am. Physicians **58:** 86, 1944.

42. BLATZ, W. E.: The cardiac, respiratory and electrical phenomena involved in the emotion of fear. J. Exp. Psychol. **8:** 109, 1925.

43. BLISS, C. I. AND SEVRINGHAUS, E. L.: A collaborative study of methods for assaying analgesic drugs. Fed. Proc. **6:** 310, 1947.

44. BLIX, M.: Experimentelle Beiträge zur Lösung der Frage über die spezifische Energie der Hautnerven. Ztschr. f. Biol. **20**: 141, 1884.

45. BOLDYREFF, V. B.: On the change of rhythmical light sensation in man caused by pain stimulation. Bull. Biol. Med. exp. URSS **8**: 384, 1939.

46. BOLTON, B.: Vasoconstriction following deep inspiration. J. Physiol. **86**: 83, 1936.

47. BONNER, F., BOBB, S., SWEET, W. H. AND WHITE, J. C.: Frontal Lobe Surgery: Its Value in the Treatment of Pain with Consideration of Postoperative Psychological Changes. Proc. Assn. Res. Nerv. & Ment. Dis. Vol. XXXI, The Williams & Wilkins Company, 1952.

48. BORING, E. G.: Cutaneous sensation after nerve-division. Quart. J. Exper. Physiol. **10**: 1, 1916.

49. BORING, E. G.: The Physical Dimensions of Consciousness. New York, The Century Co., 1933.

50. BORING, E. G.: The sensations of the alimentary canal. Am. J. Psychol. **26**: 1, 1951.

51. BORING, E. G.: Sensation and Perception in the History of Experimental Psychology. New York, D. Appleton-Century Co., Inc., 1942.

52. BOUASSE, H.: Émission chaleur solaire. Éclairage théorie de émission. Paris, Libairie Delagrave, 1925.

53. BOURNE, A. W. AND BURN, J. H.: Action on human uterus of anaesthetics and other drugs commonly used in labour. Brit. Med. J. **2**: 87, 1930.

54. BRACK, W.: Die Bedeutung des vegetativen Systems für die Entstehung des Juckens. Deliberationes, Ninth International Congress of Dermatology, Budapest. **1**: 129, 1935.

55. BRAMWELL, J. M.: Hypnotism: Its History, Practice and Theory. Philadelphia, J. B. Lippincott, 1930.

56. BRENMAN, M. AND GILL, M. M.: Hypnotherapy. New York, Josiah Macy Foundation, 1944.

57. BRICKNER, R. M.: An interpretation of frontal lobe function based upon the study of a case of partial bilateral frontal lobectomy. Proc. Assn. Res. Nerv. & Ment. Dis., The Williams & Wilkins Co., **13**: 259, 1934.

58. BRINK, F. JR.: Excitation and conduction in the neuron. Handbook of Experimental Psychology, p. 50. John Wiley & Sons, 1951.

59. BRODMAN, K.: Vergleichende Localizationslehre der Grosshirnrinde in ihren Prinzipien dargestellt auf Grund des Zellenbaues. Leipzig, J. A. Barth, 1909.

60. BRONK, D. W. AND STELLA, G.: Response to steady pressures of single end organs in isolated carotid sinus. Am. J. Physiol. **110**: 708, 1935.

61. BROWN, R. R. AND VOGEL, V. H.: Psychophysiological reactions following painful stimuli under hypnotic analgesia contrasted with gas anesthesia and novocain block. J. Appl. Psychol. **22**: 408, 1938.

62. BRUNS, O. AND MAYER, K.: Change in pain perception produced by morphine alone and in combination with d-desoxyephedrine; experimental and clinical studies. Klin. Wochensch. **24–25**: 24, 1946.

63. BUETTNER, K.: Effects of extreme heat on man. Protection of man against conflagration heat. J. A. M. A. **144**: 732, 1950.

64. BUMKE, O. AND FOERSTER, O.: Handbuch der Neurologie. Berlin, J. Springer, 1936.

65. Burns, M. and Dallenbach, K. M.: The adaptation of cutaneous pain. Am. J. Psychol. **45**: 111, 1933.

66. Burrill, D. Y., Goetzl, F. R. and Ivy, A. C.: The pain threshold raising effects of amphetamine. J. Dent. Res. **23**: 337, 1944.

67. Cajal, S. R.: Histologie du Système Nerveux de l'Homme et des Vertébrés. Maloine, Paris, Vol. I, 1909; Vol. II, 1911.

68. Cajal, S. R.: La fine structure des centres nerveux. Proc. Roy. Soc. **55**: 444, 1894.

69. Campbell, C. J.: Pain threshold apparatus. J. Nerv. Ment. Dis. **109**: 363, 1949.

70. Cannon, W. B.: Bodily Changes in Pain, Hunger, Fear and Rage. New York, D. Appleton & Co., 1929, 2nd ed.

71. Cannon, W. B.: Wisdom of the Body. New York, W. W. Norton & Co., 1932.

72. Capps, J. A.: Pain from the pleura and pericardium. Proc. Assn. Res. Nerv. & Ment. Dis., The Williams & Wilkins Co., **23**: 263, 1943.

73. Cattell, McK.: The action and use of analgesics. Pain, Proc. Assn. Res. Nerv. & Ment. Dis., The Williams & Wilkins Co., **23**: 365, 1943.

74. Chapman, W. P., Arrowood, J. G. and Beecher, H. K.: The analgetic effects of low concentrations of nitrous oxide compared in man with morphine sulphate. J. Clin. Invest. **22**: 871, 1943.

75. Chapman, W. P.: Measurements of pain sensitivity in normal control subjects and in psychoneurotic patients. Psychosomatic Med. **6–7**: 252, 1944–45.

76. Chapman, W. P., Cohen, M. E. and Cobb, S.: Measurements related to pain in neurocirculatory asthenia, anxiety neurosis, or effort syndrome: Levels of heat stimulus perceived as painful and producing wince and withdrawal reactions. J. Clin. Invest. **25**: 890, 1946.

77. Chapman, W. P., Herrera, R., and Jones, C. M.: Comparison of pain produced experimentally in lower esophagus, common bile duct, and upper small intestine with pain experienced by patients with diseases of biliary tract and pancreas. Surg., Gynec. & Obst. **89**: 573, 1949.

78. Chapman, W. P., Finesinger, J. E., Jones, C. M. and Cobb, S.: Measurements of pain sensitivity in patients with psychoneurosis. Arch. Neurol. & Psychiat. **57**: 321, 1947.

79. Chapman, W. P. and Jones, C. M.: Variations in cutaneous and visceral pain sensitivity in normal subjects. J. Clin. Invest. **23**: 81, 1944.

80. Chapman, W. P., Rose, A. S. and Solomon, H. C.: Measurements of heat stimulus producing motor withdrawal reaction in patients following frontal lobotomy. Proc. Assn. Res. Nerv. & Ment. Dis., The Williams & Wilkins Co., **27**: 754, 1948.

81. Claiborne, J. H.: A case of subjective pain. Psychol. Revs. **2**: 599, 1895.

82. Clark, D., Hough, H. B. and Wolff, H. G.: Experimental studies on headache: Observations on headache produced by histamine. Arch. Neurol. & Psychiat. **35**: 1054, 1936.

83. Clark, D., Hughes, J. and Gasser, H. S.: Afferent function in the group of nerve fibers of slowest conduction velocity. Am. J. Physiol. **114**: 69, 1935.

84. Clausen, J. and King, H. E.: Determination of pain threshold on untrained subjects. J. Psychol. **30**: 299, 1950.

85. Cleland, J. P. G.: Paravertebral anesthesia in obstetrics: Experimental and clinical basis. Surg., Gynec. & Obstet. **57**: 51, 1933.

86. COBLENTZ, W. W.: The diffuse reflecting power of various substances. Bull. U. S. Bur. Standards 9: 238, 1913.
87. COHEN, H.: Visceral pain. Lancet 2: 933, 1947.
88. COHEN, H.: Mechanism of visceral pain. Lancet 246: 764, 1944.
89. COHEN, H. AND WALLACE-JONES, H.: The reference of cardiac pain to a phantom left arm. Brit. Heart J. 5: 67, 1943.
89a. CRITCHLEY, MacD.: Observations on pain. Bristol Med.-Chir. J. 52: 191, 1935.
90. CRONHOLM, B.: Phantom limbs in amputees. A study of changes in the integration of centripetal impulses with special reference to referred sensations. Acta Psych. et Neurol. Scan. Suppl. 72, Ejnar Munksgaard, Copenhagen, 1951.
91. CUSHING, H.: A note upon the faradic stimulation of the postcentral gyrus in conscious patients. Brain 32: 44, 1909.
92. DALLENBACH, K. M.: Pain: History and present status. Am. J. Psychol. 52: 331, 1939.
93. D'AMOUR, F. E. AND SMITH, D. L.: A method for determining loss of pain sensation. J. Pharm. & Exp. Therap. 72: 74, 1941.
94. DARROW, C. W.: The galvanic skin response and the blood pressure as preparatory and facilitative functions. Psychol. Bull. 33: 73, 1936.
95. DARROW, C. W.: Neural mechanisms controlling palmar galvanic skin reflex and palmar sweating; consideration of available literature. Arch. Neurol. & Psychiat. 37: 641, 1937.
96. DARWIN, E.: Zoonomia. 1, sec. 14, pp. 76–90, 1794.
97. DAVENPORT, H. A. AND RANSON, S. W.: Ratios of cells to fibers and of myelinated to unmyelinated fibers in spinal nerve roots. Am. J. Anat. 49: 193, 1931.
98. DAVIS, R. C.: Modifications of the galvanic reflex by daily repetition of a stimulus. J. Exp. Psychol. 17: 504, 1934.
99. DENTON, J. E. AND BEECHER, H. K.: New analgesics. I. Methods in the clinical evaluation of new analgesics. J. A. M. A. 141: 1051, 1949.
100. DODEK, S. M.: New method for graphically recording contractions of parturient human uterus; study of effects of certain sedatives, anaesthetics and stimulants upon uterus in labor. Surg., Gynec. & Obst. 55: 45, 1932.
101. DONALDSON, H. H.: On the temperature sense. Mind 10: 399, 1885.
102. DOUPE, J., MILLER, W. R. AND KELLER, W. K.: Vasomotor reactions in the hypnotic state. J. Neurol. & Psychiat. 2: 97, 1939.
102a. DU BOIS-REYMOND, R.: Le centre du sommeil. Comp. Rendu Soc. Biol., Paris 53: 229, 1901.
103. DUKE-ELDER, W. S.: Text Book of Ophthalmology. St. Louis, C. V. Mosby Co., 1941, Vol. 1, Chap. 22.
104. DUNBAR, F.: Emotions and Bodily Changes. New York, Columbia University Press, 1946, pp. 85–95.
105. DYNES, J. B.: Hypnotic anesthesia. J. Abn. & Soc. Psychol. 27: 79, 1932.
106. DYNES, J. B. AND POPPEN, J. L.: Lobotomy for intractable pain. J.A.M.A. 140: 15, 1949.
107. EBAUGH, F. G. JR., BIRD, R. M. AND HARDY, J. D.: Observations on pain and temperature perception within the sternal marrow cavity. Proc. Soc. Exper. Biol. & Med. 74: 844, 1950.
108. EBAUGH, F. G. JR. AND THAUER, R.: Influence of various environmental temperatures on the cold and warmth thresholds. J. Appl. Physiol. 3: 173, 1950.

109. ECKARDT, L. B., McLEAN, J. M. AND GOODELL, H.: Experimental studies on headache. The genesis of pain from the eye. Proc. Assoc. Res. Nerv. & Ment. Dis., The Williams & Wilkins Co. **23**: 209, 1943.

110. EDDY, N. B.: Pharmacological Studies. Nat'l Res. Counc. Report on Committee on Drug Addiction, 1929–1941.

111. EDDY, N. B.: Studies on hypnotics of barbituric acid series. J. Pharm. **33**: 43, 1928.

112. EDDY, N. B.: Studies of morphine, codeine and their derivatives. J. Pharm. & Exp. Therap. **45**: 339, 1932.

113. EDES, B. AND DALLENBACH, K. M.: The adaptation of pain aroused by cold. Am. J. Psychol. **48**: 307, 1936.

114. EDWARDS, W.: Recent research on pain perception. Psychol. Bull. **47**: 449, 1950.

115. EHRENWALD, H. AND KÖNIGSTEIN, H.: Klinische und experimentelle Untersuchungen über das Juckgefühl. Vorläufige Mitteilung. Wien. klin. Wchnschr. **42**: 1397, 1929.

116. ELO, J. AND NIKULA, A.: Zur Topographie des Wärmesinnes. Skan. Arch. für Physiol. **24**: 226, 1910.

117. ERCOLI, N. AND LEWIS, M. N.: Studies on analgesics. J. Pharm. & Exp. Therap. **84**: 301, 1945.

117a. ERICKSON, T. C., BLECKWENN, W. J., AND WOOLSEY, C. N.: Observations on the post central gyrus in relation to pain. A. N. A. Program, 77th An. Meeting, 1952, p. 14.

118. EVANS, J. P.: Quoted in Walker, A. E.: Central Rep. of Pain. Proc. Assn. Res. Nerv. & Ment. Dis., The Williams & Wilkins Co. **23**: 63, 1943.

119. FALCONER, M. A.: Relief of intractable pain of organic origin by frontal lobotomy. ibid. **27**: 706, 1948.

120. FECHNER, G. T.: Elemente der Psychophysik, Leipsig, Breitkopf & Härtel, 1860.

121. FEINDEL, W. H., WEDDELL, G. AND SINCLAIR, D. C.: Pain sensibility in deep somatic structures. J. Neurol, Neurosurg. & Psychiat. **11**: 113, 1948.

122. FENDER, F. A.: Precision device for faradic stimulation. Science **89**: 491, 1939.

123. FERRY, E. J.: Persistence of vision. Am. J. Science **44**: 192, 1892.

124. FLEMING, J. A.: Utilization of induced currents. The Alternate Current Transformer, Vol. II. London, Electrician Printing & Publishing Co., 1892.

125. FLINN, F. B. AND CHAIKELIS, A. S.: An improved instrument for the determination of changes in the pain threshold caused by drugs. Am. J. Psychiat. **103**: 349, 1946–47.

126. FLODMARK, S. AND WRAMNER, T.: The analgetic action of morphine, eserine, and prostigmine studied by a modified H-W-G method. Acta Phys. Scandinav. **9**: 88, 1945.

127. FORBES, A. AND MILLER, R. H.: The effect of ether anesthesia on afferent paths in the decerebrate animal. Am. J. Physiol. **62**: 113, 1922.

128. FOERSTER, O.: Die Leitungsbahnen des Schmerzgefühls und die chirurgische Behandlung der Schmerzzustände. Berlin & Vienna, Urban and Schwarzenberg, 1927.

129. FOERSTER, O.: Symptomatologie der Erkrankungen des Rückenmarks und seiner Wurzeln, in: Bumke, O. and Foerster, O., Handbuch der Neurologie. Berlin, Springer, 1936, Vol. 5, p. 1.

130. FOSTER, R. H. K. AND CARMAN, A. J.: Studies in analgesia: Piperidine derivatives with morphine-like activity. J. Pharm.& Exp. Therap. **91**: 195, 1947.

131. FREEMAN, W. AND WATTS, J. W.: Psychosurgery. Springfield, Illinois, C. C. Thomas, 1950, 2nd ed.

132. FREEMAN, W.: Personal communication, re transorbital lobotomy.

133. FREEMAN, L. W., SHUMACKER, H. B. JR., WAYSON, E. E. AND STAHL, N. M.: Conduction of painful impulses from the extremities via the sympathetic nervous system. Fed. Proc. **7**: 36, 1948.

134. FREEMAN, W. AND WATTS, J. W.: Psychosurgery. Springfield, Illinois, C. C Thomas, 1942. Ibid, 1950, 2nd Ed.

135. FREEMAN, W. AND WATTS, J. W.: Pain of organic disease relieved by prefrontal lobotomy. Lancet **250**: 953, 1946.

136. FREEMAN, W. AND WILLIAMS, J. M.: The lesions of transorbital lobotomy. Program Abstract, Am. Neurol. Assn., 76th Annual Meeting, June 1951.

137. FRIEDLANDER, J. W. AND SARBIN, T. R.: The depth of hypnosis. J. Abn. & Soc. Psychol. **33**: 453, 1938.

138. FURER, M. AND HARDY, J. D.: The reaction to pain as determined by the galvanic skin response. Proc. Assn. Res. Nerv. & Ment. Dis., The Williams & Wilkins Co., **29**: 72, 1949.

139. GAD, J. AND GOLDSCHEIDER, A.: Über die Summation von Hautreizen. Ztschr. f. klin. Med. **21**: 339, 1892.

140. GAENSLER, E. A.: Quantitative determination of the visceral pain threshold in man. J. Clin. Invest. **30**: 406, 1951.

141. GAMMON, G. D. AND STARR, I.: Studies on the relief of pain by counterirritation. J. Clin. Invest. **20**: 13, 1941.

142. GASSER, H. S.: Conduction in nerves in relation to fiber types. Proc. Assn. Res. Nerv. & Ment. Dis., The Williams & Wilkins Co., **15**: 35, 1934.

143. GASSER, H. S.: Pain-producing impulses in peripheral nerves. Proc. Assn. Res. Nerv. & Ment. Dis., The Williams & Wilkins Co., **23**: 44, 1943.

144. GASSER, H. S.: The control of excitation in the nervous system. Harvey Lectures, Baltimore, The Williams & Wilkins Co., 1937.

145. GASSER, H. S. AND ERLANGER, J.: The role of fiber size in the establishment of nerve block by pressure or cocaine. Am. J. Physiol. **88**: 581, 1929.

146. GELLHORN, E. AND THOMPSON, L.: The influence of muscle pain on cortically induced movements. Am. J. Physiol. **142**: 231, 1944.

147. GEORGI, F.: Beiträge zur Kenntnis des psycho-galvanischen Phänomens. Arch. f. Psychiat. u. Nervenkrankheit. **62**: 571, 1921.

148. GERARD, R. W., MARSHALL, W. H. AND SAUL, L. J.: Electrical activity of the cat's brain. Arch. Neurol. & Psychiat. **36**: 675, 1936.

149. GLASSTONE, S., LAIDLER, K. J. AND EYRING, H.: The Theory of Rate Processes. New York, McGraw-Hill Book Co., 1941.

150. GLUZEK, L. J. B.: Dolorimetry: A quantitative method of measuring pain and deep sensibility. Ohio State Med. J. **40**: 49, 1944.

151a. GOETZL, F. R.: Experimental evidence for analgesic properties of antipyretic drugs: Critical review of literature with report on additional experiments. Permanente Found. M. Bull. **4**: 49, 1946.

151b. GOETZL, F. R., BIEN, C. W. AND GO LU: Changes in blood pressure in response to presumably painful stimuli. J. App. Physiol. **4**: 161, 1951.

152. GOETZL, F. R., BURRILL, D. Y. AND IVY, A. C.: A critical analysis of algesimetric methods with suggestions for a useful procedure. Quart. Bull. North western U. Med. Sch. **17**: 280, 1943.

153. GOLD, H., KWIT, N. T. AND MODELL, W.: The effect of extra-cardiac pain on the heart. Proc. Assn. Res. Nerv. & Ment. Dis., The Williams & Wilkins Co., **23**: 345, 1943.

154. GOLDSCHEIDER, A.: Über Irradiation und Hyperästhesie im Bereich der Hautsensibilität. Arch. f. d. ges. Physiol. **165**: 1, 1916.

155. GOLDSCHEIDER, A.: Über die Summation von Hautreizen. Arch. f. Physiol. 164, 1891. (Gesammelte Abhandlungen, **1**: 397, 1898.)

156. GOLDSCHEIDER, A.: Über den Schmerz: Physiologischer und Klinischer Hinsicht. 1894.

157. GOLDSCHEIDER, A.: Die spezifische Energie der Gefühlsnerven der Haut. Monatschr. Prakt. Dermatol. **3**: 283, 1884.

158. GOLDSTEIN, K.: Frontal lobotomy and impairment of abstract attitude. J. Nerv. & Ment. Dis. **110**: 93, 1949.

159. GOLLA, F. L.: The objective study of neurosis. Lancet **99**: 373, 1921.

160. GOODELL, H., McDOWELL, F. AND WOLFF, H. G.: Unpublished observations.

161. GOODRICH, F. W. AND THOMS, H.: Natural Childbirth. Pediatrics **3**: 613, 1949.

162. GORDON, G. AND WHITTERIDGE, D.: Conduction time for human pain sensation. Lancet **2**: 700, 1943.

163. GORTON, B. E.: The physiology of hypnosis II. Psych. Quart., pp. 457–485, July 1949.

164. GRACE, C. M., McGUIRE, J. H. AND MARTIN, E. G.: The influence of drugs on the human sensory threshold. J. Pharm. & Exper. Therap. **6**: 527, 1915.

165. GRACE, W. J., WOLF, S. AND WOLFF, H. G.: The Human Colon. New York, Paul B. Hoeber, Inc., 1951.

166. GRAHAM, D. T., GOODELL, H. AND WOLFF, H. G.: Neural mechanisms involved in itch, "itchy skin", and tickle sensations. J. Clin. Invest. **30**: 37, 1951.

167. GRAHAM, J. R. AND WOLFF, H. G.: Mechanism of migraine headache and action of ergotamine tartrate. Proc. Assn. Res. Nerv. & Ment. Dis., Williams & Wilkins Co., **18**: 638, 1937. Arch. Neurol. & Psychiat. **39**: 737, 1938.

168. GRANIER-DOYEUX, M.: Determination of pain threshold—applications in pharmacology. Rev. sau. y. asest. soceal **11**: 257, 1946.

169. GRANIT, R. AND HARPER, P.: Comparative studies on peripheral and central retina. II. Synaptic reactions in the eye. Am. J. Physiol. **95**: 211, 1930.

169a. GREGOR, A.: Beiträge zur Kenntnis des psychogalvanischen Phänomens. Ztschr. f. d. g. Neurol. u. Psychiat. **8**: 393, 1912.

170. GROSS, E. G., HOLLAND, H., CARTER, H. R. AND CHRISTENSEN, E. M.: The role of epinephrine in analgesia. Anesthesiology **9**: 459, 1948.

171. GRUNDFEST, H.: Bioelectric potentials. Ann. Rev. Physiol. **2**: 213, 1940.

171a. GUTHRIE, T., BERLIN, L., GOODELL, H., AND WOLFF, H. G.: Unpublished observations.

172. GUTTMANN, L. AND WHITTERIDGE, D.: Effects of bladder distention on autonomic mechanisms after spinal cord injuries. Brain **70**: 361, 1947.

173. HAGGARD, E. A. AND GARNER, W. R.: Studies in affective processes: II. On the quantification and evaluation of measured changes in skin resistance. J. Exp. Psychol. **35**: 46, 1945.

174. HAGGARD, E. A. AND GARNER, W. R.: An empirical test of a derived measure of changes in skin resistance. J. Exp. Psychol. **36:** 59, 1946.
175. HALSTEAD, W. C. AND SETTLAGE, P. H.: The dynamic visual field. Arch. Neurol. & Psychiat. **49:** 633, 1943.
176. HARDY, J. D.: Physiological responses to heat and cold. Ann. Rev. Physiol., p. 119, 1950.
177. HARDY, J. D. AND CATTELL, McK.: Measurement of pain threshold-raising action of aspirin, codeine, and meperidine (Demerol). Fed. Proc. **9:** 282, 1950.
178. HARDY, J. D. AND DuBois, E. F.: The technique of measuring radiation and convection. J. Nutrition **15:** 461, 1938.
179. HARDY, J. D., GOODELL, H. AND WOLFF, H. G.: Studies on pain: Observations on hyperalgesia associated with referred pain. Am. J. Physiol. **133:** 316, 1941.
180. HARDY, J. D. AND JAVERT, C. T.: Studies on Pain: Measurement of pain intensity in childbirth. J. Clin. Invest. **28:** 153, 1949.
181. HARDY, J. D. AND OPPEL, T. W.: Studies in temperature sensation. III. The sensitivity of the body to heat and the spatial summation of the end organ reponses. J. Clin. Invest. **16:** 533, 1937.
182. HARDY, J. D. AND OPPEL, T. W.: Studies in temperature sensation. IV. The stimulaton of cold sensation by radiation. J. Clin. Invest. **17:** 771, 1938.
183. HARDY, J. D., POTELUNAS, C. B. AND MEIXNER, M. D.: Pain threshold measurements on human skin following application of topical analgesics. J. Invest. Dermat. **16:** 369, 1951.
184. HARDY, J. D. AND SODERSTROM, G. F.: An improved apparatus for measuring surface and body temperature. Rev. Sci. Ins. **8:** 419, 1937.
185. HARDY, J. D., WOLFF, H. G. AND GOODELL, H.: Studies on pain. A new method for measuring pain threshold: Observations on the spatial summation of pain. J. Clin. Invest. **19:** 649, 1940.
186. HARDY, J. D., WOLFF, H. G. AND GOODELL, H.: Experimental evidence on the nature of cutaneous hyperalgesia. J. Clin. Invest. **29:** 115, 1950.
187. HARDY, J. D., WOLFF, H. G. AND GOODELL, H.: Threshold and discrimination of differences in intensity of stimulus for deep pain. Fed. Proc. **10:** 60, 1951.
188. HARDY, J. D., WOLFF, H. G. AND GOODELL, H.: Studies on pain: Discrimination of differences in intensity of a pain stimulus as a basis of a scale of pain intensity. J. Clin. Invest. **26:** 1152, 1947.
189. HARDY, J. D., WOLFF, H. G. AND GOODELL, H.: The effect of skin temperature upon the pain threshold evoked by thermal radiation. Science **114:** 149, 1951.
189a. HARDY, J. D., WOLFF, H. G., AND GOODELL, H.: Pricking pain threshold in different body areas. Proc. Soc. Exp. Biol. and Med. **80:** 425, 1952.
190. HARDY, J. D., WOLFF, H. G. AND GOODELL, H.: Pain threshold in man. Proc. Assn. Res. Ner. & Ment. Dis., The Williams & Wilkins Co., **23:** 1, 1943.
191. HARDY, J. D., WOLFF, H. G. AND GOODELL, H.: Unpublished observations.
192. HARELL, A., MEAD, S. AND MUELLER, E.: The problem of spasm in skeletal muscle; a clinical and laboratory study. J. A. M. A. **143:** 640, 1950.
193. HARMAN, J. B.: The localization of deep pain. Brit. Med. J. **1:** 188, 1948.
194. HARPUDER, K. AND STEIŃ, I. D.: Studies on the nature of pain arising from an ischemic limb. II. Biochemical studies. Am. Heart J. **25:** 438, 1943.
195. HARRISON, I. AND BIGELOW, N. H.: Quantiative studies of visceral pain

produced by the contraction of ischemic muscle. Proc. Assn. Res. Nerv. & Ment. Dis., The Williams & Wilkins Co., **23:** 154, 1943.

196. HART, E. R.: Toxicity and analgetic potency of salicylamide and certain of its derivatives as compared with established analgetic-antipyretic drugs. J. Pharm. & Exp. Therap. **89:** 205, 1947.

197. HART, E. R. AND WEAVER, O. M.: Analgesia in rats as a result of administration of barbiturates, and its relation to hypnosis. Fed. Proc. **6:** 336, 1947.

198. HARTLINE, H. K.: The effects of spatial summation in retina on excitation of fibers of optic nerve. Am. J. Physiol **130:** 700, 1940.

199. HAZOURI, L. A. AND MUELLER, A. D.: Pain threshold studies on paraplegic patients. Arch. Neurol. & Psychiat. **64:** 607, 1950.

200. HEAD, H.: On disturbances of sensation with especial reference to the pain of visceral disease. Brain **19:** 153, 1896.

201. Head, H.: Studies in Neurology. London, Oxford University Press, 1920.

202. HEAD, H.: On disturbances of sensation with especial reference to the pain of visceral disease. Brain **16:** 1, 1893.

203. HEAD, H.: On disturbances of sensation with especial reference to the pain of visceral disease. Brain **17:** 339, 1894.

204. HEARDMAN, H.: A Way to Natural Childbirth. Baltimore, The Williams & Wilkins Co., 1948.

205. HEATON, C. E.: History of anesthesia and analgesia in obstetrics. J. Hist. Med. & Allied Sci. **1:** 567, 1946.

206. HEINBECKER, P., BISHOP, G. H. AND O'LEARY, J.: Analysis of sensation in terms of the nerve impulse. Arch. Neurol. & Psychiat. **31:** 34, 1934.

207. v. HELMHOLTZ, H.: Über die Dauer und den Verlauf der durch Strömesschwankungen inducisten elektrischen Ströme. Poggendorf's Annalen der Physik und Chemie **83:** 505, 1851.

208. v. HELMHOLTZ, H.: Müller's Archiv., 1852, p. 330.

209. HENRIQUES, F. C.: The predictability and the significance of thermally induced rate processes leading to irreversible epidermal injury. Arch. Path. **43:** 489, 1947.

210. HENSEN, H.: Über den Einfluss des Morphines und des Aethers auf die Wehentäligkeit des Uterus. Arch. f. Gynäk. **144:** 500, 1898.

211. HERGET, C. M., GRANATH, L. P. AND HARDY, J. D.: Thermal sensation and discrimination in relation to intensity of stimulus. Am. J. Physiol. **134:** 645, 1941.

212. HERGET, C. M. AND HARDY, J. D.: Temperature sensation: The spatial summation of heat. Am. J. Physiol. **135:** 426, 1942.

213. HERSHENSON, B. B. AND BRUBAKER, E. R.: Scopolamine and apomorphine in labor. Am. J. Obst. &. Gynec. **53:** 980, 1947.

214. HERZEN, A.: Über die Spaltung des Temperatursinnes in zwei gesonderte Sinne. Arch. f. d. ges. Physiol. **38:** 93, 1885.

215. HEWER, A. J. H. AND KEELE, C. A.: A method of testing analgesics in man. Lancet **2:** 683, 1948.

216. HINSEY, J. C. AND PHILLIPS, R. A.: Observations upon diaphragmatic sensation. J. Neurophysiol. **3:** 175, 1940.

217. HODGKIN, A. L.: Evidence for electrical transmission in nerve. Part I. J. Physiol. **90:** 183, 1937.

218. HOLBROOK, T. J. AND DE GUTIERREZ-MAHONEY, C. G.: Diffusion of painful stimuli over segmental, infrasegmental and suprasegmental levels of the spinal cord. Fed. Proc. **6:** 22, 1947.

219. HOLLANDER, B.: Hypnosis and anesthesia. Proc. R. Soc. Med. **25:** 598, 1932.

220. HOLLANDER, E.: A clinical guage for sensitivity to pain. J. Lab. Clin. Med. **24:** 537, 1939.

220a. HOLMAN, C. W. AND GOODELL, H.: Unpublished observations.

221. HOLMES, T. H., GOODELL, H., WOLF, S. AND WOLFF, H. G.: The Nose. An Experimental Study of Reactions within the Nose in Human Subjects during Varying Life Experiences. Springfield, Illinois, C. C. Thomas, 1950.

221a. HOLMES, T. H., AND WOLFF, H. G.: Life situations, emotions and backache. Psychosom. Med. **14:** 18, 1952.

222. HORRAX, G.: Experiences with cortical excisions for the relief of intractable pain in the extremities. Surgery, **20:** 593, 1946.

223. HUETTER, T.: Experiences with ultra sound treatment. Condensed by Dr. Demmel, "Deutsche Medizinische Rundschau", July, 1948.

224. HUTCHINS, H. C. AND REYNOLDS, O. E.: Experimental investigation of the referred pain of aerodontalgia. J. Dent. Res. **26:** 3, 1947.

225. INMAN, V. T. AND SAUNDERS, J. B. D. M.: Referred pain from skeletal structures. J. Nerv. & Ment. Dis. **99:** 660, 1944.

226. IRWIN, S., HOUDE, R. W., BENNETT, D. R., HENDERSHOT, L. C., AND SEEVERS, M. H.: The effects of morphine, methadone and meperidine on some reflex responses of spinal animals to nociceptive stimulation. J. Pharm. & Exp. Therap. **101:** 132, 1951.

227. IVY, A. C., GOETZL, F. R. AND BURRILL, D. Y.: Morphine-dextroamphetamine analgesia: The analgesic effects of morphine sulfate alone and in combination with dextroamphetamine sulfate in normal human subjects. War Med. **6:** 67, 1944.

228. IVY, A. C., GOETZL, F. R., HARRIS, S. C. AND BURRILL, D. Y.: The analgesic effect of intracarotid and intravenous injection of epinephrine in dogs and of subcutaneous injection in man. Quart. Bull. Northwestern U. Med. Sch. **18:** 298, 1944.

229. JAVERT, C. T. AND HARDY, J. D.: Influence of analgesics on pain intensity during labor. Anesth. **12:** 189, 1951.

230. JAVERT, C. T. AND HARDY, J. D.: Measurement of pain intensity in labor and its physiologic, neurologic, and pharmacologic implications. Am. J. Obs. & Gynec. **60:** 552, 1950.

231. JONES, C. M.: Digestive Tract Pain. Diagnosis and Treatment. New York, MacMillan Co., 1938.

232. JONES, C. M.: Pain from the digestive tract. Proc. Assn. Res. Nerv. & Ment. Dis., The Williams & Wilkins Co., **23:** 302, 1943.

233. JONES, C. M. AND CHAPMAN, W. P.: Comparative study of analgesic effect of morphine sulfate and monoacetylmorphine. Arch. Int. Med. **73:** 322, 1944.

234. JONES, F. N. AND JONES, M. H.: The chronaxy of pain. Am. J. Psychol. **54:** 240, 1941.

235. KARL, R. C., PEABODY, G. E. AND WOLFF, H. G.: The mechanism of pain in trigeminal neuralgia. Science **102:** 12, 1945.

236. KEATS, A. S., BEECHER, H. K. AND MOSTELLER, F. C.: Measurement of path-

ological pain in distinction to experimental pain. J. App. Physiol. **3: 35,** 1950.

237. KEEGAN, J. J. AND GARRETT, F. D.: The segmental distribution of the cutaneous nerves in the limbs of man. Anat. Rec. **102:** 409, 1948.
238. KELLGREN, J. H., McGOWAN, A. J. AND WOOD, D. R.: Effect of d-tubocurarine chloride on sensation in man. Brit. Med. J. **2:** 898, 1946.
239. KERNWEIN, G. AND KELIKIAN, H.: Errors in interpretation of referred pain of bone origin. Am. J. Surg. **56:** 663, 1942.
240. KIESOW, F.: The problem of the condition of arousal of the pure sensation of cutaneous pain. J. Gen. Psychol. **1:** 199, 1928.
241. KING, H. E., CLAUSEN, J. AND SCARFF, J. E.: Cutaneous thresholds for pain before and after unilateral prefrontal lobotomy. J. Nerv. & Ment. Dis. **112:** 93, 1950.
242. KOLB, L. C.: Evaluation of lobotomy and its potentialities for future research in psychiatry and basic sciences. J. Nerv. & Ment. Dis. **110:** 112, 1949.
243. KOLB, L. C.: Psychiatric aspects of treatment for intractable pain in the phantom limb. Med. Clin. North Amer. **34:** 1029, 1950.
244. KOSKOFF, Y. D., DENNIS, W., LAZOVIK, D. & WHEELER, E. T.: The Frontal Lobes. Proc. Assn. Res. Nerv. & Ment. Dis., The Williams & Wilkins Co., **27:** 723, 1948.
245. KRUEGER, H., EDDY, N. B. & SUMWALT, M.: The Pharmacology of the Opium Alkaloids. Vol. 1 and 2, Supplement #165, U. S. Pub. Health Serv. Reports, U. S. Govt. Printing Office, 1941.
246. KÜLPE, O.: Outlines of Psychology. 1893. Eng. trans. E. B. Titchener, 1905.
247. KUNKLE, C. E.: Phasic pains induced by cold. J. App. Physiol. **1:** 811, 1949.
248. KUNKLE, E. C., ARMISTEAD, G. C., AND GOODELL, H.: Unpublished observations.
249. KUNKLE, E. C. AND CHAPMAN, W. P.: Insensitivity to pain in man. Proc. Assn. Res. Nerv. & Ment. Dis., The Williams & Wilkins Co., **23:** 100, 1943.
250. KUNKLE, E. C., GOODELL, H. AND WOLFF, H. G.: Unpublished observations.
251. KUNKLE, E. C. KIBLER, R. F., ARMISTEAD, G. C. AND GOODELL, H.: Central sensory excitation and inhibition in response to induced pain. Tr. Am. Neurol. Assn., Vol. 62, 1949.
252. KUNKLE, E. C., RAY, B. AND WOLFF, H. G.: Studies on headache: The mechanism and significance of the headache associated with brain tumor. Bull. N. Y. Acad. Med. **18:** 400, 1942.
253. KUNKLE, E. C., RAY, B. AND WOLFF, H. G.: Studies on headache: An analysis of the headache associated with changes in intracranial pressure. Arch. Neurol. & Psychiat. **49:** 323, 1943.
254. KUNO, F.: The Physiology of Human Perspiration. London, J. & A. Churchill, Ltd., 1934.
255. KUNTZ, A.: The Autonomic Nervous System, Philadelphia, Lea and Febiger, 1934.
256. KUNTZ, A. AND HAMILTON, J. W.: Afferent innervation of the skin. Anat. Rec. **11:** 387, 1938.
257. LACEY, J. I., LACEY, B. C. AND DALLENBACH, K. M.: Areal and temporal variations in pain sensitivity. Am. J. Psychol. **54:** 413, 1941.
258. LANDIS, C.: Psychology and the psychogalvanic reflex. Psychol. Rev. **37:** 381. 1930.

259. LANDIS, C.: Electrical phenomena of the skin (GSR). Psychol. Bull. **29:** 693, 1932.

260. LANDIS, C. AND DE WICK, H. N.: The electrical phenomena of the skin (PGR). Psychol. Bull. **26:** 64, 1929.

261. LANDIS, C. AND HUNT, W. A.: The conscious correlates of the galvanic skin response. J. Exp. Psychol. **18:** 505, 1935.

262. LANIER, L. H.: An experimental study of cutaneous innervation. Proc. Assn. Res. Nerv. & Ment. Dis., The Williams & Wilkins Co., **15:** 437, 1935.

263. LANIER, L. H.: Variability in the pain threshold. Science **97:** 49, 1943.

264. LE BEAU, J. AND GACHEO, J.: Effect of topectomy on irreducible pain with regard to 2 cases of causalgia. J. A. M. A. **141:** 1104, 1949.

265. LE BEAU, J.: Experience with topectomy for relief of intractable pain. J. Neurosurgery **7:** 79, 1950.

266. LEDUC, E. H. AND SLAUGHTER, D.: The effects of a combination of acetanilid, caffeine and sodium bromide on the pain threshold in man. Anesthesia & Analgesia **24:** 147, 1945.

267. LEE, L. E.: Clinical studies of morphine, methyldihydromorphinone, and desomorphine. J. Pharm. & Exp. Therap. **75:** 161, 1942.

268. LEE, R. F. AND HASEGAWA, A. K.: Human analgesic testing of experimental drugs: Nisentil (NU-1196) and (NU-2206). Am. Soc. Pharm. & Exp. Therap., Fall Meeting, November 1949.

269. LEE, R. F. AND PFEIFFER, C. C.: A warm wire algesimeter. Fed. Proc. **8:** 314, 1949.

270. LEE, R. F. AND PFEIFFER, C. C.: Influence of analgesics, Dromoran, Nisentil and morphine on pain thresholds in man. J. Appl. Physiol. **4:** 193, 1951.

271. LENNANDER, K. G.: Über lokale Anästhesie und über sensibilität in Organ und Gewebe, weitere Beobachtungen II. Mitt. a. d. Grenzgeb d. Med. u. Chir. **15:** 465, 1906.

272. LERICHE, R. AND FONTAINE, R.: Chirurgie des Nerfs du coeur. P. Verb. Congr. Fr. Chir. **41:** 89, 1932.

273. LERICHE, R. AND STRICKER, P.: Recherches expérimentals sur le nerf présacre. Bull. Soc. Nat. Chir. **53:** 819, 1927.

273a. LEVINE, M.: Electrical skin resistance during hypnosis. Arch. Neurol. & Psychiat. **24:** 937, 1930.

273b. LEWIS, C. S.: Problem of Pain. New York, MacMillan Co., 1944.

274. LEWIS, T.: Pain. New York, MacMillan Co., 1942.

275. LEWIS, T.: Pain in muscular ischemia: Its relation to anginal pain. Arch. Int. Med. **49:** 713, 1932.

276. LEWIS, T.: The nocifensor system of nerves and its reactions. I & II. Brit. Med. J. **1:** 431, 1937.

277. LEWIS, T.: Experiments relating to cutaneous hyperalgesia and its spread through somatic nerves. Clin. Sc. **2:** 373, 1936.

278. LEWIS, T., GRANT, R. T. AND MARVIN, H. M.: Vascular reactions of the skin to injury. X. The intervention of a chemical stimulus illustrated especially by the flare. The response to faradism. Heart **14:** 139, 1927.

279. LEWIS, T. AND HESS, W.: Pain derived from the skin and the mechanism of its production. Clin. Sc. **1:** 39, 1933–34.

280. LEWIS, T. AND KELLGREN, J. H.: Observations relating to referred pain,

viscero-motor reflexes and other associated phenomena. Clin. Sci. **4**: 47, 1939.

281. LEWIS, T., PICKERING, G. AND ROTHSCHILD, P.: Observations upon muscular pain in intermittent claudication. Heart **15**: 359, 1929–31.

282. LEWIS, T., AND POCHIN, E. E.: Effects of asphyxia and pressure on sensory nerves of man. Clin. Sci. **3**: 141, 1938.

283. LEWIS, T. AND POCHIN, E. E.: The double pain response of the human skin to a single stimulus. Clin. Sci. **3**: 67, 1937–38.

284. LIBMAN, E.: Observations on individual sensitiveness to pain. J. A. M. A. **102**: 335, 1934.

285. LIDDELL, H. S.: Some specific factors that modify tolerance for environmental stress. Life Stress and Bodily Disease. Proc. Assn. Res. Nerv. & Ment. Dis. The Williams & Wilkins Co., **29**: 155, 1950.

286. LIDZ, T.: Analysis of prefrontal lobe syndrome and its theoretic implications. Arch. Neurol. & Psychiat. **62**: 1, 1949.

287. LIVINGSTON, W. K.: Pain Mechanisms. New York, MacMillan Co., 1943.

288. LLOYD, D. P. C.: Functional organization of the spinal cord. Physiol. Rev. **24**: 1, 1944.

289. LLOYD-SMITH, D. L. AND MENDELSSOHN, K.: Tolerance limits to radiant heat. Brit. Med. J., p. 975, 1948.

290. LORENTE DE NÓ, R.: A study of nerve physiology. New York, Vols. 131 and 132 of: Studies from the Rockefeller Institute for Medical Research, 1947.

291. LORENTE DE NÓ, R.: Analysis of the activity of the chains of internuncial neurons. J. Neurophysiol. **1**: 207, 1938.

292. LORENTE DE NÓ, R.: Synaptic stimulation of motoneurons as a local process. J. Neurophysiol. **1**: 195, 1938.

293. LULL, C. B., AND HINGSON, R. A.: Control of Pain in Childbirth. Philadelphia, J. B. Lippincott Co., 1949.

294. LUND, C. J. AND HARRIS, J. W.: Use of heroin (diacetyl-morphine) in labor; Report of 454 deliveries. Am. J. Obst. & Gynec. **45**: 890, 1943.

295. LYERLY, J. G.: Prefrontal lobotomy for the relief of intractable pain. Am. J. Surg. **81**: 526, 1951.

296. McAULIFFE, G. W. GOODELL, H. AND WOLFF, H. G.: Experimental studies on headache: Pain from the nasal and paranasal structures. Proc. Assn. Res. Nerv. & Ment. Dis., The Williams & Wilkins Co., **23**: 185, 1943.

297. McAULIFFE, G. W.: Unpublished observations.

298. McLELLAN, A. AND GOODELL, H.: Pain from the bladder, ureter, and kidney pelvis. Proc. Assn. Res. Nerv. & Ment. Dis., The Williams & Wilkins Co., **23**: 252, 1943.

299. McMURRAY, G.: Experimental study of a case of insensitivity to pain. Arch. Neurol. & Psychiat. **64**: 650, 1950.

300. MACHT, D. I., HERMAN, N. B. AND LEVY, C. S.: A quantitative study of the analgesia produced by opium alkaloids individually and in combination with each other, in normal man. J. Pharm. & Exp. Therap. **8**: 1, 1916.

301. MACHT, D. I. AND MACHT, M. B.: Quantitative studies on pain threshold after administration of various drugs. J. Am. Pharm. Assn. **29**: 193, 1940.

302. MACKENZIE, J.: Symptoms and Their Interpretation. London, Shaw & Sons, 1918, 3rd Ed.

303. MACKENZIE, J.: Some points bearing on the association of sensory disorders and visceral disease. Brain 16 (Part III): 21, 1893.

304. MALMO, P. B. AND SHAGASS, C.: Physiologic studies of reaction to stress in anxiety and early schizophrenia. Psychosom. Med. 11: 9, 1949.

305. MARGOLIN, S. G., ORRINGER, D., KAUFMAN, M. R., WINKELSTEIN, A., HOLLANDER, F., JANOWITZ, H. AND STEIN, A.: Variations of gastric functions during conscious and unconscious conflict states. Proc. Assn. Res. Nerv. & Ment. Dis., The Williams & Wilkins Co., 29: 656, 1950.

306. MARSHALL, H. R.: Are there special nerves for pain? J. Nerv. & Ment. Dis. 21: 71, 1894.

307. MARTIN, E. G.: A quantitative study of faradic stimulation. II. The calibration of the inductorium for break shocks. Am. J. Physiol. 22: 116, 1908.

308. MARTIN, E. G.: The measurement of induction shocks. Am. J. Physiol. 27: 76 and 230, 1910.

309. MASON, T. H. AND HAMBY, W. B.: Relief of morphine addiction by prefrontal lobotomy. J. A. M. A. 136: 1039, 1948.

310. MAYR, J. K.: Tests of cutaneous sensation in early syphilis. Munch. med. Wchnshr. 78: 1433, 1931.

311. MICHELSEN, J. J.: Subjective disturbances of the sense of pain from lesions of the cerebral cortex. Proc. Assn. Res. Nerv. & Ment. Dis. The Williams & Wilkins Co., 23: 86, 1943.

312. MILLER L. C.: A critique of analgesic testing methods. Ann. N. Y. Acad. Sci 51: 34, 1948.

313. MIRSKY, I. A., KAPLAN, S. AND BROH-KALHN, R. H.: Pepsinogen excretion (uropepsin) as an index of the influence of various life situations on gastric secretion. Life Stress and Bodily Disease. Proc. Assn. Res. Nerv. & Ment. Dis., The Williams & Wilkins Co., 29: 628, 1950.

314. MOORE, R. M.: Some experimental observations relating to visceral pain. Surgery 3: 534, 1938.

315. MORAVCSIK, E. E.: Experimente über das Psychogalvanische Reflexphänomen. J. f. Psychol. u. Neurol. 18: 186, 1912.

316. MORITZ, A. R. AND HENRIQUES, F. C. JR.: Studies of thermal injury. II. The relative importance of time and surface temperature in the causation of cutaneous burns. Am. J. Path. 23: 695, 1947.

317. MORLEY, J.: Abdominal Pain. New York, Wm. Wood. & Co., 1931.

318. MORRISON, L. M. AND SPIEGEL, E. A.: Demonstration of visceral pain by determination of skin potentials. Ann. Int. Med. 22: 827, 1945.

318a. MORTON, D. R., KLASSEN, K. P. AND CURTIS, G. M.: The effect of high vagus section upon the clinical physiology of the bronchus. A.N.A. Program, 1950.

319. MOWRER, O. H.: A stimulus response analysis of anxiety and its role as a reinforcing agent. Psychol. Rev. 46: 553, 1939.

320. MÜLLER, J.: Handbuch der Physiologie des Menschen. 2: 249, 1840.

321. MULLIN, F. J. AND LUCKHARDT, A. B.: The effect of alcohol on cutaneous tactile and pain sensitivity. Am. J. Physiol. 109: 77, 1934.

322. MULLIN, F. J. AND LUCKHARDT, A. B.: Effects of certain analgesic drugs on cutaneous, tactile and pain sensitivity. Am. J. Physiol. 113: 100, 1935.

323. MURPHY, D. P.: Uterine Contractility in Pregnancy. Philadelphia, J. B. Lippincott Co., 1947, p. 118.

324. MURRAY, E.: A qualitative analysis of tickling; its relation to cutaneous and organic sensation. Am. J. Psychol. **19**: 289, 1908.

325. MYASISCHEV, L.: Experimental evidence on the problem of objective indices in sensory disorders. Nov. Refl. Fiziol. Nerv. Sist. **3**: 458, 1929. (Psychol. Abst. **4**: 4349, 1930)

326. NAFE, J. P.: The Pressure, Pain and Temperature Senses. in: Handbook of General Experimental Psychology. Worcester, The International University Series in Psychology, 1934.

327. NORTHFIELD, D. W. C.: Some observations on headache. Brain **61**: 133, 1938.

328. OBERST, F. W.: Chairman of a Symposium on "Can the Euphoric, Analgetic, and Physical Dependence Effects of Drugs Be Separated?" Fed. Proc. **2**: 187, 1943.

329. OLLENDORF, H.: Systematic study of sensitivity of various syphilitic and non-syphilitic abnormal conditions in skin. Arch. f. Dermat. u. Syph. **149**: 310, 1925.

330. OPPEL, T. W. AND HARDY, J. D.: Studies in temperature sensation. I. A comparison of the sensation produced by infra-red and visible radiation. J. Clin. Invest. **16**: 517, 1937.

331. PALMER, W. L.: The pain of peptic ulcer. Proc. Assn. Res. Nerv. & Ment. Dis., The Williams & Wilkins Co., **23**: 302, 1943.

332. PARSONS, C. M. AND GOETZL, F. R.: Effect of induced pain on pain threshold. Proc. Soc. Exp. Biol. **60**: 327, 1945.

333. PARSONS, C. M. AND GOETZL, F. R.: The influence of acetylsalicylic acid upon analgesic effects of induced pain. Permanente Found. Med. Bull. **4**: 15, 1946.

334. PAYNE, W. W. AND POULTON, E. P.: Experiments on visceral sensation: Relation of pain to activity in the human oesophagus. J. Physiol. **63**: 217, 1927.

335. PEIPER, A.: Untersuchungen über den galvanischen Hautreflex (psychogalvanischen reflex) im Kindeslter. Jahrbuch für Kinderheilkunde, **107**: 139, 1924.

336. PELNER, L.: The determination of sensitivity to pain. J. Lab. & Clin. Med. **27**: 248, 1941.

337. PENFIELD, W. AND BOLDREY, E.: Somatic motor and sensory representations in cerebral cortex of man as studied by electrical stimulation. Brain **60**: 389, 1937.

338. PENFIELD, W.: Personal communication.

339. PETRIE, A.: Personality and the Frontal Lobes. London, Routledge and Kegan Paul, 1952.

340. PFEIFFER, C. C., SONNENSCHEIN, R. R., GLASSMAN, L., JENNEY, E. H. AND BOGOLUB, S.: Experimental methods for studying analgesia. Ann. N. Y. Acad. Sci. **51**: 21, 1948.

341. PICKERING, G. W. AND HESS, W.: Observations on the mechanism of headache produced by histamine. Clin. Sci. **1**: 77, 1933.

342. POOL, J. L.: Pain disturbances associated with certain war wounds. Arch. Neurol. & Psychiat. **59**: 810, 1948.

343. POPPEN, J. L.: Prefrontal lobotomy for intractable pain. Lahey Clinic Bull. **4**: 205, 1946.

344. PORTER, T. C.: Contributions to the study of flicker. Proc. Roy. Soc. **70**: 313, 1902.

345. POTELUNAS, C. B., MEIXNER, M. D. AND HARDY, J. D.: Measurement of pain threshold and superficial hyperalgesia in diseases of the skin. J. Invest. Dermat. **12:** 307, 1949.

346. PRIDEAUX, E.: The psychogalvanic reflex. Brain **43:** 50, 1920.

347. PRINCE, M. AND PETERSON, F.: Experiments in psychogalvanic reactions from co-conscious (subconscious) ideas in multiple personality. J. Abn. Psychol. **3:** 114, 1908–09.

348. PRITCHARD, E. A. B.: The clinical significance of variations in tickle sensibility. Proc. Roy. Soc. Med. **26:** 697, 1933.

349. RADO, Sandor: An adaptational view of sexual behavior (pp. 159–189). in: Psychosexual Development in Health and Disease. New York, Grune and Stratton, 1949.

350. RANSON, S. W.: The Anatomy of the Nervous System. Philadelphia. W. B. Saunders Co., 1943.

351. RAY, B. S.: Personal communication.

352. RAY, B. S. AND NEILL, C. L.: Abdominal visceral sensation in man. Ann. Surg. **126:** 709, 1947.

353. RAY, B. S. AND WOLFF, H. G.: Experimental studies on headache. Pain sensitive structures of the head and their significance in headache. Arch. Surg. **41:** 813, 1940.

354. RAY, B. S. AND WOLFF, H. G.: Studies on pain; "spread of pain"; evidence on site of spread within neuraxis of effects of painful stimulation. Arch. Neurol. & Psychiat. **53:** 257, 1945.

355. READ, G. D.: Childbirth Without Fear. New York, Harper & Brothers, 1944.

356. REDLICH, F. C.: Organic and hysterical anesthesia: A method of differential diagnosis with the aid of the galvanic skin response. Am. J. Psychiat. **102:** 318, 1945.

357. REIN, F. H.: Zur Physiologie des Schmerzes. Schmerz **12:** 129, 1939.

358. REVICI, E. AND RAVICH, R. A.: The painful focus. I. Physiological and pathological pain. Bull. Inst. Appl. Biol. **1:** 12, 1949.

359. REVICI, E., STOOPEN, E., FRENK, E. AND RAVICH, R. A.: The painful focus. II. The relation of pain to local physico-chemical changes. Bull. Inst. Appl. Biol **1:** 21, 1949.

360. REY, A.: Normal and pathologic cutaneous sensitivity; description of apparatus, technique and standardization. Arch. de psychol. **30:** 1, 1943.

361. REYNOLDS, S. R. M.: Physiology of the Uterus. New York, Paul B. Hoeber, Inc., 1949.

362. RICHTER, C. P. AND WOODRUFF, B. G.: Changes produced by sympathectomy in the electrical resistance of the skin. Surgery, **10:** 957, 1941.

363. RICHTER, C. P.: Significant changes in the electrical resistance of the body during sleep. Proc. Nat. Acad. Sci. **12:** 214, 1926.

364. RICHTER, C. P.: High electrical resistance of the skin of new born infants and its significance. Am. J. Dis. Child. **40:** 18, 1930.

365. RICHTER, C. P.: Electrical skin resistance, diurnal and daily variations in psychopathic and normal persons. Arch. Neurol. Psychiat. **19:** 488, 1928.

366. RIDDOCH, G.: The reflex functions of the completely divided spinal cord in man, compared with those associated with less severe lesions. Brain **40:** 266, 1917.

367. RIECHERT, U. T.: Cutting of thalamofrontal tracts in uncontrollable pain. J. A. M. A. **141**: 877, 1949.

368. RINZLER, S. H. AND TRAVELL J.: Therapy directed at the somatic component of cardiac pain. Am. Heart J. **35**: 248, 1948.

369. RIOCH, D. McK.: Personal communication to L. C. Kolb and quoted, J. Nerv. & Ment. Dis. **110**: 112, 1949.

370. ROBERTSON, H. S., GOODELL, H. AND WOLFF, H. G.: Studies on headache: The teeth as a source of headache and other pain. Arch. Neurol. & Psychiat. **57**: 277, 1947.

371. ROSENBLUM, D. E.: Nature and origin of altitude pains. Am. Rev. of Soviet Med. **1**: 303, 1944.

372. ROSENTHAL, S. R.: Histamine as possible chemical mediator for cutaneous pain. Dual pain response to histamine. Proc. Soc. Exp. Biol. & Med. **74**: 167, 1950.

373. ROSS, J.: On the segmental distribution of sensory disorders. Brain **10**: 333, 1888.

374. ROTHMAN, S.: Physiology of itching. Physiol. Rev. **21**: 357, 1941.

375. ROWE, S. N. AND MOYAR, J. B.: Unilateral prefrontal lobotomies for pain. J. Neurosurgery **7**: 121, 1950.

376. RUCKER, M. P.: The action of various anesthetics upon uterine contractions. Anesth. & Analg. **5**: 235, 1926.

377. RYLANDER, GÖSTA: Personality analysis before and after frontal lobotomy. The Frontal Lobes: Proc. Assn. Res. Nerv. & Ment. Dis., The Williams & Wilkins Co., **27**: 691, 1948.

378. SARNOFF, S. J. AND ARROWOOD, J. G.: Differential spinal block. II. The reaction of sudomotor and vasomotor fibers. J. Clin. Invest. **26**: 203, 1947.

379. SATTLER, D. G.: Absence of local sign in visceral reaction to painful stimulation. Proc. Soc. Res. Nerv. Ment. Dis., The Williams & Wilkins Co., **23**: 143, 1943.

380. SCARFF, J. E.: Unilateral prefrontal lobotomy for the relief of intractable pain and termination of narcotic addiction. Surg., Gynec. & Obst. **89**: 385, 1949.

381. SCARFF, J. E.: Unilateral prefrontal lobotomy for the relief of intractable pain. J. Neurosurg. **7**: 330, 1950.

382. SCHAMP, J. R. AND SCHAMP, H. M.: Variability of pain threshold in man. J. Dent. Res. **25**: 101, 1946.

383. SCHILLING, R. F. AND MUSSER, M. J.: The pain reaction threshold in the menopausal syndrome. Am. J. Med. Sci. **218**: 204, 1949.

384. SCHIFF, J. M.: Lehrbuch der Physiologie, 1858.

385. SCHNECK, J. M.: Psychosomatic reactions to the induction of hypnosis. Dis. Nerv. Syst. **11**: 118, 1950.

386. SCHRIEVER, H.: Über den Wärmeschmerz. Zeitschr. f. Biologie **85**: 67, 1926-27.

387. SCHUMACHER, G. A.: The influence of inflammation on the pain threshold of the skin in man. Proc. Assn. Res. Nerv. & Ment. Dis., The Williams & Wilkins Co., **23**: 166, 1943.

388. SCHUMACHER, G. A., GOODELL, H., HARDY, J. D. AND WOLFF, H. G.: Uniformity of the pain threshold in man. Science **92**: 110, 1940.

389. SCHUMACHER, G. A. AND GUTHRIE, T. C.: Studies on headache: Mechanism of headache and observations on other effects induced by distention of

bladder and rectum in subjects with spinal cord injuries. Arch. Neurol. & Psychiat. **65**: 568, 1951.

390. SCHUMACHER, G. A., RAY, B. S., AND WOLFF, H. G.: Experimental studies on headache: Further analysis of histamine headache and its pain pathways. Arch. Neurol. & Psychiat. **44**: 701, 1940.

391. SCHUMACHER, G. A. AND WOLFF, H. G.: Experimental studies on headache. a) Contrast of histamine headache with the headache of migraine and that associated with hypertension. b) Contrast of vascular mechanisms in pre-headache and in headache phenomena of migraine. Arch. Neurol. & Psychiat. **45**: 199, 1941.

392. SCOTT, C. G., ROBBINS, E. B., AND CHEN, K. K.: Comparison of some new analgesic compounds. Science **104**: 587, 1946.

393. SEARS, R. R.: Experimental study of hypnotic anesthesia. J. Exp. Psychol. **15**: 1, 1932.

394. SEARS, R. R. AND COHEN, L. H.: Hysterical anesthesia, analysis and astereognosis. Arch. Neurol. & Psychiat. **29**: 260, 1933.

395. SEEVERS, M. H., BENNETT, J. H., POHLE, H. W. AND REINARDY, E. W.: The analgesia produced by nitrous oxide, ethylene and cyclopropane in the normal human subject. J. Pharm. & Exp. Therap. **59**: 291, 1937.

396. SEEVERS, M. H. AND PFEIFFER, C. C.: A study of the analgesia, subjective depression, and euphoria produced by morphine, heroine, dilaudid and codeine in the normal human subject. J. Pharm. & Exp. Therap. **56**: 166, 1936.

397. SELYE, HANS: The Physiology and Pathology of Exposure to Stress. Montreal, ACTA Inc., 1950.

398. SETÜRNER, F. W. A.: Darstellung der reinen Mohnsäure (Opiumsäure) nebst einer chemischen Untersuchung des Opiums mit vorzülicher Hinsicht auf einem darin neu entdeckten Stoff und die dahin gehörigen Bemerkungen. J. d. Pharm. f. Aerzte, Apoth. u. Chem. **14**: 47, 1806.

399. SHERMAN, E. D.: Sensitivity to pain. Can. M. A. J. **48**: 437, 1943.

400. SHERRINGTON, C. S.: Some functional organization of the spinal cord. Proc. Roy. Soc. **B-105**: 332, 1929.

401. SHERRINGTON, C. S.: The Integrative Action of the Nervous System. New Haven: Yale University Press, 1920.

402. SIMONS, D. J.: Personal communication quoted by SCHUMACHER, G. A., RAY, B. S. AND WOLFF, H. G., in: Experimental studies on headache; further analysis of histamine headache and its pain pathways. Arch. Neurol. & Psychiat. **44**: 701, 1940.

403. SIMONS, D. J., DAY, E., GOODELL, H. AND WOLFF, H. G.: Experimental studies on headache: Muscles of the head and neck as sources of pain. Proc. Assn. Res. Nerv. & Ment. Dis., The Williams & Wilkins Co., **23**: 228, 1943.

404. SIMONS, D. J. AND WOLFF, H. G.: Studies on headache: Mechanisms of chronic post-traumatic headache. Psychosom. Med. **8**: 227, 1946.

405. SINCLAIR, D. C., WEDDELL, G. AND FEINDEL, W. H.: Referred pain and associated phenomena. Brain **71**: 184, 1948.

406. SLAUGHTER, D.: New concepts of morphine analgesia. Anesthesiology **5**: 508, 1944.

407. SLAUGHTER, D. AND MUNSELL, D. W.: Some new aspects of morphine action: Effects on pain. J. Pharm. & Exp. Therap. **68**: 104, 1940.
408. SLAUGHTER, D., PARSONS, J. C. AND MUNAL, H. D.: New clinical aspects of the analgesic action of morphine. J. A. M. A. **115**: 2058, 1940.
409. SLAUGHTER, D. AND WRIGHT, F. T.: A modification of the Hardy-Wolff-Goodell pain threshold apparatus. Anesthesia & Analgesia **23**: 115, 1944.
410. SMALL, L. F., EDDY, N. B., MOSETTIG, E. AND HIMMELSBACH, C. K.: Studies on Drug Addiction. Supplement #138, U. S. Pub. Health Serv. Reports, U. S. Govt. Printing Office, 1938.
411. SMOLIK, E. A.: Lobotomy in management of intractable pain and narcotic addiction. Dis. Nerv. System **11**: 327, 1950.
412. SNYDER, F. F.: Obstetric Analgesia and Anesthesia. Philadelphia, W. B. Saunders Co., 1949.
413. SONNE, C.: The mode of action of the universal light bath: Visible and invisible heat rays. Acta Med. Scandinav. **54**: 350, 1921.
414. SONNENSCHEIN, R. R. AND IVY, A. C.: Failure of oral antipyretic drugs to alter human pain threshold. J. Pharm. & Exper. Therap. **97**: 308, 1949.
415. SONNENSCHEIN, R. R., JAMISON, R., LOVSETH, L., CASSELS, W. AND IVY, A. C.: The mechanism of nitrous oxide analgesia. Fed. Proc. **7**: 118, 1948.
416. SORESI, A. L.: Is pain a physiological or a pathological sensation? Med. Rec., N. Y. **161**: 563, 1948.
417. SPIEGEL, E. A. AND WOHL, M. G.: The viscerogalvanic reaction. Arch. Int. Med. **56**: 327, 1935.
418. STEVENS, S. S.: Psychology and the science of science. Psychol. Bull. **36**: 221, 1939.
419. STEVENS, S. S.: On the theory of scales of measurement. Science **103**: 677, 1946.
420. STEVENS, S. S.: Mathematics, Measurement and Psychophysics. Handbook of Experimental Psychology. New York, John Wiley & Son, 1951.
421. STEVENS, S. S. AND DAVIS, H.: Hearing. New York, John Wiley & Son, 1938.
422. STEVENS, S. S., MORGAN, C. T. AND VOLKMANN, J.: Theory of the neural quantum in the discrimination of loudness and pitch. Am. J. Psychol. **54**: 315, 1941.
423. STOKES, J., CHAPMAN, W. P. AND SMITH, L. H.: Effects of hypoxia and hypercapnia on perception of thermal cutaneous pain. J. Clin. Invest. **27**: 299, 1948.
424. STOLL, A. M. AND HARDY, J. D.: Study of thermocouples as skin thermometers. J. App. Physiol. **11**: 531, 1950.
425. STONE, L. J. AND DALLENBACH, K. M.: Adaptation to the pain of radiant heat. Am. J. Psychol. **46**: 229, 1934.
426. STRONG, C. A.: The psychology of pain. Psychol. Rev. **2**: 329, 1895.
427. STURGE, W. A.: The phenomena of angina pectoris, and their bearing upon the theory of counter-irritation. Brain **5**: 492, 1883.
428. SUN, K. C.: Spontaneous contraction of pregnant human uterus. Bull. Johns Hopkins Hosp. **36-37**: 280, 1925.
429. SUTHERLAND, A. M. AND WOLFF, H. G.: Experimental studies on headache. Further analysis of the mechanism of headache in migraine, hypertension, and fever. Arch. Neurol. & Psychiat. **44**: 929, 1940.
430. TAINTER, M. L.: Pain. Ann. N. Y. Acad. Sci. **51**: 3, 1945.

431. TAINTER, M. L.: Estudio comparativo del algunas aciones del demeral y del methadon. Bol. Asoc. med del Puerto Rico **40**: 1, 1948.

432. TAINTER, M. L. AND BUCHANAN, O. H.: Buve relato sobre el alivio del dolor por la meperidine (demerol) y la metadona. Prensa med mex. **14**: 357, 1949.

433. THÖLE: Über Jucken und Kitzeln in Beziehung zu Schmerzgefühl und Tastempfindung. Neurol. Centralbl. **31**: 610, 1912.

434. THOMPSON, L. AND GELLHORN, E.: The influence of muscle pain on spinal reflexes. Proc. Soc. Exp. Biol. & Med. **58**: 105, 1945.

435. THOMPSON, M. B. AND GELLHORN, E.: Influence of muscle pain on electrical resistance of the human skin. Proc. Soc. Exp. Biol. **58**: 146, 1945.

436. TITCHENER, E. B.: A Text Book of Psychology. Part I. New York, MacMillan Co., 1909.

437. TÖRÖK, L.: Über das Wesen der Juckempfindung. Ztschr. f. Psychol. **46**: 23, 1907.

438. TOWER, S.: Pain: Definition and properties of the unit for sensory reception. Proc. Assn. Res. Nerv. & Ment. Dis., The Williams & Wilkins Co., **23**: 16, 1943.

439. TRAVELL, J., BERRY, C. AND BIGELOW, N.: Effects of referred somatic pain on structures in the reference zone. Fed. Proc. **3**: 49, 1944.

440. TRAVELL, J. AND BIGELOW, N. H.: Referred somatic pain does not follow a simple "segmental" pattern. Fed. Proc. **5**: 106, 1946.

441. TRAVELL, J. AND RINZLER, S. H.: Relief of cardiac pain by local block of somatic trigger areas. Proc. Soc. Exp. Biol. & Med. **63**: 480, 1946.

442. VAN WAGENEN, W. P.: Personal communication.

443. VAN WAGENEN, W. P.: Personal communication to Dr. A. Earl Walker and quoted in "Central representation of pain", Pain, Proc. Assn. Res. Nerv. & Ment. Dis., The Williams & Wilkins Co. **23**: 63, 1943.

444. VERAGUTH, O.: Das psychogalvanische reflex Phänomen. Berlin, S. Karger, 1909.

445. VON FREY, M.: Versuche über schmerzerregende Reize. Ztschr. f. Biol. **76**: 1, 1922.

446. VON FREY, M.: Beitrage zur Physiologie des Schmerzsinnes. Ber. u. d. Verhandl. d. k. sachs. Ges. d. Wiss. z. Leipzig; math.-phys. K. **46**: 283, 1894.

447. VON FREY, M.: Beitrage zur Physiologie des Schmerzsinnes. Ber. u. d. Verhandl. d. k. sachs Ges. d. Wiss. z. Leipzig; math.-phys. K. **46**: 185, 1894.

448. VON FREY, M.: Beitrage zur Sinnesphysiolgie des Haut. Ber. u. d. Verhandl. d. k. sachs. Ges. d. Wiss. z. Leipzig; math.-phys. K. **47**: 166, 1895.

449. VON FREY, M.: Untersuchungen über die Sinnesfunctionen der menschlichen Haut; Druckempfindungen und Schmerz. Abh. sachs. Ges. d. Wiss. z. Leipzig; math.-phys. K. **23**: 169, 1897.

450. VON FREY, M.: The distribution of afferent nerves in the skin. J. A. M. A. **47**: 645, 1906.

451. VON FREY, M.: Die Tangoreceptoren des Menschen. Handbuch der normalen und pathologischen Physiologie **11**: 94, 1926.

452. VOYLES, H. E.: Cited by Lull, C. G. and Hingson, R. A.: Control of Pain in Childbirth. Philadelphia, J. B. Lippincott Co., 1948.

453. WALKER, A. E.: Central representation of pain. Proc. Assn. Res. Nerv. & Ment. Dis., The Williams & Wilkins Co., **23**: 63, 1943.

454. WANGEMAN, C. P. AND HAWK, M. H.: The effects of morphine, atropine, and scopolamine on human subjects. Anesthesiology **3**: 24, 1942.

455. WATTS, J. W. AND FREEMAN, W.: Psychosurgery for relief of unbearable pain. J. A. M. A. **133**: 891, 1947. J. Internat. Coll. of Surgeons **9**: 679, 1946.

456. WATTS, J. W. AND FREEMAN, W.: Frontal lobotomy in the treatment of unbearable pain. The Frontal Lobes, Proc. Assn. Res. Nerv. & Ment. Dis., The Williams & Wilkins Co. **27**: 715, 1948.

457. WATTS, J. W. AND FREEMAN, W.: Development of prefrontal lobotomy in the treatment of intolerable pain. Southern Med. & Surg. **110**: 1, 1948.

458. WEBER, E. H.: De Pulsu, resorptione, audita et tactu; annotationes, anatomiea et physiologiae, 1834, p. 44–175, De Tactu.

459. WEBER, E. H.: Der Tastsinn und das Gemeingefühl, in: Rudolph Wagner's Handwörtenbuch der Physiologie **3**: 481, 1846.

460. WEDDELL, G.: The multiple innervation of sensory spots in the skin. J. Anat. **75**: 441, 1940–41.

461. WEDDELL, G.: The pattern of cutaneous innervation in relation to cutaneous sensibility. J. Anat. **75**: 346, 1940–41.

462. WEDDELL, G., SINCLAIR, D. C. AND FEINDEL, W. H.: An anatomical basis for alterations in quality of pain sensibility. J. Neurophys. **11**: 99, 1948.

463. WEISS, S. AND DAVIS, D.: The significance of the afferent impulses from the skin in the mechanism of visceral pain. Skin infiltration as a useful therapeutic measure. Am. J. Med. Sci. **176**: 517, 1928.

464. WEITZ, J.: A further study of the relation between skin temperature and cutaneous sensitivity. J. Exp. Psychol. **30**: 426, 1942.

465. WELLS, H. S.: Temperature equalization for the relief of pain. Arch. Phys. Med. **28**: 135, 1947.

465a. WERTHEIMER, M. AND WARD, W. D.: The influence of skin temperature upon the pain threshold as evoked by thermal radiation—A confirmation. Science **115**: 499, 1952.

466. WHITE, J. C. AND SMITHWICK, R. H.: The Autonomic Nervous System. 2nd ed. New York, MacMillan Co., 1941.

467. WHITE, J. C.: Sensory innervation of the viscera: Studies on visceral afferent neurones in man based on neurosurgical procedures for relief of intractible pain. Proc. Assn. Res. Nerv. & Ment. Dis., The Williams & Wilkins Co. **23**: 273, 1943.

468. WHITE, J. C. AND SWEET, W. H.: Effectiveness of cordotomy in phantom pain after amputation. Am. Neurol. Assn. **18-20**: 23, 1951.

469. WHYTE, H. M.: The effect of aspirin and morphine on heat pain. J. Clin. Sci. **10**: 333, 1951.

470. WIKLER, A., GOODELL, H. AND WOLFF, H. G.: The effects of analgesic agents on sensations other than pain. J. Pharm. & Exp. Therap. **83**: 294, 1945.

471. WIKLER, A., PESCOR, M. J., KALBAUGH, E. P. AND ANGELUCCI, R. J.: The effects of frontal lobotomy on the morphine abstinence syndrome in man. An experimental study. Arch. Neurol. & Psychiat., **67**: 510, 1952.

472. WILDER, R. M.: Sensitivity to pain. Proc. Staff Meeting, Mayo Clinic **15**: 551, 1940.

473. WILLIAMS, H. S.: Painless Childbirth. New York, Goodhue Co., 1914.

474. WINDER, C. V., PFEIFFER, C. C. AND MAISON, G. L.: The nociceptive contraction of the cutaneous muscle of the guinea pig as elicited by radiant

heat, with observations on the mode of action of morphine. Arch. internat. de Pharmacody. **72**: 329, 1946.

475. WINN, R. C.: The psychogalvanometer in practice. Australian J. Psychol. & Phil. Vol. 7, 1929.

476. WINSLOW, C. E. A., HERRINGTON, L. P. AND GAGGE, A. P.: Physiological re-actions of human body to varying environmental temperatures. Am. J. Physiol. **120**: 1, 1937.

477. WITMER, L.: The psychological analysis and physical basis of pleasure and pain. J. Nerv. & Ment. Dis. **19**: 209, 1894.

478. WOLBERG, L.: Medical Hypnosis. New York, Grune and Stratton, 1948.

479. WOLF, G. A. JR.: The effect of pain on renal function. Proc. Assn. Res. Nerv. & Ment. Dis., The Williams & Wilkins Co. **23**: 358, 1943.

480. WOLF, G. A. JR.: Mechanism of reflex anuria. Ann. Int. Med. **23**: 99, 1945.

481. WOLF, S. G.: Sustained contraction of the diaphragm; the mechanism of a common type of dyspnea and precordial pain. J. Clin. Invest. **26**: 1201, 1947.

482. WOLF, S. G., GOODELL, H. AND WOLFF, H. G.: Unpublished observations on comparisons of intensity of pain arising from various sources.

483. WOLF, S. G. AND HARDY, J. D.: Studies on pain. Observations on pain due to local cooling and on factors involved in the "cold pressor" effect. Res. Pub. Assoc. Res. Nerv. & Ment. Dis., The Williams & Wilkins Co. **23**: 123, 1943.

484. WOLF, S. G., PFEIFFER, J. B., RIPLEY, H. S., WINTER, O. S. AND WOLFF, H. G.: Hypertension as a reaction pattern to stress; summary of experimental data on variations in blood pressure and renal blood flow. Ann. Int. Med. **29**: 1056, 1948.

484a. WOLF, S. G. AND WOLFF, H. G.: Pain. Charles C. Thomas, Springfield, Ill., 2nd Ed., 1951.

485. WOLF, S. G., WOLFF, H. G. AND GOODELL, H.: Unpublished observations.

486. WOLF, S. G. AND WOLFF, H. G.: Human Gastric Function. New York, Oxford University Press, 1943 and 1947.

487. WOLF, S. G., WOLFF, H. G. AND GOODELL, H.: Unpublished observations.

488. WOLFF, H. G.: Headache and Other Head Pain. New York, Oxford University Press, 1947.

489. WOLFF, H. G.: Some observations on pain. Harvey Lect. **39**: 39, 1943.

490. WOLFF, H. G. AND GOODELL, H.: The relation of attitude and suggestion to the perception of and reaction to pain. Proc. Assoc. Res. Ner. Ment. Dis., The Williams & Wilkins Co., **23**: 434, 1943.

491. WOLFF, H. G., HARDY, J. D. AND GOODELL, H.: Measurement of the effect on the pain threshold of acetylsalicylic acid, acetanilid, acetophenetidin, aminopyrine, ethyl alcohol, trichlorethylene, a barbiturate, quinine, ergotamine tartrate, and caffeine: an analysis of their relation to the pain experience. J. Clin. Invest. **20**: 63, 1941.

492. WOLFF, H. G., HARDY, J. D. AND GOODELL, H.: Studies on pain. Measurement of the effect of morphine, codeine, and other opiates on the pain threshold and an analysis of their relation to the pain experience. J. Clin. Invest. **19**: 659, 1940.

493. WOLFF, H. G., HARDY, J. D. AND GOODELL, H.: Studies on pain. Measurement of the effect of ethyl alcohol on the pain threshold and on the "alarm" reaction. J. Pharm. & Exp. Therap. **75**: 38, 1942.

494. WOLFF, H. G., SIMONS, D. J. AND GOODELL, H.: Unpublished observations.
495. WOLFF, H. G., WOLF, S. G. AND HARE, C. C., EDITORS: Life Stress and Bodily Disease. Proc. Assn. for Res. in Nerv. & Ment. Dis., The Williams & Wilkins Co., volume 29, 1950.
495a. WOLFF, H. G. AND HARDY, J. D.: On the nature of pain. Physiol. Rev. **27**: 167, 1947.
496. WOODWARD, R. S.: Experimental Psychology. New York, Henry Holt & Co., 1938, pp. 276–298.
497. WOOLFE, G. AND MACDONALD, A. D.: The evaluation of the analgesic action of pethidine hydrochloride (Demerol). J. Pharm. & Exp. Therap. **80**: 300, 1944.
498. WOOLLARD, H. H., ROBERTS, J. E. H. AND CARMICHAEL, E. A.: An inquiry into referred pain. Lancet **1**: 337, 1932.
499. WOOLLARD, H. H., WEDDELL, G. AND HARPMAN, J. A.: Observations on the neurohistological basis of cutaneous pain. J. Anat. **74**: 413, 1940.
500. WORTIS, H., STEIN, M. H. AND JOLIFFE, N.: Fiber dissociation in peripheral neuropathy. Arch. Int. Med. **69**: 222, 1942.
501. WUNDT, W.: Grundzüge der Physiologischen Psychologie. Leipzig, W. Engelmann, 1874.
502. YOUNG, THOMAS: Phil. Trans. **19**: 23, 1801.
503. ZISKIN, D. E. AND WALD, A.: Observations on electrical pulp testing. J. Dent. Res. **17**: 79, 1938.
504. ZOTTERMAN, Y.: Touch, pain and tickling: An electro-physiological investigation on cutaneous sensory nerves. J. Physiol. **95**: 1, 1939.
505. ZUBIN, JOSEPH: Personal communication.

AUTHOR INDEX

417

SUBJECT INDEX

Acetanilid
 influence on pain threshold, 355
Acetophenetidin
 influence on pain threshold, 356
Acetylsalicylic acid
 as a therapeutic agent, 354
 influence on intensity of pain above
 threshold, 362
 influence on pain threshold, 33, 354
Aching pain (see also Pain threshold
 measurement of)
 different causes of headache pain, 135
 intensity of, 161, 171
 methods of study of, 140
 no spatial summation of, 142
 production of, by three types of mechanisms:
 1) true visceral and deep somatic
 pain, 139
 2) referred pain, 139
 3) pain secondary to skeletal muscle contraction, 140
 production of deep somatic
 by nerve root ischemia, 135
 by muscle ischemia, 135
 quality of, 134, 145
 spread of, 142
 structures involved, 134
Action potentials, 5, 12, 296
Adaptation to pain
 effect of hypnotic suggestion upon
 283
 effect of repetitive stimulation upon,
 272
 radiant heat studies, 2, 66
Adequate stimulus for pain, 379
 definition of, 53
 tissue damage in relation to, 23, 103
Age
 influence of on pain threshold, 87, 119
Alarm reaction
 effect of alcohol on, 264
 "   " anxiety on, 278
 "   " extremes of environmental
 temperature on, 277
 effect of hypnotic suggestion on, 289,
 291
 effect of painful stimulation on, 272
 indicated by drop in electrical skin
 resistance, 263
 threshold of, 263
 to pain, 263
Alcohol—see Ethyl alcohol
Algesimeter
 tests with, 56
Alkalinizing agents
 effects on gastric pain, 327, 377

Analgesia
 definition of, 282
 under hypnotic suggestion, 283
Analgesic action, 325, 328, 331
Analgesic agents
 affecting intensity of pain (experimental) 337
 central action of, 331
 clinical value of, 378
 definition of, 325
 features of, 325
 influence on labor pains, 367
 "   " pain intensity above
 threshold, 361
 influence on pain threshold under prolonged stimulation, 360
 methods for studying effectiveness
 (four), 328
 modes of action of, listing of eight,
 325, 376
 narcotics as, 340
 no influence on secondary hyperalgesia, 205
Analgesic agents, listing of
 acetanilid—see Acetanilid
 acetophenetidin—see Acetophenetidin
 acetylsalicylic acid—see Aspirin
 apomorphine—see Apomorphine
 aspirin—see Acetylsalicylic acid
 barbiturates—see Barbiturates, Evipal
 cocaine—see Procaine
 codeine—see Codeine
 demerol—see Meperidine
 diacetylmorphine—see Diacetylmorphine
 Dilaudid—see Dihydromorphinone
 hydrochloride
 ethyl alcohol—see Ethyl alcohol
 heroin—see Diacetylmorphine
 Meperidine—see Meperidine
 methyldihydromorphinone—see Methyldihydromorphinone
 Metopon—see Methyldihydromorphinone
 morphine—see Morphine sulfate
 pantopium hydrochloride—see Pantopium hydrochloride
 Pantopon—see Pantopium hydrochloride
 procaine—see Procaine
 scopolamine—see Scopolamine
 trichlorethylene—see Trichlorethylene
Anesthesia
 hypnotic suggestion of, 290
 effect on pain sensation, 290